66/-

10

)'

)

14

5

Scalar and Vector Fields:

A Physical Interpretation

Scalar and Vector Fields:

A Physical Interpretation

Richmond B. McQuistan

Staff Scientist

Honeywell Research Center

John Wiley & Sons, Inc., New York / London / Sydney

Library of Congress Catalog Card Number: 65-16418
Printed in the United States of America

To My Wife Marilyn

and My Parents Alistair and Jean

Preface

The increasingly rapid advances made by science and engineering have exerted a profound influence on the curricula of educational institutions. It has been said that the transient, almost ephemeral, importance of existing materials, components, and devices has placed universities in the position of attempting to educate students for professions that have no names and for jobs which do not yet exist. Curricula developed to meet this situation have generally omitted the presentation of specialized training relating to existing devices, soon to be made obsolete by newer developments. Instead, it has been considered more desirable to give a student a firmer foundation in the basic aspects of the physical sciences and engineering and to leave the more specialized training to the student or to the industry which hires him. As a result of such reasoning, more courses of a fundamental nature are now being presented to a student early in his academic career. For example, an increasing number of educational institutions have initiated undergraduate courses such as classical mechanics, electromagnetic fields, and hydrodynamics which involve field theory. Unfortunately, however, it has been my experience and that of many of my colleagues that a student at this level usually lacks the physical insight necessary for an understanding of field concepts. This deficiency impedes his understanding of the material if it is presented properly, that is, with free use of field notation and field operations. If the material is not presented in this manner, many of the advantages gained by its early introduction are lost. An undergraduate student usually has not had sufficient time to take a specialized course in vector analysis prior to taking field courses. Even if he had, the elegant mathematical treatment usually given vector field concepts is of little help to a student who generally lacks the mathematical maturity to appreciate it or to associate the mathematics with physical situations.

Most undergraduate, as well as graduate, books written on subjects which require the extensive use of field concepts contain only a cursory treatment of the physical aspects of the subject which, at best, is sufficient as a review for those who have already been exposed to such material. This book has been written in an attempt to correct this situation and is intended therefore to supplement these more specialized books.

The genesis of this book was an undergraduate course in electromagnetic fields that I presented at the University of Minnesota. It was my experience, during this time, that performing the mathematical manipulations associated with fields presents comparatively little difficulty for the students. Instead, the primary difficulty lies in understanding the physical interpretation of field concepts and operations. As a result of this observation, I prepared supplementary class notes (from which large portions of this book were taken) in an attempt to emphasize the physical meaning of the algebra, calculus, operators, and transformation theory associated with fields. In a book of finite length, this emphasis on the physical interpretation has meant that certain aspects of the mathematical rigor have been neglected.

Since it is my intention to write a book which can serve as supplementary material for undergraduate as well as some graduate work, the level of presentation is not uniform but varies considerably, depending on the sophistication of the topic.

In Chapter 1 scalar and vector quantities are introduced; the concept of a field is discussed and the more common methods of representing them graphically are treated. The meaning of certain fundamental field characteristics, for example, single-valuedness and continuity, are discussed in physical terms. Addition, subtraction, multiplication, and division involving vector quantities are treated in Chapter 2. Chapter 3 is concerned with the processes of differentiation and integration as they relate to vector fields. The role of the coordinate system in the representation of vector fields and the transformation of the representation of a vector field from one coordinate system to another are discussed in Chapter 4. Orthogonality, the right-handedness of coordinate systems, frames of reference, and vector and function spaces are also considered in this chapter. Chapters 5, 6, 7, and 8 are a discussion of the physical aspects of the differential properties of fields, as well as the operator notation associated with these field properties. The integral properties of fields, Stokes, Gauss's, and Green's theorems are the subjects of Chapter 9. The subject of Chapter 10 is the representation of field operators in orthogonal curvilinear coordinate systems. Field potentials and consideration of the Helmholtz theorem for vector fields are discussed in Chapter 11. Chapter 12 is concerned with time-dependent fields, motion relative to a field, and retarded potentials.

The problems of notation are always difficult to solve. No attempt has been made to be elegant; rather, the philosophy has been adopted that the learning of the notation should not impede the understanding of the physical significance of a topic.

It is a pleasure to acknowledge the cooperation and encouragement given by Minneapolis-Honeywell. The effort and diligence of Mrs. L. Lehr in preparing this manuscript are very gratefully appreciated. To J. W. Schultz and R. E. Consoliver, who helped in manuscript preparation and proof reading, I am very grateful. I wish also to thank many of my colleagues, particularly D. Lichtman, L. D. McGlauchlin, J. F. Ready, F. N. Simon, and J. D. Zook, for many valuable comments and enlightening discussions. I am particularly indebted to my wife and family for their forebearance, assistance, and consideration during the writing of the manuscript.

R. B. McQuistan
Honeywell Research Center

February 1965

Contents

Scalar and Vector Fields:

A Physical Interpretation

1

The Concept of Scalar
and Vector Fields

1.1 Introduction

When we say that a certain physical phenomenon is understood, what do we mean? We usually mean that the phenomenon can be described in a quantitative manner in terms of defined physical quantities. In many instances this description involves the way in which physical quantities depend on position. For example, the force experienced by an electron in the presence of another electron depends on the relative position of the two electrons; similarly, the pressure at a point within an ideal liquid is determined by the position of that point. To describe such situations, it has proved extremely useful to employ the concept of a field. In addition to providing a succinct framework whereby the spatial dependence of physical quantities can be described, the concept of a field permits us to do so without recourse to any coordinate system. Thus the use of field notation provides a means of formulating physical laws in an *invariant* form, that is, in a form which does not depend on any coordinate system.* Furthermore, the mathematical symbolism associated with fields provides an excellent means of emphasizing and clarifying the physical aspects of a phenomenon. We shall see that the study of fields is not just a mathematical exercise but is a valuable and practical tool for understanding many of the underlying principles of geometry, classical mechanics, electromagnetism, and fluid mechanics.

It is the purpose of this chapter to introduce the fundamental concepts of scalar and vector fields. We shall first define and attempt to characterize scalar and vector quantities. Next we shall discuss fields by showing their utility as a means of describing a physical situation in which the value of a scalar or vector quantity at a particular point depends on the location of

---

* The reader is not to infer that the concept of a field is the only manner by which a coordinate-free description of physical laws can be given; however, field descriptions have proved to be extremely useful.

that point in space. We shall discuss several physical examples of two- and three-dimensional fields. There are a variety of ways in which fields can be represented graphically. The most frequently used of these will be treated in an effort to aid the visualization of scalar and vector fields.

1.2 Definitions

One aspect of the physical sciences and engineering which differentiates them from other academic disciplines is that they are concerned with quantities which can be defined in an unambiguous manner. Although the number of physical quantities considered in science and engineering is very large, they can be classified into a relatively few groups according to the number of "pieces" of information necessary to specify them completely. Among these physical quantities are many which are characterized by giving one piece of information only—their magnitude. Such quantities are called *scalar quantities* or, more simply, *scalars*.

Strictly speaking, a quantity is to be called a scalar only if it is invariant under a transformation of space coordinates. As an example of a true scalar quantity, consider the numerical value of the electrostatic voltage at a point; it is the same regardless of the coordinate system used to describe that point. Conversely, a quantity such as the numerical value of the magnitude of the x component of the wind, which depends on the orientation of what we take to be the x axis, is not a true scalar. Such quantities are called *pseudoscalars*. For the purposes of this book, however, we shall neglect these differences.

A pure number is the simplest type of scalar. Usually, scalar quantities connected with physical ideas express the ratio of the size of that quantity to the size of some unit accepted as a standard for its measurement. For example, the mass of this book is approximately 654 grams; that is, its mass is 654 times the unit of mass—the gram. Other examples of scalar quantities are volume, temperature, voltage, and entropy. The concept of a scalar need not be restricted to real numbers, but it may include, for example, complex numbers.

In addition to scalar quantities, science and engineering are concerned with quantities which require two "pieces" of information: their magnitude and direction. Physical quantities of this nature are called vector quantities.

The word "direction" used here is sometimes replaced by "direction and sense" to denote the fact that a vector is an oriented line segment which points in a particular sense. To make this distinction clear and illustrate the concept of a vector let us consider the following example. To say that a

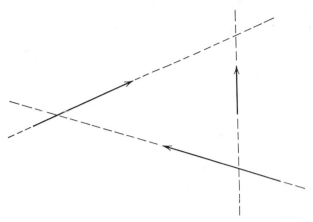

Figure 1.1   The graphical representation of vector quantities.

person is located five miles from a certain tree does not locate him uniquely. If we are to characterize his position completely, we must specify along what direction he is located, for example, the northeast-southwest direction, and in what sense along that direction we must look for him. In other words, the position of a person relative to some reference point is a vector quantity, and if we are to locate the person we must specify the magnitude, sense, and direction of the vector from that reference point to the person.

A vector quantity may be represented graphically by a straight line segment drawn in a particular direction, with an arrowhead at one end to indicate the sense of the vector quantity. The length of such a line segment is representative of the magnitude of the vector quantity in some prescribed scale (see Fig. 1.1); the orientation of the line segment is characteristic of the direction of the vector quantity, and the arrow indicates the sense of the vector quantity.

It is important for someone sailing a boat to ascertain the force of the wind on his sail. To do so, he must determine the capacity of the wind to push his boat through the water and *also* the sense and direction in which the wind will blow him. The fact that this sailor must determine these factors to characterize the force of the wind indicates that the force of the wind may be a vector quantity. However, to qualify as a true vector, a quantity must follow the *law of composition*. To illustrate this characteristic of a true vector, consider the following. Suppose we displace a ball from the origin to a point P (see Fig. 1.2). Now such a displacement has magnitude, sense, and direction and we therefore consider it a vector quantity. We may first move the ball along direction (1), then parallel to direction (2), and finally parallel to direction (3). However, the result

Scalar and Vector Fields

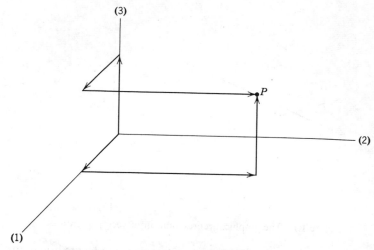

Figure 1.2   The displacement of a ball.

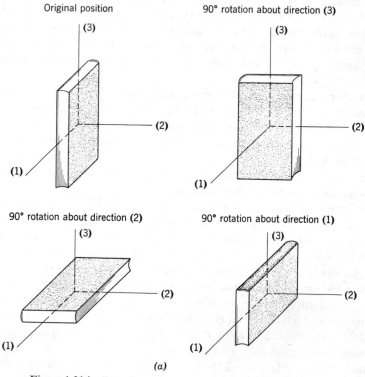

(a)

Figure 1.3(a)   Rotations about the (3), (2), and (1) directions.

would be the same if the ball were first moved along direction (3), then parallel to direction (1), and then along direction (2). In fact, there are six different combinations involving displacements along all these three directions by which a ball could be moved from the origin to *P*. We see that the order in which we execute the individual displacements does not influence the final total displacement. Thus we may say that a physical quantity is a true vector if it can be characterized by a magnitude, direction, and sense *and* if the sum of a number of such vector quantities produces a unique vector quantity regardless of the order in which these quantities are added.

In contradistinction to this behavior the result of several angular displacements is *not* independent of the order of their execution (see Fig. 1.3*a* and *b*). If the book is rotated 90 degrees about direction (3), this rotation may be represented by an arrow whose orientation is along the axis of rotation, whose length is proportional to the amount of rotation, and whose sense is that in which a right-hand screw would advance if rotated in the same manner. We might be tempted, at this point, to call the angular displacement a vector quantity. However, let us first examine

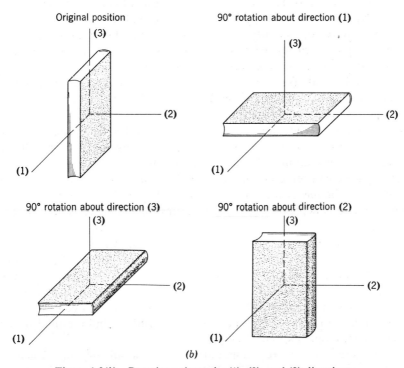

(b)

Figure 1.3(*b*)   Rotations about the (1), (3), and (2) directions.

the result of two successive angular displacements to see if it is independent of the order in which the angular displacements are executed. By examining Fig. 1.3*a*, which shows a 90 degree angular displacement in the (3) direction followed by similar 90 degree rotations about the (2) direction and (1) direction, and comparing it with Fig. 1.3*b* which represents the same rotations but in different order, we see that the final orientation of the book *does* depend on the order of rotation. We conclude therefore that an angular displacement, although characterized by a sense, direction, and magnitude, is not a true vector quantity. We will treat this topic in more detail in Section 4.6.

Although it is not germane to this book, it is sometimes necessary to distinguish between true (polar) vectors such as displacement, force and velocity, and pseudovectors (axial vectors) such as infinitesimal angular displacements and angular momentum. Since the properties of both polar and axial vectors are almost identical, we shall not distinguish between them.

Although angular displacement is not a vector, we shall see in Section 4.6 that an infinitesimal angular displacement is a vector quantity. Since the instantaneous angular velocity is an infinitesimal angular displacement divided by an infinitesimal period of time, we shall consider the angular velocity as a vector quantity. One reason is that the motion of, say, a spinning top is characterized by the orientation of its axis and the number of revolutions per unit time, in other words, it is characterized by a direction and magnitude (see Fig. 1.4). The positive sense of ω, the angular velocity, is taken as the sense that a right-handed screw would advance if rotated in the same manner as the rotating body.

In addition to the more or less obvious vector quantities already mentioned, other physical quantities are also conveniently represented by vectors. We shall now discuss these quantities.

The space curve representing the path that a particle may take through space cannot be represented by a vector (see Fig. 1.5) since it would have many directions depending on which portion of the curve is considered. However, we can think of the space curves with which we deal in the physical world as composed of many infinitesimal straight-line segments having directions that depend on their position on the curve. By assigning a sense to these infinitesimal line segments (usually the positive sense is specified by the sense in which the independent variable(s) increase), we see that a small element of such space curves can be represented by a vector $d\mathbf{l}$. We may thus use vector notation to describe an infinitesimal linear displacement along a specified curve.

Let us suppose we are using radar to follow an airplane which is traveling the path shown in Fig. 1.5. The direction and path length of the radar signal serve to locate the aircraft at any instant. Consequently, the sense, direction, and the path length of the radar signal constitute a vector which describes the position of the airplane. We can therefore think of the location of a point in terms of a vector that tells us the sense, direction, and distance of the point from an arbitrary but fixed origin. Such a vector **R** is called a *position vector*. It can be used to describe a field, for example, a scalar field can be represented as $h(\mathbf{R})$, where h is the value of the scalar quantity at the point located by the vector **R**; similarly, $\mathbf{F}(\mathbf{R})$ represents the value of the vector field at the point located by the vector **R**.

Just as we can think of a space curve as composed of many infinitesimal line elements, we can consider a space surface as made up of many plane surface elements (see Fig. 1.6). Each element of surface is oriented in space in a way that is unique to that surface element. Then, since each surface element may be considered to have a magnitude (its area) and a sense and direction (its orientation), it is reasonable to ascribe to it a vector quality. By convention it has been agreed that the vector representing a surface element is normal to that element and of magnitude which is proportional to the area of the surface element. So we say that the surface

Figure 1.4　An example of the vector representation of the angular velocity.

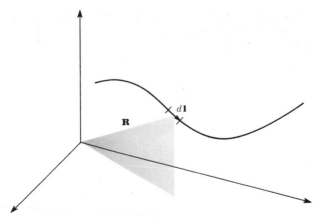

Figure 1.5　An example of the vector representation of a displacement along a space curve.

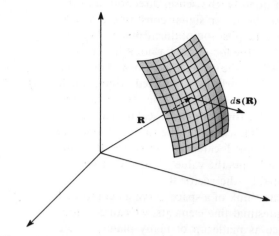

Figure 1.6   Vector representation of the differential area *ds*.

element shown in Fig. 1.6 may be written as *ds*(**R**), where **R** locates that particular element of area relative to some origin.

The sense of *ds*(**R**) is decided in the following manner.

1. If the surface is closed, as, for example, a balloon or doughnut, *ds* points outward from the interior of the body (see Fig. 1.7*a*).

2. If the surface is open, the sense of *ds* is taken to be the direction that a right-hand screw would take if rotated in a direction coinciding with whatever is considered to be the positive direction around the periphery (see Fig. 1.7*b*).

Vector quantities encountered in physical situations are further classified into one of three categories: (*a*) free vectors, (*b*) sliding vectors, and (*c*) point or fixed vectors.

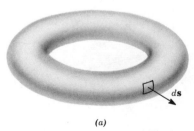

(*a*)

Figure 1.7(*a*)   An example of the sense of *ds* for a closed surface.

A *free vector* is not located at any unique point in space. If we wish to describe the distance traveled by a flight of ducks in 10 seconds when all the ducks are flying with the same velocity, a displacement vector associated with any individual duck or any group of ducks in the flock will be representative of the flock (see Fig. 1.8). The displacement of the flock is considered a free vector.

In the study of geometry we usually consider vectors to be free. Such vectors may be relocated in space provided that they are moved rigidly to a position parallel to their original orientation so that their magnitude and sense are not changed.

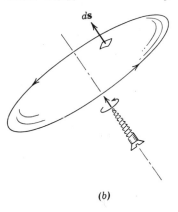

(b)

Figure 1.7(b)   An example of the sense of d**s** for an open surface.

A *sliding vector* has a unique line of action along which it may act. Its effect at one point is identical to that at any other point along that line of action (see Fig. 1.9). Pulling a toy wagon at a constant velocity requires the same force whether it is pulled by its handle or by a spring attached

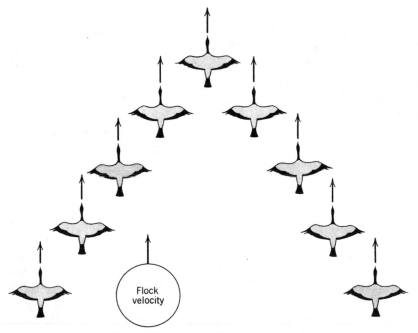

Figure 1.8   An example of a free vector.

Figure 1.9   An example of a sliding vector.

to the end of the handle. Thus the force applied in this situation is a sliding vector.

A *point* or *fixed vector* is associated with a particular point in space. If, for example, we wish a billiard ball to execute a certain motion, say a particular path with a desired spin, we must strike the billiard ball with a force of a particular magnitude and direction and at a particular point on the ball. In this example the vector force can be applied at only one point in space to achieve the desired result. If we consider an elastic body, the position of the application of a force is most important. In one place the force may compress an elastic body, whereas, applied at another place, it may stretch the body. When, as in the foregoing examples, the vector is bound to one point in space, it is called a point or fixed vector. It is this type of vector in which we will be interested when discussing vector fields.

1.3   Fields

We have presented two main categories of physical quantities: scalars and vectors. Let us now extend our discussion to include the situation where a physical quantity, either a scalar or a vector, varies from point to point in space. If the value of a physical quantity at a point depends on the position of that point, the physical quantity is said to be a point function, and the association of a particular value of a physical quantity with each point in a region of space is said to constitute a field. When a scalar quantity is involved, the field is called a *scalar field*; when a vector quantity varies from point to point in a region of space, a *vector field* is said to exist. Let us now examine these ideas in more detail.

SCALAR FIELDS

Suppose we are asked to determine the steady-state temperature distribution on a thin aluminum sheet under which a Bunsen burner is placed and where along its edges an infinite supply of ice is maintained so that the edges are always at 0°C (see Fig. 1.10). After a time, sufficiently long so that the temperature at a point does not change, we may determine the temperature at selected points by a thermocouple. To describe the position of these points, we could scribe a rectangular coordinate system on the aluminum sheet with the origin at the center. We could, then

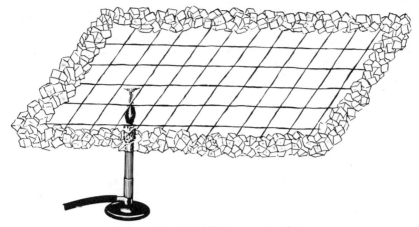

Figure 1.10   Establishing a scalar field.

record the temperature at many points on the sheet and the position of each point in a manner shown in Table 1.1.

This process could be continued as long as we wish in an attempt to determine the temperature at a large number of points on the aluminum sheet. All these data, describing the temperature at certain points and the location of these points, constitute a two-dimensional temperature, that is, scalar, field.

Obviously, this concept of a scalar field is not limited to temperature fields. We may wish to determine the elevation of each point on a mountain as a function of position. To do so we could measure the altitude of points on the mountain and record the latitude and longitude of such points and again present the data in tabular form (see Table 1.2).

The data shown in Table 1.2 could be presented by indicating on a map the elevation of selected points (see Fig. 1.11a). However, this mode of

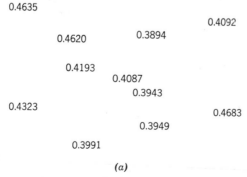

(a)

Figure 1.11(a)   One method of representing a scalar field.

Table 1.1

Temperature at various points on aluminum sheet

Position (ft)		
x	y	Temperature °C
−0.5	−0.5	0
.	.	.
.	.	.
.	.	.
−0.3	−0.2	736
.	.	.
.	.	.
.	.	.
0	−0.4	134
.	.	.
.	.	.
.	.	.
+0.1	+0.4	87
.	.	.
.	.	.
.	.	.
+0.4	+0.3	36
.	.	.
.	.	.
+0.05	+0.5	0

Table 1.2

Elevation of a mountain as a function of position

Position		
Longitude	Latitude	Elevation (ft)
120° 40′ 16″	45° 20′ 35″	4635
120° 40′ 20″	45° 20′ 39″	4620
.	.	.
.	.	.
.	.	.
.	.	.
120° 37′ 18″	45° 15′ 18″	3894
.	.	.
.	.	.
.	.	.
.	.	.
.	.	.
120° 33′ 55″	45° 18′ 50″	3943

presentation does not aid in visualizing the physical situation. To facilitate the process of visualization, the data could be illustrated in a perspective drawing, but it would be necessary to present at least two such drawings to show the entire mountain. One of the better methods used to represent graphically the data of Table 1.2 is by a contour maps These maps are formed by first connecting points of equal elevation to form three-dimensional curves (see Fig. 1.11*b*). The three-dimensional space curves can then be projected onto a two-dimensional surface (see Fig. 1.11*c*). The resulting two-dimensional curves are called *contour lines*. The advantage of this mode of presentation is that it displays the data so that the actual mountain may be readily visualized.

Other examples of two-dimensional scalar fields are the illuminance of a wall or floor resulting from the radiant power emanating from a light and the instantaneous population density in the United States.

If we were to measure the steady-state temperature at various points in the room where you are reading this book, our measurements would indicate the presence of a three-dimensional temperature field. We cannot illustrate a three-dimensional scalar field directly, because there

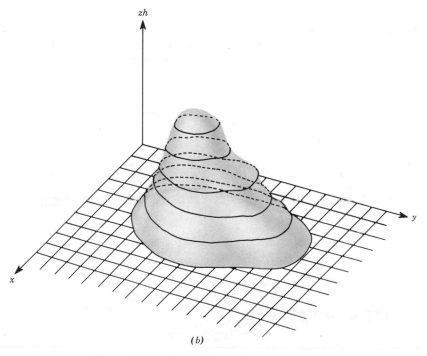

(*b*)

Figure 1.11(*b*).   The construction of contour lines.

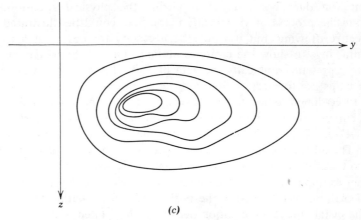

(c)

Figure 1.11(c)   Contour lines.

are four variables (three coordinates and the temperature);   however,
we can connect points in space which are at the same temperature by
surfaces called isothermal surfaces (see Fig. 1.12).

Other examples of three-dimensional scalar fields are the instantaneous
pressure around the wing of an airplane and the mass density of water in
the oceans of the earth.

We can generalize the foregoing by stating that a scalar field exists
in a region of space if at every point in that region a scalar quantity is

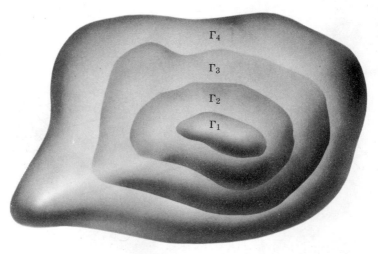

Figure 1.12   Isothermal surfaces.

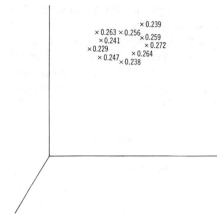

Figure 1.13   One means of representing a three-dimensional scalar field.

defined. We can also think of a scalar field as an assembly of numbers in space, each of which is associated with the point at which it appears and each of which specifies the value of the scalar quantity at that point (see Fig. 1.13).

We have discussed scalar fields that are functions of two and three variables only. In general, the number of variables on which a scalar field depends is dependent on the physical quantity involved. For example, the hydrostatic pressure at a point within a stationary, isothermal incompressible fluid depends on one variable only—the depth below the surface of the fluid; on the other hand, the temperature at a point in the atmosphere depends on the altitude, the latitude and longitude, and the time of the day and year as well as local meteorological conditions of the moment. Here, however, we shall be concerned initially with quantities depending on position only, that is, which are point functions and therefore constitute a field.

VECTOR FIELDS

By analogy with scalar point functions, we find, in science and engineering, vector quantities whose value varies from point to point in space. That is, the magnitude and/or sense and direction of the vector quantity depend on position. To describe this situation, we may consider a vector field to be a region of space at every point of which a vector quantity is defined.

As an example of a two-dimensional vector field, let us consider the instantaneous velocity of the surface water of a stream or river. After establishing a coordinate system to describe the position of points on the surface of the water and agreeing on a consistent means of specifying sense and direction—let us say the compass—we can measure the surface velocity at selected points by using light cork bobs constrained to float on the surface. The resulting data can be presented in tabular form similar to that used for a scalar field. Now, however, we must give the magnitude, sense, and direction of the velocity for each of the selected points on the surface of the stream (see Table 1.3).

Table 1.3

Surface velocity of a stream

Position (ft)		Velocity of Surface Water (ft/sec)	
x	y	Magnitude	Direction from N (as measured in a clockwise direction)
+6	+3	6.2	6°
.	.	.	.
.	.	.	.
+4.37	−8.29	1.3	43
.	.	.	.
.	.	.	.
−8.5	+7.3	8.6	163
.	.	.	.
.	.	.	.
41	−9.00	0.4	94
.	.	.	.
.	.	.	.
2.9	−5.80	.9	68

Just as a scalar field may be visualized as a region of space filled with numbers, each associated with a particular point, we may think of a vector field as an assembly of vectors, each associated with a particular point, that is, an assembly of point vectors. We shall now discuss several of the more commonly used methods for the graphical description of a vector field.

Suppose we wish to describe graphically the two-dimensional vector field of the surface velocity of a stream. We can choose a number of

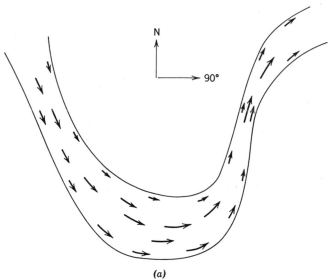

(a)

Figure 1.14(*a*)   One means of representing a two-dimensional vector field.

points and draw at each point a vector whose magnitude, sense, and direction are representative of the velocity at that point (see Fig. 1.14*a*).

We can also let the thickness of the line segment illustrating a vector represent the magnitude of the vector quantity at that point (see Fig. 1.14*b*).

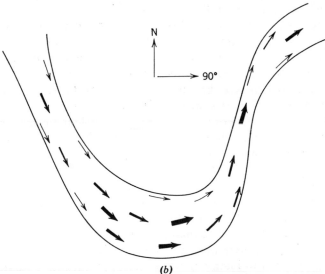

(b)

(*b*)   One means of representing a two-dimensional vector field.

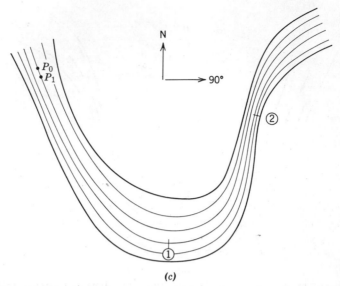

Figure 1.14(c)   One means of representing a two-dimensional vector field.

Another mode of representing a two-dimensional field is to indicate a vector field by drawing continuous lines, whose orientation at any point is the direction of the vector field (see Fig. 1.14c).

To represent a vector field in this manner, we draw at a point P_0 a line element whose direction at P_0 is that of the field we wish to represent. We thereby arrive at a point P_1, close to P_0. Through P_1 we draw another line element whose direction is that of the vector field at P_1. This process is continued until a curve is constructed in the region of interest. Other starting points are chosen and the process repeated until a sufficient number of curved lines is produced. Such lines are called field lines, flow lines, flux lines, or stream lines, depending on the vector quantity involved. The magnitude or intensity of a vector field in the neighborhood of a point is proportional to the number of field lines per unit length of a line (if it is a two-dimensional field) or per unit area of a surface (if it is a three-dimensional field) drawn perpendicular to the field lines. For example, in Fig. 1.14c the number of lines crossing a line at point 1 is one, whereas the number crossing a line of the same length at point 2 is two; this signifies that the magnitude of the surface velocity, the surface speed, is two times greater at point 2 than at point 1.

It should be noted here that two different field lines cannot intersect, because at the point of intersection the direction of the field would not be single-valued.

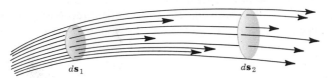

Figure 1.15 A tube of field lines.

We shall now consider the possibility that these field lines may have a beginning and an end. In the three-dimensional vector field $\mathbf{F}$ whose field lines have been constructed in the manner shown previously, let us insert at some point a surface element $d\mathbf{s}_1$ which is essentially at right angles to the field lines (see Fig. 1.15). Now the number of field lines passing through $d\mathbf{s}_1$ is $|\mathbf{F}_1|\,|d\mathbf{s}_1|$, where $|\mathbf{F}_1|$ is the intensity of $\mathbf{F}$ at $d\mathbf{s}_1$ and $|d\mathbf{s}_1|$ is the magnitude of $d\mathbf{s}_1$—its area. If we follow that bundle of lines, they will form a tube containing the field lines of the field $\mathbf{F}$. Let us section the tube at some point near $d\mathbf{s}_1$ and let $d\mathbf{s}_2$ designate the cross-sectional area of the bundle at that point. The number of lines through $d\mathbf{s}_2$ is $|\mathbf{F}_2|\,|d\mathbf{s}_2|$, where $|\mathbf{F}_2|$ is the intensity of $\mathbf{F}$ at $d\mathbf{s}_2$. Then, if $|\mathbf{F}_1|\,|d\mathbf{s}_1|$ is different from $|\mathbf{F}_2|\,|d\mathbf{s}_2|$, we conclude that field lines must have originated or terminated in the tube between the surfaces $d\mathbf{s}_1$ and $d\mathbf{s}_2$ because no field lines can enter or leave through the sides of the tube.

The instantaneous velocity of raindrops on a gusty day is an example of a three-dimensional vector field. Such fields can be represented graphically by a group of vectors drawn at selected points in a region of space, each indicating the magnitude, sense, and direction of the velocity of the raindrops at those points (see Fig. 1.16).

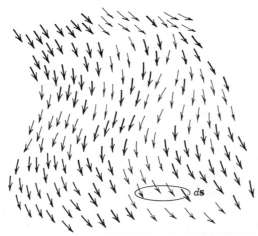

Figure 1.16 One means of representing a three-dimensional vector field.

In this section we have attempted to represent scalar and vector fields in a region of space by choosing selected points to represent the value of a scalar or vector quantity. If we try, at a reasonable number of points, to represent a field over a considerable area or volume, there will be points and regions where we have indicated nothing. We should not allow our graphical field representations to mislead us into thinking that the scalar or vector quantity is zero at these points. The fields with which we shall deal permeate a region, that is, exist at all points of that region; and the points in the field drawings at which no value is indicated merely signify the fact that we cannot represent *graphically* a scalar or vector quantity at *every* point of a region.

1.4 Fundamental Characteristics of Fields

The fields encountered in science and engineering are usually (1) single-valued, (2) bounded, (3) continuous, (4) differentiable, and (5) linear. However, sometimes fields may not conform to (1), (2), (3), and (4) at a number of selected locations. An understanding of these fundamental characteristics and the physical significance of a field not possessing these characteristics is basic to the entire theory of fields.

By the words "single-valued," we mean that given the position of a point (by stipulating the coordinates of a point), the value of the scalar or vector quantity at that point is uniquely defined. For example, in our discussion of a mountain as illustrative of a scalar field, we saw that for each position on the earth, the height of the mountain was uniquely specified. If there had been an overhanging portion (see Fig. 1.17, which is a section of the mountain), the elevation at a point specified by a particular latitude and longitude is 643 ft, 654 ft, and 665 ft, and the elevation of the mountain is then not a single-valued function of position. The fields with which we shall deal will not be of this type, but they will be single-valued; that is, given the position of a point, the scalar or vector quantity involved will be uniquely defined at that point.

If, in a region of space, a number exists such that the magnitude of a field is less than that number, the field is *bounded*.

The fields we shall treat are continuous, except possibly at a finite or countable infinite number of points, lines, and surfaces. We shall therefore be concerned primarily with fields that vary smoothly from one point to a nearby point. A field is continuous at a point if the values of the field as we approach that point from any direction are equal, finite, and coincide with the value of the field at that point. The continuity of a field at a point Q means that Q may be surrounded by a sphere within which the

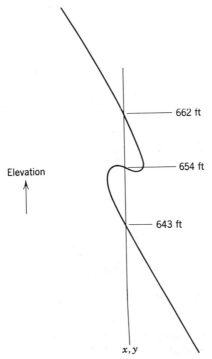

Figure 1.17   Mountain elevation as an example of a multivalued function of position.

field is not a great deal different from its value at Q (see Fig. 1.18). The size of the sphere surrounding Q where the field is approximately that at Q may change as the position of Q changes. If, however, at all points in a region of space the radii of the spheres surrounding Q are always greater than a specified small value, the field is said to be *uniformly continuous* in that region.

If the mountain discussed previously had a sharp, right-angle cliff on its side (see Fig. 1.19), at that point the altitude would not be continuous, because the value of the height of the mountain as we approach $x = x_0$ depends on the direction from which we approach that point. At this point the height of the mountain is also not single-valued.

There may be a certain finite number of points, lines, or surfaces in a region of space where a field is not continuous. The fields we shall consider are also differentiable at all but a finite number of points, lines, and surfaces; that is, the spatial rates of change of these fields are bounded and are uniquely defined regardless of the manner a point in space is approached. These fundamental field properties are extremely important, and we shall discuss them further in many of the following sections.

Scalar and Vector Fields

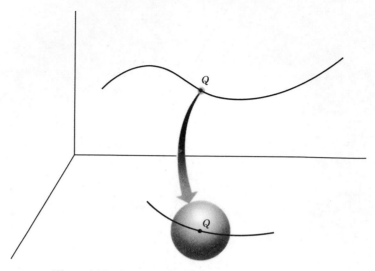

Figure 1.18   A geometrical interpretation of continuity.

In addition to the properties of single-valuedness, boundedness, continuity, and differentiability, we shall deal with fields that are *linear*. This means that the point vectors, of which an n-dimensional vector field is composed, can be expressed as the linear combination of n bases vectors whose direction, sense, and magnitude are prescribed. For example, as we shall see in Chapter 2, a vector in a plane **A** can be

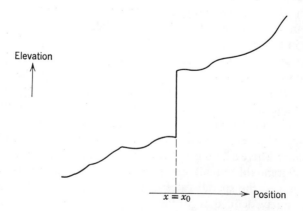

Figure 1.19   Elevation of a mountain as an example of a discontinuous function of position.

represented by the linear sum of two vectors,

$$\mathbf{A} = \mathbf{u}_x A_x + \mathbf{u}_y A_y$$

where $\mathbf{u}_x$ and $\mathbf{u}_y$ are vectors whose sense, direction, and magnitude are prescribed; A_x and A_y are real scalar constants. In the more general case the constants appearing in the linear combination of the prescribed or bases vectors may be complex.

2

Vector Algebra

2.1 Introduction

In Chapter 1, the concept of a field was presented, and we discussed the graphical and symbolic representations of both scalar and vector fields. The primary value of these ideas to scientists and engineers is that they can be employed to describe physical concepts and phenomena in a quantitative manner. However, before the concept of scalar and vector fields can be utilized in a quantitative manner, we must develop certain rules which govern the mathematical manipulation of the symbols representing such fields. To be physically meaningful, these rules must be unambiguous and, furthermore, they must be capable of describing physical processes involving the addition, subtraction, multiplication, and, if possible, the division of field quantities.

Because a vector field may be thought of as an assembly of point vectors, it is important to examine the rules governing point vectors. We shall find that the algebra (rules) governing the mathematical manipulation of the symbols representing scalar fields is, in some respects, different from those which are applicable when treating the symbols representing vector fields. We shall, in the following discussion, assume that the reader is familiar with scalar algebra.

Throughout the discussion in this chapter, we shall attempt to emphasize geometrical considerations as opposed to a discussion based entirely on vector components. The justification for this approach is that we wish to point out further that a vector is a unique quantity, independent of the frame of reference or coordinate system which may be utilized to describe it.

2.2 Vector Addition and Subtraction

Before discussing vector addition and subtraction, we must decide what we mean by "equal" when discussing vectors and vector fields. Two free

24

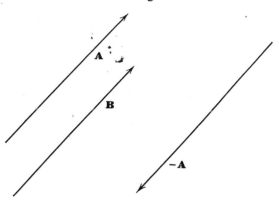

Figure 2.1   Free vectors.

vectors **A** and **B** are said to be equal,

$$\mathbf{A} = \mathbf{B} \tag{2.1}$$

when they have the same magnitude, direction, and sense. This definition of equality does not imply that these two vectors are coincident in space. The free vectors **A** and **B** shown in Fig. 2.1 are therefore considered equal. On the other hand, two vector fields are said to be equal in a region of space when they are equal at all points of that region. Since vector fields constitute an assembly of point or fixed vectors, the equality of two fields implies the coincidence of the two fields.

To illustrate the physical interpretation of vector addition, let us consider two tugboats which are pulling a barge with ropes that have a common point of attachment on the barge (see Fig. 2.2a). The force $\mathbf{F}_T$ on the barge produced by the effect of both tugs is that which would be produced by a single tug pulling with a force, whose direction and magnitude are determined by the forces $\mathbf{F}_1$ and $\mathbf{F}_2$ exerted by each tug individually. This single resultant force $\mathbf{F}_T$ can be determined by adding the forces as illustrated in Fig. 2.2b. Forces added in this manner are said to have been added geometrically or vectorially. This idea may be generalized in the following way: by **C** the sum of two vectors **A** and **B**,

$$\mathbf{C} = \mathbf{A} + \mathbf{B} \tag{2.2}$$

we mean that the vector **B** may be moved parallel to itself, so that its initial point coincides with the final point of **A**; then the vector **C**, joining the initial point of **A** with the final point of **B**, is said to represent the vector sum of **A** and **B**. By referring to Fig. 2.3 we see that

$$\mathbf{C} = \mathbf{A} + \mathbf{B} = \mathbf{B} + \mathbf{A} \tag{2.3}$$

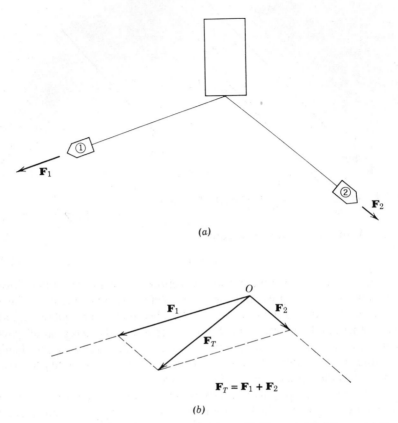

(a)

(b)

$$\mathbf{F}_T = \mathbf{F}_1 + \mathbf{F}_2$$

Figure 2.2 (a) An example of vector addition. (b) The graphical representation of vector addition.

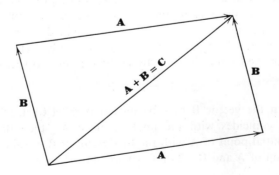

Figure 2.3 Commutation of vector addition.

that is, if we construct a parallelogram whose sides are the vectors **A** and **B**, the diagonal vector **C** from the initial point of **A** to the terminal point of **B** is the same as the vector from the initial point of **B** to the terminal point of **A**. We conclude therefore that vector addition is *commutative*. The result is the same regardless of whether we add **B** to **A** or **A** to **B**.

If we wish to add another vector **D** to **C** = **A** + **B**, we proceed as before.

$$E = D + C = D + (A + B) \tag{2.4}$$

Here the grouping of the vectors may be changed without altering the result,

$$E = (D + A) + B = D + (A + B) \tag{2.5}$$

We see that the *associative law* is valid for vector addition.

The subtraction of one vector **B** from another vector **A** may be considered as the sum of the vector **A** and the vector (−**B**):

$$C = A - B = A + (-B) \tag{2.6}$$

This can be interpreted geometrically by considering Fig. 2.4. If two vectors **A** and **B** are drawn from a common origin **C**, the difference **A** − **B** may be considered as a vector extending from the final point of **B** to the final point of **A** such that

$$B + C = A \tag{2.7}$$

In the introductory discussion of vector addition, we treated the problem of determining the direction and magnitude of the force exerted by a single tugboat which would be equivalent to that exerted by two tugs pulling as indicated in Fig. 2.2a. Suppose instead we wish to discuss the inverse problem: If F_T, the total force provided by a single tugboat, is to be duplicated by two tugboats pulling in the directions shown in Fig. 2.2a, what force must be exerted by each tugboat? To determine

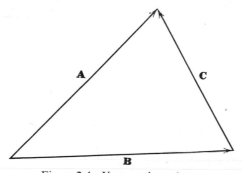

Figure 2.4 Vector subtraction.

Scalar and Vector Fields

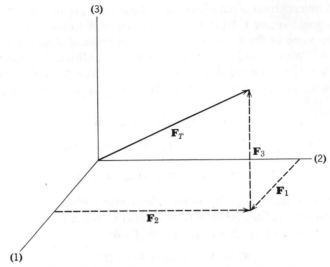

Figure 2.5   Resolving a vector into its components.

these forces, we project $\mathbf{F}_T$ onto the lines indicating each direction (see Fig. 2.2b). $\mathbf{F}_T$ and these direction lines have a common initial point 0. To project $\mathbf{F}_T$ along direction 1, we draw a line parallel to direction 2 from the final point of $\mathbf{F}_T$ until it intersects the line indicating direction 1. The length of the line segment from 0 to this point of intersection is the magnitude of the force which one tugboat must exert. By a similar projection onto a line in direction 2, we can determine the force which the other tug must exert if the result of the forces of both tugs is to be equivalent to that exerted by a single tug pulling with a force $\mathbf{F}_T$. We now speak of $\mathbf{F}_1$ and $\mathbf{F}_2$ as the components of $\mathbf{F}_T$ in the directions 1 and 2, or we say that $\mathbf{F}_T$ has been *resolved* into vectors in the directions 1 and 2.

We have discussed the resolution of a vector along directions which lie in the plane of the vector. This idea can be generalized to include the resolution of a vector along three noncoplanar directions (see Fig. 2.5). In this figure the vector $\mathbf{F}_T$ is resolved into components along directions 1, 2, and 3 which are mutually orthogonal. If two vectors are equal, then the components of one of the vectors are equal to the corresponding components of the other vector.

2.3   Multiplication Processes Involving Vectors

If we are asked to multiply one scalar by another, we find that the desired operation and its result are unambiguous. Similarly, if we multiply a vector by a scalar, we shall see presently that we can do so in a straight-forward manner. If, however, we are asked to multiply one vector by another, the request is ambiguous and requires a further stipulation as to the manner in which these two vectors are to be multiplied. In other words, we must define what we mean when we "multiply" two vectors together. In this section we shall discuss multiplication processes where a vector is a multiplicand.

MULTIPLICATION OF A VECTOR BY A SCALAR

In Section 2.2 we defined the process of vector addition involving two vectors **A** and **B**. Suppose in this process we wish to let **B** = **A**; that is, we wish to add **A** to itself. The result of this addition would be 2**A**, a vector in the same direction and having the same sense as **A** but with twice the magnitude. If to 2**A** we add **A**, the result, of course, is 3**A**, etc.

We can generalize threse results as follows: If m is a scalar and **A** a vector, then m**A** is a vector in the direction of **A** if $m > 0$ or in the opposite sense from **A** if $m < 0$. The magnitude of the vector m**A** is m times that of **A**. If $m = 0$, we obtain a zero vector **0** which is a vector of zero length and which by convention is considered to have any direction; that is, it is parallel to all vectors.

It follows from an examination of Fig. 2.6 that if m is a scalar and **C** is a vector given by Eq. (2.2), then

$$m\mathbf{C} = m(\mathbf{A} + \mathbf{B}) = m\mathbf{A} + m\mathbf{B} \qquad (2.8)$$

If m is a scalar given by $m = p + q$, where p and q are scalars, then

$$m\mathbf{A} = (p + q)\mathbf{A} = p\mathbf{A} + q\mathbf{A} \qquad (2.9)$$

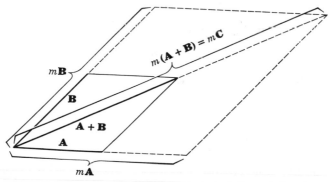

Figure 2.6   Multiplication of a vector sum by a scalar.

SCALAR OR DOT MULTIPLICATION

The scalar product of two vectors **A** and **B** is defined to be a scalar given by

$$\mathbf{A} \cdot \mathbf{B} = |\mathbf{A}|\,|\mathbf{B}|\cos[\mathbf{A}, \mathbf{B}] \qquad (2.10)$$

read, "**A** dot **B**," where [**A**, **B**] is the angle between **A** and **B** as measured from **A** to **B**. Sometimes this type of vector multiplication is called the inner product of **A** and **B**.

The scalar product is commutative (see Fig. 2.7).

$$\mathbf{A} \cdot \mathbf{B} = \mathbf{B} \cdot \mathbf{A} \qquad (2.11)$$

That this is true can be seen by considering that

$$\mathbf{B} \cdot \mathbf{A} = |\mathbf{B}|\,|\mathbf{A}|\cos[\mathbf{B}, \mathbf{A}] \qquad (2.12)$$

But in Fig. 2.7 we see that

$$[\mathbf{B}, \mathbf{A}] = [\mathbf{A}, \mathbf{B}]$$

Thus

$$\begin{aligned}
\mathbf{B} \cdot \mathbf{A} &= |\mathbf{B}|\,|\mathbf{A}|\cos[\mathbf{B}, \mathbf{A}] \\
&= |\mathbf{A}|\,|\mathbf{B}|\cos[\mathbf{A}, \mathbf{B}] \\
&= \mathbf{A} \cdot \mathbf{B}
\end{aligned} \qquad (2.13)$$

Furthermore, it follows that

$$\mathbf{A} \cdot (\mathbf{B} + \mathbf{C}) = \mathbf{A} \cdot \mathbf{B} + \mathbf{A} \cdot \mathbf{C} \qquad (2.14)$$

that is, scalar multiplication of vectors is distributive.

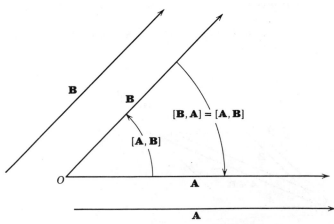

Figure 2.7   Angles involved in the scalar multiplication of two vectors.

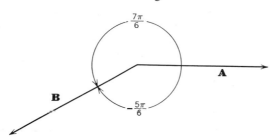

Figure 2.8   For discussion of scalar multiplication.

If **B** = **A**, then from Eq. 2.13

$$\mathbf{A} \cdot \mathbf{A} = |\mathbf{A}|\,|\mathbf{A}| \cos \theta = |\mathbf{A}|\,|\mathbf{A}| \equiv A^2 \qquad (2.15)$$

If **A** is perpendicular to **B**, the angle [**A, B**] is $\pi/2$ and $\cos \pi/2 = 0$ so that

$$\mathbf{A} \cdot \mathbf{B} = 0 \qquad (\text{if } \mathbf{A} \perp \mathbf{B}) \qquad (2.16)$$

However, if **A** · **B** = 0, we can only conclude that either **A** $\perp$ **B** or **A** = 0 or **B** = 0, or both **A** and **B** are zero.

If **A** is parallel to **B**, then **A** · **B** = |**A**| |**B**|; and if **A** is antiparallel (has the opposite sense) to **B**, then **A** · **B** = $-$|**A**| |**B**|, because $\cos (\pi) = -1$.

As an example of the foregoing ideas, consider the scalar product of the two vectors shown in Fig. 2.8. Here the angle from **A** to **B** is $7\pi/6$ or $-5\pi/6$, depending on whether we measure the angle from **A** to **B** in a counterclockwise direction (which we have called positive) or in a clockwise direction (which we consider negative). Then

$$\mathbf{A} \cdot \mathbf{B} = |\mathbf{A}|\,|\mathbf{B}| \cos \left(\frac{7\pi}{6}\right) = -\frac{|\mathbf{A}|\,|\mathbf{B}|\sqrt{3}}{2}$$

$$= |\mathbf{A}|\,|\mathbf{B}| \cos \left(-\frac{5\pi}{6}\right) = -\frac{|\mathbf{A}|\,|\mathbf{B}|\sqrt{3}}{2} \qquad (2.17)$$

or, in general,

$$\mathbf{A} \cdot \mathbf{B} = |\mathbf{A}|\,|\mathbf{B}| \cos [\mathbf{A, B}] = |\mathbf{A}|\,|\mathbf{B}| \cos \{360 \pm [\mathbf{A, B}]\}$$

$$= |\mathbf{A}|\,|\mathbf{B}| \cos \{360 \pm [\mathbf{B, A}]\} \qquad (2.18)$$

$$= |\mathbf{A}|\,|\mathbf{B}| \cos [\mathbf{B, A}]$$

$$= \mathbf{B} \cdot \mathbf{A}$$

The product of |**B**| and $\cos$ [**A, B**] represents the magnitude of the component of **B** in the direction of **A** and |**A**| $\cos$ [**A, B**] is the magnitude of **A** in the direction of **B** (see Figure 2.9). We see then that **A** · **B** may be interpreted as the magnitude of the component of **B** along **A** times |**A**| or, equivalently, **A** · **B** may be thought of as the magnitude of the component of **A** along the direction of **B** times |**B**|.

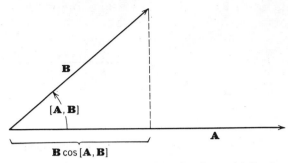

Figure 2.9   For the interpretation of scalar multiplication.

To indicate the utility of the scalar product of two vectors, consider
the work done in moving a sled a small distance $d\mathbf{l}$ by pulling on the sled
with a rope which makes an angle θ with the displacement $d\mathbf{l}$ of the sled
(see Fig. 2.10).

Work, a scalar, is defined as the product of a force component in the
direction of displacement times the magnitude of the displacement. The
component of the force $\mathbf{F}$ along the rope with which the sled is pulled is

$$|\mathbf{F}| \cos [\theta] = |\mathbf{F}| \cos [\mathbf{F}, d\mathbf{l}] \tag{2.19}$$

so that the work done dW in displacing a sled a distance $d\mathbf{l}$ is

$$dW = |\mathbf{F}| \, |d\mathbf{l}| \cos [\mathbf{F}, d\mathbf{l}] \tag{2.20}$$

However, according to our definition of the scalar product of two vectors,
this equation may be written

$$dW = \mathbf{F} \cdot d\mathbf{l} \tag{2.21}$$

where dW is a scalar. There are many other applications involving the
scalar product; we shall now discuss one of the most important of them,
the component representation of a vector in a rectangular or Cartesian
coordinate system.

We have discussed the resolution of a vector into components along
specific directions. By adding the component vectors in each direction, we

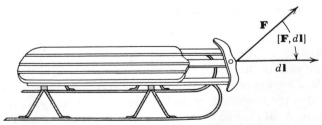

Figure 2.10   Work as an example of scalar multiplication.

can reconstitute the vector so that the stipulation of components along known directions serves to specify the vector uniquely. One reasonable set of directions along which to specify the components of a vector are the directions given by the x-, y-, and z-axes of a rectangular coordinate system. If we denote the component vectors along these directions by $\mathbf{A}_x$, $\mathbf{A}_y$, and $\mathbf{A}_z$, then, as before, the sum of these components equals the vector $\mathbf{A}$,

$$\mathbf{A} = \mathbf{A}_x + \mathbf{A}_y + \mathbf{A}_z \qquad (2.22)$$

(see Fig. 2.11).

Now a vector with a specified magnitude, sense, and direction, for example, the vector $\mathbf{A}_x$ already discussed, may be written

$$\mathbf{A}_x = \mathbf{u}_x |\mathbf{A}_x| \qquad \text{or simply} \qquad \mathbf{u}_x A_x \qquad (2.23a)$$

where $|\mathbf{A}_x|$ is the magnitude or length of $\mathbf{A}_x$ and where $\mathbf{u}_x$ is a vector in the $+x$-direction whose magnitude is one, that is, $|\mathbf{u}_x| = 1$. By means of the concept of a unit vector, we can express the component vector $\mathbf{A}_x$ in terms of a scalar A_x and a vector $\mathbf{u}_x$, whose direction and magnitude are specified. This notation is very useful in the symbolic representation of vector quantities.

If we desire, we can ascribe units such as one mile per hour to the unit vector. However, following the same convention as when writing algebraic equations involving scalars, we refrain from ascribing units to a unit vector.

By analogy with Eq. (2.23a), we may write

$$\mathbf{A}_y = \mathbf{u}_y A_y \qquad \text{and} \qquad \mathbf{A}_z = \mathbf{u}_z A_z \qquad (2.32b,c)$$

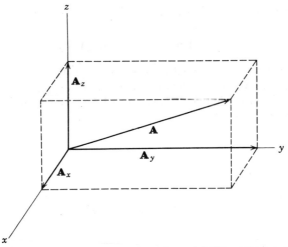

Figure 2.11 The resolution of a vector into three mutually orthogonal components.

so that Eq. (2.22) becomes

$$\mathbf{A} = \mathbf{u}_x A_x + \mathbf{u}_y A_y + \mathbf{u}_z A_z \tag{2.24}$$

Because $\quad \mathbf{u}_x \cdot \mathbf{u}_x = 1 = \mathbf{u}_y \cdot \mathbf{u}_y = \mathbf{u}_z \cdot \mathbf{u}_z \quad$ since $\cos 0 = 1$

and $\quad \mathbf{u}_x \cdot \mathbf{u}_y = 0 = \mathbf{u}_y \cdot \mathbf{u}_z = \mathbf{u}_z \cdot \mathbf{u}_x \quad$ since $\cos \dfrac{\pi}{2} = 0$

the dot product may be written

$$\mathbf{A} \cdot \mathbf{B} = (\mathbf{u}_x A_x + \mathbf{u}_y A_y + \mathbf{u}_z A_z) \cdot (\mathbf{u}_x B_x + \mathbf{u}_y B_y + \mathbf{u}_z B_z)$$
$$= A_x B_x + A_y B_y + A_z B_z \tag{2.25}$$

If we dot Eq. (2.24) with itself, that is, $\mathbf{A} \cdot \mathbf{A}$, we obtain

$$\mathbf{A} \cdot \mathbf{A} \equiv A^2 = (\mathbf{u}_x A_x + \mathbf{u}_y A_y + \mathbf{u}_z A_z) \cdot (\mathbf{u}_x A_x + \mathbf{u}_y A_y + \mathbf{u}_z A_z)$$
$$= A_x^2 + A_y^2 + A_z^2 \tag{2.26}$$

From Eq. (2.26) we see that

$$|\mathbf{A}| = A = (A_x^2 + A_y^2 + A_z^2)^{1/2} \tag{2.27}$$

That the magnitude of a vector is the square root of the sum of the squares of the magnitude of its components results from the fact that the coordinate system (in this case the Cartesian or rectangular) is orthogonal. We shall return to this important point in Chapter 4.

VECTOR OR CROSS MULTIPLICATION

The vector or cross product of two vectors $\mathbf{A}$ and $\mathbf{B}$ is defined to be a vector given by

$$\mathbf{A} \times \mathbf{B} = \mathbf{u}_n \, |\mathbf{A}| \, |\mathbf{B}| \sin [\mathbf{A}, \mathbf{B}] \tag{2.28}$$

(see Fig. 2.12) read "A cross B," where $\mathbf{u}_n$ is a unit vector normal to a plane containing $\mathbf{A}$ and $\mathbf{B}$ in the direction that a right-handed screw would advance if turned so that $\mathbf{A}$ rotates toward $\mathbf{B}$ through the smaller angle, $0 \leq \theta \leq \pi$. Here $\mathbf{A}$ and $\mathbf{B}$ may be moved parallel to themselves until

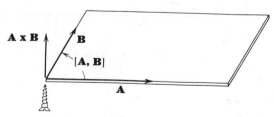

Figure 2.12   The vector product of two vectors.

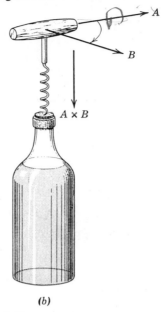

(a)

(b)

Figure 2.13.

they are coplanar and have a common origin. They then define the plane to which $\mathbf{u}_n$ is normal. Other names for this type of multiplication are the skew and outer products.

As an aid in deciding the direction of the vector $\mathbf{A} \times \mathbf{B}$, see Fig. 2.13a. If the fingers of the right hand are curled so that they point from $\mathbf{A}$ toward $\mathbf{B}$ through the smaller angle, then the thumb points in the direction of $\mathbf{u}_n$. This concept is called the *right-hand rule*. In this figure we have shown another example of the cross product. The direction and sense of $\mathbf{A} \times \mathbf{B}$ is that which a right-handed corkscrew will take if $\mathbf{A}$ is rotated toward $\mathbf{B}$ through the smaller angle between them (Fig. 2.13b).

The vector product is not commutative, that is,

$$\mathbf{A} \times \mathbf{B} \neq \mathbf{B} \times \mathbf{A} = \mathbf{u}'_n \, |\mathbf{B}| \, |\mathbf{A}| \sin [\mathbf{B}, \mathbf{A}] \qquad (2.29)$$

where from the definition of the cross product we see that $\mathbf{u}'_n$ has a sense opposite to that of $\mathbf{u}_n$; thus $\mathbf{u}_n = -\mathbf{u}'_n$, so that

$$\mathbf{B} \times \mathbf{A} = -\mathbf{A} \times \mathbf{B} \qquad (2.30)$$

We see therefore that the order of the multiplier and the multiplicand must be maintained.

The distributive law is valid,

$$\mathbf{A} \times (\mathbf{B} + \mathbf{C}) = \mathbf{A} \times \mathbf{B} + \mathbf{A} \times \mathbf{C} \qquad (2.31)$$

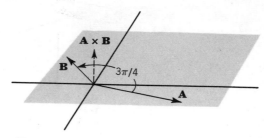

Figure 2.14   The vector product of two vectors.

If **A** is normal to **B**, then

$$\mathbf{A} \times \mathbf{B} = \mathbf{u}_n \, |\mathbf{A}| \, |\mathbf{B}| \qquad (2.32)$$

and if **A** is parallel to **B**, then

$$\mathbf{A} \times \mathbf{B} = 0 \qquad (2.33)$$

Conversely, if the vector product $\mathbf{A} \times \mathbf{B} = 0$, then either one or more of the following are true: $\mathbf{A} = 0$, $\mathbf{B} = 0$, or $\mathbf{A} \parallel \mathbf{B}$. Obviously, then, a vector crossed into itself is zero.

As an example of the mechanics of the vector product, consider the vectors **A** and **B** shown in Fig. 2.14. Here the smaller angle from **A** to **B**, is $3\pi/4$, so that $\sin [\mathbf{A}, \mathbf{B}] = \frac{1}{2}\sqrt{2}$. Since $\mathbf{u}_n$ points upward,

$$\mathbf{A} \times \mathbf{B} = \frac{|\mathbf{A}| \, |\mathbf{B}| \, \sqrt{2}}{2} \, \mathbf{u}_n$$

is a vector that points upward.

The vector product of two vectors may be interpreted geometrically as follows (see Fig. 2.15).

Since the height h of the parallelogram shown in Fig. 2.15 is given by

$$h = |\mathbf{B}| \sin [\mathbf{A}, \mathbf{B}] \qquad (2.34)$$

then $|\mathbf{A} \times \mathbf{B}|$ represents the magnitude of the area of a parallelogram whose

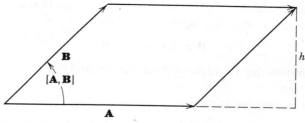

Figure 2.15   An illustration showing that the area of a parallelogram is **A** × **B**.

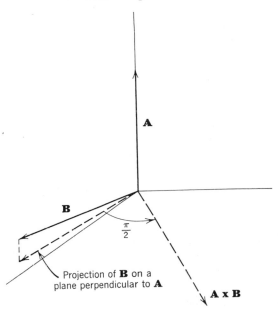

Figure 2.16 A geometrical interpretation of A × B.

sides are the vectors **A** and **B**. The fact that this area is represented by the vector $\mathbf{u}_n h = \mathbf{u}_n |\mathbf{A}| |\mathbf{B}| \sin [\mathbf{A}, \mathbf{B}]$ indicates the consistency of the idea discussed in Chapter 1 that a plane area is a vector quantity whose direction is normal to the plane.

The product **A** × **B** can also be considered as the result of rotating the projection of **B** onto a plane normal to **A** by $\pi/2$ in a positive or counterclockwise direction about **A** and multiplying the resulting vector by $|\mathbf{A}|$ (see Fig. 2.16). In other words, the vector product of two vectors is a vector whose sense and direction are given by the right-hand rule and whose magnitude is that of the first vector times the magnitude of the component of the second vector which lies in a plane normal to the first vector.

The utility of the cross product is illustrated by the following example. Suppose a thumbtack in Fig. 2.17 is spinning on its point with an angular velocity **ω** rad/sec and we wish to calculate the linear velocity **v** of a point on the periphery of its head. We can consider the point of the thumbtack as the origin, and the angular velocity **ω** with which the tack is spinning is considered to be a vector whose sense and direction are upward along the axis about which the tack is spinning and whose magnitude is proportional to the angular velocity. The magnitude of the linear velocity $|\mathbf{v}|$ is given by

$$|\mathbf{v}| = |\boldsymbol{\omega}| |\mathbf{R}'| = |\boldsymbol{\omega}| |\mathbf{R}| \sin [\boldsymbol{\omega}, \mathbf{R}] \qquad (2.35)$$

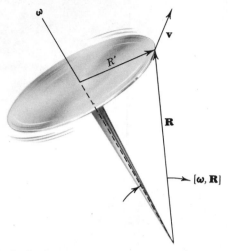

Figure 2.17   A physical example of the utility of the vector product.

and, in accordance with the direction of **v** which is normal to **ω** and **R**, we may then write

$$\mathbf{v} = \boldsymbol{\omega} \times \mathbf{R} \tag{2.36}$$

Another physical concept which can be used to demonstrate the utility of the vector product of two vectors is *torque* or the *moment of force*. If we wish to describe the torque resulting from a force **F** acting at a point *P* about a center *O* (see Fig. 2.18), we must specify the magnitude and direction of the torque. The magnitude of the moment of force is the product of the magnitude of the force and *l*, the shortest distance from *O* to the direction along which **F** acts. If |**R**| is the distance from *O* to *P* and

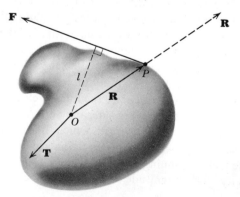

Figure 2.18   Torque, as an example of the vector product of two vectors.

[R, F] is the angle between **R** and **F**, where $0 \leq [R, F] \leq \pi$, then

$$|T| = l\,|F| = |R|\,|F|\,\sin\,[R, F]$$

The direction of **T** is the direction of the axis of rotation about O, normal to the plane containing **R** and **F**. We observe in Fig. 2.18 that the direction of rotation about O is that which moves the vector **R**, so that it tends to assume the direction of **F**. Adopting this convention, we see that

$$T = u_n\,|R|\,|F|\,\sin\,[R, F] = R \times F \tag{2.37}$$

The vector product of two vectors **A** and **B** may also be written in component form:

$$A \times B = [u_x A_x + u_y A_y + u_z A_z] \times [u_x B_x + u_y B_y + u_z B_z] \tag{2.38}$$

Since the Cartesian coordinate axes are at right angles to each other, the angles $[u_x, u_y]$, $[u_y, u_z]$, and $[u_z, u_x]$ are $\pi/2$, so that we may write

$$u_x \times u_x = u_y \times u_y = u_z \times u_z = 0$$

$$u_x \times u_y = u_z = -u_y \times u_z$$

$$u_y \times u_z = u_x = -u_z \times u_y$$

$$u_z \times u_x = u_y = -u_x \times u_z$$

Then Eq. (2.38) becomes

$$A \times B = u_x(A_y B_z - A_z B_y) + u_y(A_z B_x - A_x B_z) + u_z(A_x B_y - A_y B_x) \tag{2.39}$$

In determinant form, Eq. (2.39) is written

$$A \times B = \begin{vmatrix} u_x & u_y & u_z \\ A_x & A_y & A_z \\ B_x & B_y & B_z \end{vmatrix} \tag{2.40}$$

SCALAR TRIPLE PRODUCT

The scalar triple product is defined to be

$$A \cdot (B \times C) \tag{2.41}$$

Here the parentheses are superfluous since the multiplication involving the dot and cross can be performed in one order only because an operation $(A \cdot B) \times C$ has no meaning since $A \cdot B$ is a scalar and we have not defined the vector product of a scalar and a vector. If this is written in component form, we see that

$$\mathbf{A} \cdot \mathbf{B} \times \mathbf{C} = A_x(B_yC_z - B_zC_y) + A_y(B_zC_x - B_xC_z) + A_z(B_xC_y - B_yC_x)$$

$$= \begin{vmatrix} A_x & A_y & A_z \\ B_x & B_y & B_z \\ C_x & C_y & C_z \end{vmatrix} \tag{2.42}$$

Equation (2.42) may be rearranged to be

$$B_x(C_yA_z - C_zA_y) + B_y(C_zA_x - C_xA_z) + B_z(C_xA_y - C_yA_x) = \mathbf{B} \cdot \mathbf{C} \times \mathbf{A}$$
$$= C_x(A_yB_z - A_zB_y) + C_y(A_zB_x - A_xB_z) + C_z(A_xB_y - A_yB_x) = \mathbf{C} \cdot \mathbf{A} \times \mathbf{B} \tag{2.43}$$

This result could have been obtained by cyclically permutating columns in the determinant of Eq. (2.42), and it indicates that the value of the scalar triple product does not change if the vectors are permuted in a cyclic order; $\mathbf{A} \cdot \mathbf{B} \times \mathbf{C} = \mathbf{C} \cdot \mathbf{A} \times \mathbf{B} = \mathbf{B} \cdot \mathbf{C} \times \mathbf{A}$.

Since the scalar product is commutative, we may write

$$\mathbf{A} \times \mathbf{B} \cdot \mathbf{C} = \mathbf{C} \cdot \mathbf{A} \times \mathbf{B}$$

However, from (2.43), we see that

$$\mathbf{C} \cdot (\mathbf{A} \times \mathbf{B}) = (\mathbf{A} \times \mathbf{B}) \cdot \mathbf{C} = \mathbf{A} \cdot (\mathbf{B} \times \mathbf{C}) \tag{2.44}$$

so that the dot and cross in a scalar triple product may be interchanged without changing its value.

The scalar triple product may be interpreted geometrically to signify the volume of a parallelepiped whose sides are $\mathbf{A}$, $\mathbf{B}$, and $\mathbf{C}$ (see Fig. 2.19). The volume V of a parallelepiped is given by the magnitude of the area of a side times the altitude. The magnitude of the vector $\mathbf{B} \times \mathbf{C}$, that is, $|\mathbf{B}|\,|\mathbf{C}| \sin [\mathbf{B}, \mathbf{C}]$, is the magnitude of the area of the side; and the projection

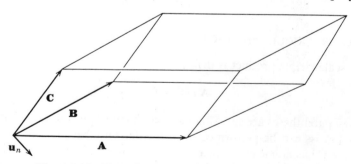

Figure 2.19   The volume of a parallelopiped is $\mathbf{A} \cdot \mathbf{B} \times \mathbf{C}$.

of **A** in the direction $\mathbf{u}_n$, that is, the direction of **B** × **C**, is $\mathbf{A} \cdot \mathbf{u}_n = |\mathbf{A}| \cos [\mathbf{A}, \mathbf{u}_n] = |\mathbf{A}| \cos [\mathbf{A}, (\mathbf{B} \times \mathbf{C})]$. The volume of the parallelepiped is therefore

$$
\begin{aligned}
V &= |\mathbf{A}| \cos [\mathbf{A}, (\mathbf{B} \times \mathbf{C})] \, |\mathbf{B}| \, |\mathbf{C}| \sin [\mathbf{B}, \mathbf{C}] \\
&= (\mathbf{A} \cdot \mathbf{u}_n)(|\mathbf{B}| \, |\mathbf{C}| \sin [\mathbf{B}, \mathbf{C}]) \\
&= \mathbf{A} \cdot \mathbf{u}_n \, |\mathbf{B}| \, |\mathbf{C}| \sin [\mathbf{B}, \mathbf{C}] \\
&= \mathbf{A} \cdot \mathbf{B} \times \mathbf{C}
\end{aligned}
\tag{2.45}
$$

If the scalar triple product of three vectors **A**, **B**, and **C** is zero, we can conclude that at least one of the following its true: (1) the vectors are coplanar; (2) two of the vectors are collinear, that is, parallel; and (3) one of the vectors is zero. Characteristics (1), (2), and (3) are most readily understood by remembering that $\mathbf{A} \cdot \mathbf{B} \times \mathbf{C}$ is the volume of a parallelepiped having sides **A**, **B**, and **C**.

VECTOR TRIPLE PRODUCT

In treating certain physical situations, the product

$$
\mathbf{A} \times (\mathbf{B} \times \mathbf{C}) \tag{2.46}
$$

will occur. The parentheses are necessary to specify the order of the operations, for, in general

$$
\mathbf{A} \times (\mathbf{B} \times \mathbf{C}) \neq (\mathbf{A} \times \mathbf{B}) \times \mathbf{C}
$$

Writing $\mathbf{A} \times (\mathbf{B} \times \mathbf{C})$ in component form, we see that

$$
\begin{aligned}
\mathbf{A} \times (\mathbf{B} \times \mathbf{C}) &= \mathbf{u}_x[A_y(B_x C_y - B_y C_x) - A_z(B_z C_x - B_x C_z)] \\
&\quad + \mathbf{u}_y[A_z(B_y C_z - B_z C_y) - A_x(B_x C_y - B_y C_x)] \\
&\quad + \mathbf{u}_z[A_x(B_z C_x - B_x C_z) - A_y(B_y C_z - B_z C_y)] \\
&= (A_x C_x + A_y C_y + A_z C_z)(\mathbf{u}_x B_x + \mathbf{u}_y B_y + \mathbf{u}_z B_z) \\
&\quad - (A_x B_x + A_y B_y + A_z B_z)(\mathbf{u}_x C_x + \mathbf{u}_y C_y + \mathbf{u}_z C_z) \\
&= \mathbf{B}(\mathbf{A} \cdot \mathbf{C}) - \mathbf{C}(\mathbf{A} \cdot \mathbf{B})
\end{aligned}
\tag{2.47}
$$

To see the significance of Eq. (2.47), we note that the vector $\mathbf{A} \times (\mathbf{B} \times \mathbf{C})$ is normal to the plane containing the two vectors **A** and $(\mathbf{B} \times \mathbf{C})$. However, the vector $(\mathbf{B} \times \mathbf{C})$ is normal to the plane containing the vectors **B** and **C**; so the vector $\mathbf{A} \times (\mathbf{B} \times \mathbf{C})$ lies in a plane which is normal to **A** and which contains **B** and **C**. Such a vector can be resolved into components along **B** and along **C**. This is what Eq. (2.47) represents.

There exist an infinitude of combinations of the scalar and vector triple products, each of which may be determined by the straightforward application of Eqs. (2.42) and (2.47).

If the vector triple product, $\mathbf{A} \times (\mathbf{B} \times \mathbf{C})$, is zero, then at least one of the following is true: (1) one of the vectors is zero; (2) $\mathbf{B}$ is parallel to $\mathbf{C}$; (3) $\mathbf{A}$ is perpendicular to the plane containing the vectors $\mathbf{B}$ and $\mathbf{C}$, that is, $\mathbf{A}$ is parallel to the vector $\mathbf{B} \times \mathbf{C}$.

2.4   The Possibility of the Division of One Vector by Another

Let us now consider the possibility of vector division. Division of a vector $\mathbf{A}$ by a scalar m can be defined as the multiplication of $\mathbf{A}$ by the scalar quantity $1/m$, a processs already treated.

We usually think of division as a process which is the inverse of multiplication. However, we shall see that this is possible only for vectors which are parallel. Consider the equation

$$m = \mathbf{A} \cdot \mathbf{X} \tag{2.48}$$

where m is a known scalar, $\mathbf{A}$ a known vector, and $\mathbf{X}$ an unknown vector. One's first reaction to determine $\mathbf{X}$ would be to multiply both sides of Eq. (2.48) by something like $1/\mathbf{A}$ or by $\mathbf{A}/\mathbf{A} \cdot 1/\mathbf{A} = \mathbf{A}/\mathbf{A} \cdot \mathbf{A}$, and, indeed $m\mathbf{A}/\mathbf{A} \cdot \mathbf{A} = \mathbf{X}$ is a solution of (2.48), as can be seen by substituting it in for $\mathbf{X}$. However,

$$\mathbf{X} = \frac{m\mathbf{A}}{\mathbf{A} \cdot \mathbf{A}} + \mathbf{Y} \tag{2.49}$$

is also a solution of Eq. (2.48), where $\mathbf{Y}$ is an arbitrary vector subject only to the condition that $\mathbf{A} \cdot \mathbf{Y} = 0$, that is, $\mathbf{A}$ is normal to $\mathbf{Y}$ and there are an infinitude of vectors perpendicular to the vector $\mathbf{Y}$. We see therefore that there are many values of X which will satisfy (2.48). In other words, the process of vector division leads to a result which is ambiguous.

In a similar fashion, consider the vector equation

$$\mathbf{C} = \mathbf{A} \times \mathbf{Z} \tag{2.50}$$

where $\mathbf{C}$ and $\mathbf{A}$ are known vectors and $\mathbf{Z}$ an unknown vector. To determine $\mathbf{Z}$ we might be tempted to multiply by $\times(1/\mathbf{A}) = \times[\mathbf{A}/(\mathbf{A} \cdot \mathbf{A})]$ and again we see that

$$\mathbf{Z} = \mathbf{C} \times \frac{\mathbf{A}}{\mathbf{A} \cdot \mathbf{A}} \tag{2.51}$$

is indeed a solution of (2.50). Again, however,

$$\mathbf{Z} = \mathbf{C} \times \frac{\mathbf{A}}{\mathbf{A} \cdot \mathbf{A}} + \mathbf{W} \tag{2.52}$$

where $\mathbf{W}$ is an arbitrary vector subject only to the condition $\mathbf{A} \times \mathbf{W} = 0$, that is, **A** is parallel to **W**, is also a solution to (2.50). So we again see that it is not possible to obtain a unique solution to an equation like (2.50) by a process of vector division.

If two vectors **A** and **B** are parallel **A** = m**B**, the quotient **A**/**B** is then given by

$$\frac{\mathbf{A}}{\mathbf{B}} = \frac{m\mathbf{B}}{\mathbf{B}} = m \qquad (2.53)$$

In other words, vector division is permissible if the vectors are parallel.

PROBLEMS

1. Vectors **A** and **B** are given by

$$\mathbf{A} = -3\mathbf{u}_x + 2\mathbf{u}_y \qquad \text{and} \qquad \mathbf{B} = \mathbf{u}_x - 4\mathbf{u}_y$$

Determine **A** + **B**, **A** − **B**, 2**A** + 3**B**, and 4**A** analytically and graphically.

2. If a plane has a ground speed of 250 mph in the direction due west, determine the true air speed and heading of the plane if there is a wind from the northwest at 25 mph.

3. If the sum and difference of two vectors is given, show graphically how the vectors can be determined.

4. If **A**, **B**, and **C** are a set of noncoplanar vectors emanating from the same origin, show that any vector **D** can be uniquely specified by

$$\mathbf{D} = p\mathbf{A} + r\mathbf{B} + s\mathbf{C}$$

where p, r, and s are real scalar constants.

5. Three vectors **A**, **B**, and **C** are mutually orthogonal. What is the magnitude of **A** + **B** + **C**, and what angle does it make with **B**?

6. Show that a line through the points located by the vectors **A** and **B** has the equation

$$\mathbf{R} = \mathbf{A} + m(\mathbf{B} - \mathbf{A})$$

where **R** is a vector locating any point on the line and m is a real scalar variable.

7. Determine the components of the unit vector **u** which is normal to the vectors

$$\mathbf{A} = 2\mathbf{u}_x - 3\mathbf{u}_y + \mathbf{u}_z$$
$$\mathbf{B} = 6\mathbf{u}_x + \mathbf{u}_y - 2\mathbf{u}_z$$

8. Show that

$$\mathbf{A} = \mathbf{u}_x \sin \alpha + \mathbf{u}_y \cos \alpha$$
$$\mathbf{B} = \mathbf{u}_x \sin \beta + \mathbf{u}_y \cos \beta$$

are unit vectors in the plane $z = 0$ which make angles α and β with the y-axis. Obtain an expression for the cosine of the angle $\alpha - \beta$ by utilizing the concept of the scalar product.

9. Show that the component of a vector **A** in the direction of another vector **B** is

$$\frac{\mathbf{A} \cdot \mathbf{B}}{B^2}\mathbf{B}$$

and that the component of A in the direction normal to B is

$$A - \frac{A \cdot B}{B^2} B$$

10. Consider the vectors A, B, and C such that $A = B - C$. By performing the scalar multiplication of each side of this relation by itself, prove the law of cosines.

11. Prove the law of sines by considering the cross products of A with

$$A = B - C$$

12. Show that

$$A \times (B \times C) + B \times (C \times A) + C \times (A \times B) = 0$$

13. Two sets of three noncoplanar unit vectors u_1, u_2, u_3, and u_4, u_5, u_6 are related by

$$u_1 = \frac{u_5 \times u_6}{u_4 \cdot u_5 \times u_6}, \qquad u_2 = \frac{u_6 \times u_4}{u_4 \cdot u_5 \times u_6}, \qquad \text{and} \qquad u_3 = \frac{u_4 \times u_5}{u_4 \cdot u_5 \times u_6}$$

(such a set constitutes a reciprocal system of vectors). Show that a vector $F = u_1 F_1 + u_2 F_2 + u_3 F_3$ can be written as $F = u_4 F_4 + u_5 F_5 + u_6 F_6$. Determine F_4, F_5, and F_6 in terms of F_1, F_2, and F_3.

3

Vector Calculus

3.1 Introduction

In order to employ the concept of a field in the description of physical phenomena, we must be able to differentiate and integrate field quantities. The material in this chapter is concerned with the ideas fundamental to and the physical interpretation associated with the operations in vector calculus. It is predicated on the assumption that the reader is familiar with scalar calculus. As we proceed, it will become apparent that the basic concepts of vector calculus are similar in many respects to the corresponding principles in scalar calculus.

3.2 Vector Fields Depending on One Variable

VECTOR DIFFERENTIATION

If, to every value of a scalar variable q there is a corresponding value of a vector quantity $\mathbf{F}$, $\mathbf{F}$ is a one-dimensional vector field usually written $\mathbf{F}(q)$. Many physical situations can be described by such a vector field. The one scalar variable involved may be a coordinate variable; for example, the force field surrounding a small electric charge is completely specified in terms of the distance from the center of the charge; or the single scalar variable may be the distance as measured along a given space curve as, for example, the tangential force on a roller coaster car is determined by its position on the track which can be stated as a distance along the track as measured from a starting point (see Fig. 3.1). In general, the scalar variable can be time, the phase of the moon, etc.; however, because of the nature of this text, we shall limit our discussion to when q is either a coordinate variable or time.

In accordance with our previous discussion (Section 1.4) concerning the continuity and differentiability of vector fields, we can say the following. When the scalar variable q approaches a particular value, say q_0, the vector

Figure 3.1 An illustration of locating a point on a space curve.

$\mathbf{F}(q)$ is said to be continuous at q_0 and approaches a finite limit $\mathbf{F}(q_0)$ if the magnitude of the difference $\mathbf{F}(q) - \mathbf{F}(q_0)$ approaches zero. This means that, so long as $\mathbf{F}(q_0)$ is not zero, $\mathbf{F}(q)$ has nearly the same direction and magnitude as $\mathbf{F}(q_0)$ when q is close to q_0. If $\mathbf{F}(q_0)$ happens to be zero, then the difference between $\mathbf{F}(q)$ and $\mathbf{F}(q_0)$ can approach zero provided only that the magnitude of $\mathbf{F}(q)$, that is, $|\mathbf{F}(q)|$ approaches zero. In this case $\mathbf{F}(q)$, as q approaches q_0, may assume any direction as long as its magnitude approaches zero. This is in agreement with our discussion in Section 2.3 concerning zero vectors.

If we define Δq to be $q - q_0$ and denote $\mathbf{F}(q) - \mathbf{F}(q_0)$ by $\Delta \mathbf{F}$, the derivative of a vector field $\mathbf{F}(q)$ is defined to be

$$\frac{d\mathbf{F}}{dq} \equiv \lim_{\Delta q \to 0} \frac{\Delta \mathbf{F}}{\Delta q}. \tag{3.1}$$

This limit must be unique regardless of the manner in which $\Delta q \to 0$. A geometrical interpretation of Eq. (3.1) will follow. For a coordinate system in which the directions of unit vectors are not functions of q, for example, Cartesian but not spherical coordinates, Eq. (3.1) may be written in component form

$$\frac{d\mathbf{F}}{dq} = \mathbf{u}_x \frac{dF_x}{dq} + \mathbf{u}_y \frac{dF_y}{dq} + \mathbf{u}_z \frac{dF_z}{dq} \tag{3.2}$$

Successive differentiation of Eq. (3.2) yields

$$\frac{d^2\mathbf{F}}{dq^2} = \mathbf{u}_x \frac{d^2F_x}{dq^2} + \mathbf{u}_y \frac{d^2F_y}{dq^2} + \mathbf{u}_z \frac{d^2F_z}{dq^2} \tag{3.3}$$

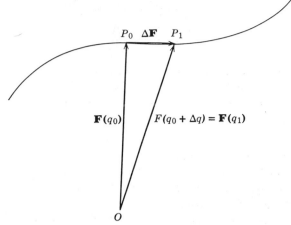

Figure 3.2 Geometrical interpretation of the rate of change of a vector.

Hence

$$\frac{d^n\mathbf{F}}{dq^n} = \mathbf{u}_x \frac{d^n F_x}{dq^n} + \mathbf{u}_y \frac{d^n F_y}{dq^n} + \mathbf{u}_z \frac{d^n F_z}{dq^n} \tag{3.4}$$

To perform the differentiation indicated in Eq. (3.4), we have assumed that $\mathbf{F}$, and hence its components, are differentiable to the nth order.

To supplement and illustrate these ideas, let us consider a geometrical interpretation of Eqs. (3.1) through (3.4). Let O be a fixed point as shown in Fig. 3.2 from which $\mathbf{F}(q)$ emanates. The end points or tips of $\mathbf{F}(q)$ as q changes will trace out a space curve Γ. The direction in which the tip of $\mathbf{F}$ moves along Γ as q increases in value is designated as the positive direction along Γ. Let P_0 be a fixed point on Γ located by the vector $\mathbf{F}(q_0)$. If q changes from q_0 by a small amount Δq to a new value q_1, $\mathbf{F}(q)$ will change from $\mathbf{F}(q_0)$ to $\mathbf{F}(q_1)$ and the point on Γ located by the tip of $\mathbf{F}(q)$ moves from P_0 to P_1. In other words,

$$\Delta q \equiv q_1 - q_0$$
$$\mathbf{F}(q_1) = \overrightarrow{OP_1} = \mathbf{F}(q_0 + \Delta q) \tag{3.5}$$

We see then that $\Delta\mathbf{F}$, the incremental change in $\mathbf{F}$ as q changes from q_0 to q_1, is given by

$$\Delta\mathbf{F} = \mathbf{F}(q_1) - \mathbf{F}(q_0) = \overrightarrow{P_0 P_1} \tag{3.6}$$

Since Δq is a scalar, we may divide Eq. (3.6) by Δq and obtain

$$\frac{\Delta\mathbf{F}}{\Delta q} = \frac{\overrightarrow{P_0 P_1}}{\Delta q} \tag{3.7}$$

As Δq approaches zero, as q_1 approaches q_0 so that P_1 approaches P_0, Eq. (3.7) becomes

$$\lim_{\Delta q \to 0} \frac{\Delta \mathbf{F}}{\Delta q} = \frac{d\mathbf{F}}{dq} \tag{3.8}$$

which represents a vector along Γ, i.e., tangent to Γ at the point P_0.

To indicate the utility of the concept of vector differentiation, consider a spectator, located at point O in Fig. 3.3, who is observing an automobile race. The race track can be considered as the curve Γ just discussed, and $\mathbf{R} = \overrightarrow{OP}$ (analogous to vector $\mathbf{F}$ already discussed) is a vector which represents the position of a particular car at a time t (t is measured from the time at which the race started). The position vector $\mathbf{R}$ gives the sense, direction, and distance the observer must look to see the car in which he is interested. Let l be the distance that car has traveled along the track Γ in the time t. l is the distance traveled by the car as measured on its odometer and is a scalar since it is not associated with any particular direction. At the time $t + \Delta t$ the car is at a new position designated by $l + \Delta l$ so that the distance and direction from the observer to the car will have changed to $\mathbf{R} + \Delta \mathbf{R}$. This change $\Delta \mathbf{R}$ in the position vector is a chord of the race track, that is, of the curve Γ. The magnitude of the ratio $\Delta \mathbf{R}/|\Delta l|$ where $|\Delta l|$ is the magnitude of a vector coincident with the infinitesimal change in l and in the direction of increasing l is

$$\left| \frac{\Delta \mathbf{R}}{\Delta l} \right| = \frac{\text{length of chord from } P \text{ to } P'}{\text{distance along } \Gamma \text{ from } P \text{ to } P'} \tag{3.9}$$

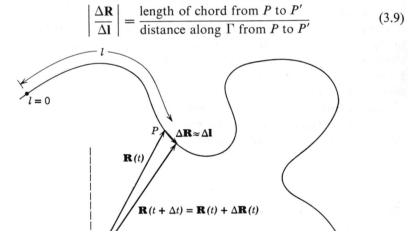

Figure 3.3   The time rate of change of a position vector.

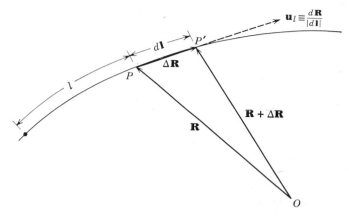

Figure 3.4   Illustration for the discussion of $\mathbf{u}_l$.

As Δt approaches zero, $\Delta \mathbf{l}$ and $\Delta \mathbf{R}$ approach zero, and their ratio, Eq. (3.9), approaches unity, that is, $\Delta \mathbf{l}$ becomes coincident with $\Delta \mathbf{R}$; then

$$\lim_{\substack{\Delta t \to 0 \\ \Delta l \to 0}} \left| \frac{\Delta \mathbf{R}}{\Delta l} \right| = 1 \tag{3.10}$$

because the chord $\Delta \mathbf{R} = \overrightarrow{PP'}$ will approach $\Delta \mathbf{l}$. In addition, $\Delta \mathbf{R}$ will approach a tangent to Γ and hence the direction of $\Delta \mathbf{R}/|\Delta \mathbf{l}|$ will be along Γ. We must then conclude that since the magnitude of $\Delta \mathbf{R}/|\Delta \mathbf{l}|$ approaches unity while its direction approached the direction of Γ at that point

$$\lim_{\Delta t \to 0} \frac{\Delta \mathbf{R}}{|\Delta \mathbf{l}|} = \mathbf{u}_l \quad \text{(see Fig. 3.4)}$$

where $\mathbf{u}_l$ is a tangent unit vector, that is, along the curve Γ in the direction of increasing l, so that

$$d\mathbf{R} = \mathbf{u}_l |d\mathbf{l}| = d\mathbf{l} \tag{3.11}$$

We may then write

$$\frac{d\mathbf{R}}{dt} = \frac{d\mathbf{R}}{|d\mathbf{l}|} \frac{|d\mathbf{l}|}{dt} = \mathbf{u}_l \frac{|d\mathbf{l}|}{dt} = \mathbf{u}_l |\mathbf{v}| \tag{3.12}$$

where $|\mathbf{v}|$ is the speed of the car along Γ and $\mathbf{u}_l |\mathbf{v}| = \mathbf{v}$ is the velocity of the car along Γ. Equation (3.12) then becomes

$$\frac{d\mathbf{R}}{dt} = \frac{d\mathbf{l}}{dt} = \mathbf{v} \tag{3.13}$$

Now **R** is a vector which could have been written

$$\mathbf{R} = \mathbf{u}_x R_x + \mathbf{u}_y R_y + \mathbf{u}_z R_z \tag{3.14}$$

so that

$$\frac{d\mathbf{R}}{dt} = \mathbf{u}_x \frac{dR_x}{dt} + \mathbf{u}_y \frac{dR_y}{dt} + \mathbf{u}_z \frac{dR_z}{dt}$$

$$= \mathbf{u}_x v_x + \mathbf{u}_y v_y + \mathbf{u}_z v_z \tag{3.15}$$

$$= \mathbf{v}_x + \mathbf{v}_y + \mathbf{v}_z$$

which also represents the velocity **v** of the car. In other words, the velocity of the car can be described as the time rate of change of the vector locating the car relative to some arbitrary reference.

The acceleration of the car at any instant, that is, at any position, can be obtained by differentiating (3.15) with respect to time, as

$$\mathbf{a} = \frac{d^2\mathbf{R}}{dt^2} = \mathbf{u}_x \frac{dv_x}{dt} + \mathbf{u}_y \frac{dv_y}{dt} + \mathbf{u}_z \frac{dv_z}{dt}$$

$$= \mathbf{u}_x a_x + \mathbf{u}_y a_y + \mathbf{u}_z a_z \tag{3.16}$$

$$= \mathbf{a}_x + \mathbf{a}_y + \mathbf{a}_z$$

so that the acceleration of the car can be described as the second derivative of the position vector with respect to time.

The following four equations (3.17 to 3.20) are theorems concerning the derivative of sums and products involving vectors. We shall state them without proof.

To determine the derivative of a field which is the sum of two fields **F** and **G** with respect to a scalar q, we proceed as in scalar calculus

$$\frac{d(\mathbf{F} + \mathbf{G})}{dq} = \frac{d\mathbf{F}}{dq} + \frac{d\mathbf{G}}{dq} \tag{3.17}$$

If **F**(q) is multiplied by $f(q)$, a scalar function of q, the derivative of the product is

$$\frac{d}{dq}[f(q)\mathbf{F}(q)] = f(q)\frac{d\mathbf{F}}{dq} + \frac{df(q)}{dq}\mathbf{F} \tag{3.18}$$

Similarly, the derivative of a quantity involving the multiplication of two vector fields is obtained in a manner similar to that employed in scalar calculus with the important difference that if the order of the factors must be preserved in the multiplication process, then the same order must be preserved in the derivative, that is,

$$\frac{d}{dq}(\mathbf{F} \cdot \mathbf{G}) = \mathbf{F} \cdot \frac{d\mathbf{G}}{dq} + \mathbf{G} \cdot \frac{d\mathbf{F}}{dq}$$

$$= \frac{d\mathbf{G}}{dq} \cdot \mathbf{F} + \frac{d\mathbf{F}}{dq} \cdot \mathbf{G} \tag{3.19}$$

but

$$\frac{d}{dq}(\mathbf{F} \times \mathbf{G}) = \mathbf{F} \times \frac{d\mathbf{G}}{dq} + \frac{d\mathbf{F}}{dq} \times \mathbf{G}$$

$$\neq \mathbf{G} \times \frac{d\mathbf{F}}{dq} + \frac{d\mathbf{G}}{dq} \times \mathbf{F} \tag{3.20}$$

As we have said, representation of higher order derivatives in the form of Eq. (3.16) is possible only if the unit vectors are constant, if they do not change with time. An example when this is not so is provided by calculating the acceleration when the velocity is given in terms of a tangential unit vector, when

$$\mathbf{v} = \mathbf{u}_t \, |\mathbf{v}| \tag{3.21}$$

Now the direction of the unit vector $\mathbf{u}_t$ along Γ changes with time, that is, $\mathbf{u}_t$ is a function of time. Taking the time derivative of $\mathbf{v}$ yields (see Eq. 3.18)

$$\mathbf{a} = \frac{d\mathbf{v}}{dt} = \frac{d}{dt}[\mathbf{u}_t \, |\mathbf{v}|] = \mathbf{u}_t \frac{d\,|\mathbf{v}|}{dt} + |\mathbf{v}| \frac{d\mathbf{u}_t}{dt} \tag{3.22}$$

To evaluate $d\mathbf{u}_t/dt$, we remember that $\mathbf{u}_t$ is a unit vector tangent to Γ. If t increased by a small amount Δt, then $\mathbf{u}_t$ will change in direction from $\mathbf{u}_t(t)$ to $\mathbf{u}_t(t + \Delta t) = \mathbf{u}_t + \Delta \mathbf{u}_t$. These two successive tangential vectors define a plane called the osculating plane of the curve Γ at the point P. Figure 3.5a shows these unit vectors at times separated by an interval Δt. If, on the osculating plane, one of these vectors is moved parallel to itself so that both vectors have a common origin (see Fig. 3.5b), a small angle $\Delta \psi$ will be between them. This angle is called the angle of contingence and is the angle between two successive tangential unit vectors and is obviously a function of time. Referring to Fig. 3.5b, we see that in the limit as Δt approaches zero,

$$|d\mathbf{u}_t| = |\mathbf{u}_t| \, d\psi = d\psi \tag{3.23}$$

Dividing Eq. (3.23) by dt yields

$$\left|\frac{d\mathbf{u}_t}{dt}\right| = \frac{d\psi}{dt} = \frac{d\psi}{|d\mathbf{l}|} \frac{|d\mathbf{l}|}{dt} = \frac{d\psi}{|d\mathbf{l}|} |\mathbf{v}| \tag{3.24}$$

The reader will recall that K, the radius of curvature at any point P of a curve Γ, is defined to be the radius of a circle drawn through P in order to be coincident with the curve in the neighborhood of P. Then $|d\mathbf{l}|$, an element of circumference of this circle which is drawn in the osculating plane and which is coincident with Γ, is given by (see Fig. 3.5c)

$$|d\mathbf{l}| = K \, d\psi \qquad \text{or} \qquad K \equiv \frac{|d\mathbf{l}|}{d\psi}$$

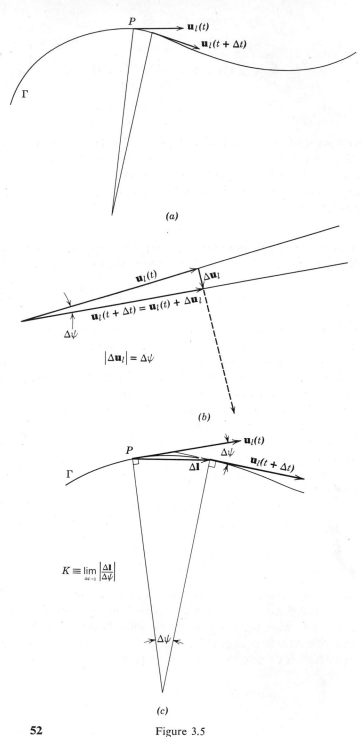

(a)

$$|\Delta\mathbf{u}_l| = \Delta\psi$$

(b)

$$K \equiv \lim_{\Delta\psi \to 0} \left|\frac{\Delta\mathbf{l}}{\Delta\psi}\right|$$

(c)

Figure 3.5

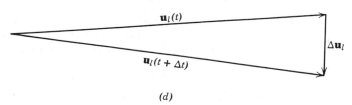

(d)

Figure 3.5 (a) Two successive unit vectors, one at time t and the other at $t + \Delta t$. (b) The time rate of change of the unit vector $\mathbf{u}_t(t)$. (c) Angular change in the osculating plane. (d) The time rate of change of the unit vector $\mathbf{u}_t$.

so that Eq. (3.24) becomes

$$\left| \frac{d\mathbf{u}_t}{dt} \right| = \frac{1}{K} |\mathbf{v}| \tag{3.25}$$

Now the direction of $d\mathbf{u}_t$, and hence of $d\mathbf{u}_t/dt$, is at right angles to $\mathbf{u}_t$. To see this, consider Fig. 3.5d. We see that as Δt approaches zero, $\Delta\mathbf{u}_t$ approaches a direction which is at right angles to $\mathbf{u}_t$. We shall designate the unit vector in the direction along $d\mathbf{u}_t$—in a direction normal to $\mathbf{u}_t$, as $\mathbf{u}_N$. Then

$$\frac{d\mathbf{u}_t}{dt} = \frac{1}{K} |\mathbf{v}| \, \mathbf{u}_N \tag{3.26}$$

The acceleration of the car, Eq. (3.22), then becomes

$$
\begin{aligned}
\mathbf{a} \equiv \frac{d\mathbf{v}}{dt} &= \mathbf{u}_t \frac{d\,|\mathbf{v}|}{dt} + \mathbf{u}_N \left(\frac{dl}{dt}\right)^2 \frac{1}{K} \\
&= \mathbf{u}_t \frac{d\,|\mathbf{v}|}{dt} + \frac{\mathbf{u}_N\,|\mathbf{v}|^2}{K}
\end{aligned}
\tag{3.27}
$$

Equation (3.27) represents the fact that the vector $\mathbf{v}$ can change in magnitude and also in direction and that acceleration is a measure of the rate at which $\mathbf{v}$ does both. We see that an acceleration may exist even if the rate of change of the speed $d\,|\mathbf{v}|/dt$ is zero. The term $\mathbf{u}_t(d\,|\mathbf{v}|/dt)$ is called the tangential acceleration, whereas $\mathbf{u}_N\,|\mathbf{v}|^2/K$ is the centripetal acceleration and is always directed toward the center of curvature at P.

It is interesting to note that there exists a unit vector $\mathbf{u}_B$ defined by

$$\mathbf{u}_B = \mathbf{u}_t \times \mathbf{u}_N \tag{3.28}$$

This vector lies in a plane normal to $\mathbf{u}_t$ and $\mathbf{u}_N$, that is, $\mathbf{u}_B$ is normal to the osculating (normal) plane at the point P. A binormal plane is defined by $\mathbf{u}_B$ together with $\mathbf{u}_N$.

As we shall see in the Chapter 4, Eq. (3.28) defines an orthogonal, right-handed coordinate system in the same way that unit vectors in the Cartesian coordinate system do. This coordinate system, called the *tangential-normal system*, may be utilized to describe the motion of a particle along Γ.

In many instances the independent scalar q may be a parameter which specifies other variables $\eta(q)$, $\xi(q)$, and $\zeta(q)$; then the derivative of a vector field $\mathbf{F}(\eta, \xi, \zeta)$ with respect to the scalar q may be written

$$\frac{d\mathbf{F}}{dq} = \frac{d\mathbf{F}}{d\eta}\frac{d\eta}{dq} + \frac{d\mathbf{F}}{d\xi}\frac{d\xi}{dq} + \frac{d\mathbf{F}}{d\zeta}\frac{d\zeta}{dq} \tag{3.29}$$

As a simple two-dimensional illustration of this relationship, let us return to the example of the automobile race discussed earlier. Suppose the race track is circular in shape, as shown in Fig. 3.6; then l, the position of a car at time t, can be determined as a function of the angle $\theta(t)$ in the following manner:

$$\begin{aligned} l(t) &= \int_0^x [(dx)^2 + (dy)^2]^{\frac{1}{2}} = \int_0^x [1 + (y')^2]^{\frac{1}{2}}\, dx \\ &= \rho \int_0^\theta \left[1 + \frac{1}{\rho^2}\left(\frac{d\rho}{d\theta}\right)^2\right]^{\frac{1}{2}} d\theta \\ &= b\theta(t) \end{aligned} \tag{3.30}$$

where $\rho = b$ is the radius of the track and $d\rho/d\theta = 0$. We assume only one trip around the track so that $0 \le \theta \le 2\pi$ specifies l uniquely. Then the time derivative of the position vector $\mathbf{R}$, locating the car, becomes

$$\frac{d\mathbf{R}}{dt} = \frac{d\mathbf{R}}{d\theta}\frac{d\theta}{dt} = \frac{d\mathbf{R}}{|d\mathbf{l}|}\frac{|d\mathbf{l}|}{d\theta}\frac{d\theta}{dt}$$

$$= \mathbf{u}_t b\, |\boldsymbol{\omega}| \tag{3.31}$$

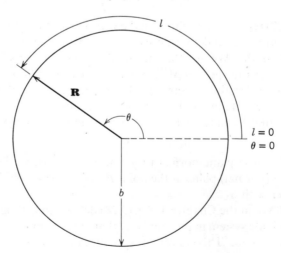

Figure 3.6   Idealized race track.

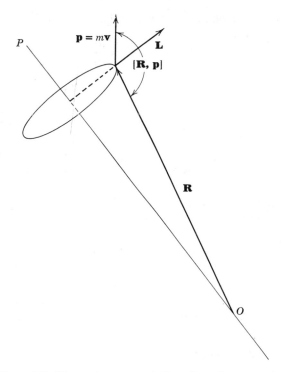

Figure 3.7   The vector representation of angular momentum.

where, from Eq. (3.30), $|d\mathbf{l}|/d\theta = b$, the radius of the track, and $|\boldsymbol{\omega}| \equiv d\theta/dt$, is the magnitude of the angular velocity of the car.

As another example of the utility of vector differentiation, consider the relationship between the angular momentum $\mathbf{L}$ and the torque $\mathbf{T}$.

$\mathbf{L}$, the angular momentum or moment of momentum, of a particle of mass m moving about the axis OP (see Fig. 3.7) with a linear velocity $\mathbf{v}$ is a vector at right angles to $\mathbf{R}$, the vector connecting 0 and the instantaneous position of the particle and also at right angles to the particle momentum $\mathbf{p} = m\mathbf{v}$. The magnitude of $\mathbf{L}$ is equal to the product of the component of $\mathbf{p}$ at right angles to $\mathbf{R}$ and $\mathbf{R}$, that is,

$$L = \mathbf{u}_n |\mathbf{R}| |\mathbf{p}| \sin [\mathbf{R}, \mathbf{p}]$$
$$= \mathbf{R} \times \mathbf{p} \tag{3.32}$$

The reader will recall from Eq. (2.37) that $\mathbf{T}$, the torque associated with a force $\mathbf{F}$ acting at a point located by $\mathbf{R}$ from a point on the axis of rotation, is

$$\mathbf{T} = \mathbf{u}_n |\mathbf{R}| |\mathbf{F}| \sin [\mathbf{R}, \mathbf{F}] = \mathbf{R} \times \mathbf{F} \tag{3.33}$$

From Newton's second law, we know that

$$\mathbf{F} = \frac{d}{dt}(m\mathbf{v}) = \frac{d\mathbf{p}}{dt}$$

Therefore

$$\mathbf{T} = \mathbf{R} \times \frac{d\mathbf{p}}{dt}$$

If we take the time derivative of $\mathbf{L} = \mathbf{R} \times \mathbf{p}$, we see that

$$\frac{d\mathbf{L}}{dt} = \frac{d}{dt}(\mathbf{R} \times \mathbf{p}) = \frac{d\mathbf{R}}{dt} \times \mathbf{p} + \mathbf{R} \times \frac{d\mathbf{p}}{dt} \tag{3.34}$$

but $d\mathbf{R}/dt$, as we have seen, is $\mathbf{v}$, so that $d\mathbf{R}/dt \times m\mathbf{v} = \mathbf{v} \times m\mathbf{v} = 0$. We see therefore that

$$\frac{d\mathbf{L}}{dt} = \mathbf{R} \times \frac{d\mathbf{p}}{dt} = \mathbf{R} \times \mathbf{F} = \mathbf{T} \tag{3.35}$$

Thus in analogy with Newton's second law, in which the force is the time derivative of the linear momentum, the torque, or moment of force, is given by the time derivative of the angular momentum.

VECTOR INTEGRATION

The result of the integration of a vector $\mathbf{F}(q)$, which depends on one variable q, is a vector which, when differentiated with respect to q, yields $\mathbf{F}(q)$. Therefore, since the derivative of a constant vector is zero, the indefinite integral of the vector field $\mathbf{F}(q)$ may be written

$$\int \mathbf{F}(q)\,dq = \mathbf{G}(q) + \mathbf{C} \tag{3.36}$$

where $\mathbf{C}$ is a constant vector, that is, $\mathbf{C}$ is not a function of q, and where $d\mathbf{G}/dq = \mathbf{F}$.

If the scalar q varies continuously between two definite limits q_1 and q_2, then

$$\int_{q_1}^{q_2} \mathbf{F}(q)\,dq = \mathbf{G}(q_2) - \mathbf{G}(q_1) \tag{3.37}$$

is the definite integral of $\mathbf{F}(q)$ between q_1 and q_2 and represents the sum of the differential vector elements $d\mathbf{G} = \mathbf{F}\,dq$ as q varies between q_1 and q_2.

Vector integration can also be considered as the scalar integration of the components of the integrand. To see this, let the components of the integrand and the constant vector be written in a coordinate system where the directions of the unit vectors are not dependent on position, for example, the Cartesian coordinate system; then

$$G(q) = \mathbf{u}_x G_x(q) + \mathbf{u}_y G_y(q) + \mathbf{u}_z G_z(q) \tag{3.38}$$
$$F(q) = \mathbf{u}_x F_x(q) + \mathbf{u}_y F_y(q) + \mathbf{u}_z F_z(q) \tag{3.39}$$

and

$$C = \mathbf{u}_x C_x + \mathbf{u}_y C_y + \mathbf{u}_z C_z \tag{3.40}$$

where C_x, C_y, and C_z are constant scalars.

Then, if the components of F and G are continuous and single-valued functions of q, Eq. (3.36) becomes three scalar equations, one for each component.

$$\int F_x \, dq = G_x(q) + C_x \tag{3.41a}$$

$$\int F_y \, dq = G_y(q) + C_y \tag{3.41b}$$

$$\int F_z \, dq = G_z(q) + C_z \tag{3.41c}$$

The definite integral of Eq. (3.37) also may be written in component form.

$$\int_{q_1}^{q_2} F_x \, dq = G_x(q_2) - G_x(q_1) \tag{3.42a}$$

$$\int_{q_1}^{q_2} F_y \, dq = G_y(q_2) - G_y(q_1) \tag{3.42b}$$

$$\int_{q_1}^{q_2} F_z \, dq = G_z(q_2) - G_z(q_1) \tag{3.42c}$$

The integral of $C \cdot F(q)$ and $C \times F(q)$, where C is a constant vector, can be evaluated by removing C from under the integral sign, that is,

$$\int C \cdot F(q) \, dq = C \cdot \int F(q) \, dq \tag{3.43}$$

and

$$\int C \times F(q) \, dq = C \times \int F(q) \, dq \tag{3.44}$$

Employing the method of integration by parts, we can evaluate the integral $\int f(q)F(q) \, dq$ where $f(q)$ is a scalar function of q, in the following manner. If $g(q) = \int f(q) \, dq$, then

$$\int f(q)F(q) \, dq = g(q)F(q) - \int g(q)F'(q) \, dq \tag{3.45a}$$

or if

$$G(q) = \int F(q) \, dq$$

then

$$\int f(q)\mathbf{F}(q)\,dq = f(q)\mathbf{G}(q) - \int \mathbf{G}(q)f'(q)\,dq \qquad (3.45b)$$

The correctness and equivalence of Eqs. (3.45a) and (3.45b) may be established by taking the derivative of each side of these equations with respect to q.

3.3   Vector Fields Which Are Functions of More Than One Variable

PARTIAL DIFFERENTIATION

The reader will recall that in scalar calculus a continuous function of more than one independent variable may be differentiated with respect to any one of them, provided the derivative exists, by differentiating the function with respect to that variable under the assumption that the other variables are held constant.   The result is called the partial derivative with respect to the variable which is permitted to vary.   Similarly, the partial derivative of a vector field with respect to one of the several variables on which it depends is defined to be the derivative of the vector field with respect to that variable assuming that all the other variables are held constant.   For example, the partial derivative with respect to x of the vector field

$$\mathbf{F}(x, y, z) = \mathbf{u}_x x^2 z + \frac{\mathbf{u}_y y}{x} + \mathbf{u}_z yz \qquad (3.46)$$

is

$$\frac{\partial \mathbf{F}(x, y, z)}{\partial x} = \mathbf{u}_x 2xz - \frac{\mathbf{u}_y y}{x^2} \qquad (3.47)$$

Let us now consider $d\mathbf{F}(x, y, z)$, the total differential of the vector field $\mathbf{F}(x, y, z)$. If the value of this vector field at the point x, y, z is $\mathbf{F}(x, y, z)$ and its value at a point $x + \Delta x$, $y + \Delta y$, $z + \Delta z$ is $\mathbf{F}(x + \Delta x, y + \Delta y, z + \Delta z)$, then $\Delta \mathbf{F}$, the difference in $\mathbf{F}$ at these two points, is

$$\Delta \mathbf{F} = \mathbf{F}(x + \Delta x, y + \Delta y, z + \Delta z) - \mathbf{F}(x, y, z)$$

If we expand $\mathbf{F}(x + \Delta x, y + \Delta y, z + \Delta z)$ in a Taylor series and neglect second and higher order terms, we see that

$$\Delta \mathbf{F} = \frac{\partial \mathbf{F}}{\partial x}\Delta x + \frac{\partial \mathbf{F}}{\partial y}\Delta y + \frac{\partial \mathbf{F}}{\partial z}\Delta z$$

which in the limit as Δx, Δy, and Δz approach zero becomes

$$
\begin{aligned}
d\mathbf{F} = {} & \frac{\partial \mathbf{F}}{\partial x}\, dx + \frac{\partial \mathbf{F}}{\partial y}\, dy + \frac{\partial \mathbf{F}}{\partial z}\, dz \\[4pt]
= {} & \mathbf{u}_x\!\left(\frac{\partial F_x}{\partial x}\, dx + \frac{\partial F_x}{\partial y}\, dy + \frac{\partial F_x}{\partial z}\, dz\right) \\[4pt]
& + \mathbf{u}_y\!\left(\frac{\partial F_y}{\partial x}\, dx + \frac{\partial F_y}{\partial y}\, dy + \frac{\partial F_y}{\partial z}\, dz\right) \\[4pt]
& + \mathbf{u}_z\!\left(\frac{\partial F_z}{\partial x}\, dx + \frac{\partial F_z}{\partial y}\, dy + \frac{\partial F_z}{\partial z}\, dz\right)
\end{aligned} \tag{3.48}
$$

We have assumed that the partial derivatives $\partial \mathbf{F}/\partial x$, $\partial \mathbf{F}/\partial y$, and $\partial \mathbf{F}/\partial z$ are continuous functions of the independent variables. The quantities within the brackets are just the magnitudes of the components in the x, y, and z directions, respectively; so that

$$
d\mathbf{F} = \mathbf{u}_x\, dF_x + \mathbf{u}_y\, dF_y + \mathbf{u}_z\, dF_z = d\mathbf{F}_x + d\mathbf{F}_y + d\mathbf{F}_z \tag{3.49}
$$

INTEGRATION—LINE, SURFACE, AND VOLUME INTEGRALS

Before discussing line, surface, and volume integrals, let us first examine the nature of the space curves, surfaces, and regions of space with which we shall deal.

We shall begin our discussion by attempting to decide what we mean by the length of a curve. At first glance, this may appear to be a trivial subject when considering a curve such as the one shown in Fig. 3.8a, but the matter is not trivial if the curve is as shown in Fig. 3.8b. In the latter figure we have some difficulty in deciding what we mean by length. To understand the fundamental ideas involved in the length of a curve, let us consider the continuous curve Γ joining the points P_A and P_B as shown in

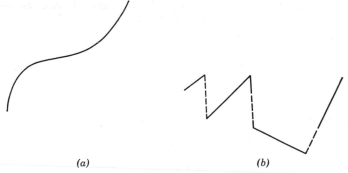

(a)   (b)

Figure 3.8   For discussion concerning rectifiable curves.

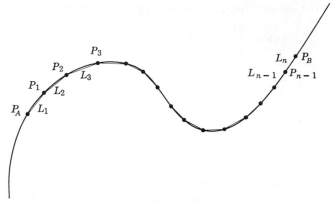

Figure 3.9   An example of a rectifiable curve.

Fig. 3.9. Let $P_1, P_2, P_3, \ldots P_{n-1}$ be a set of $n-1$ points on this curve between P_A and P_B. If we construct straight lines between successive P_j's and denote the length of these segments as $L_1, L_2, \ldots L_n$, respectively, then S_n, the sum of these lengths, given by

$$S_n = \sum_{j=1}^{n} L_j \tag{3.50}$$

is certainly less than the quantity we may wish to call the length of Γ between P_A and P_B. By increasing n in such a way that each of the line segments of the curve Γ become smaller, we expect that S_n approaches the length of Γ. If there exists a finite L such that for any given $\epsilon > 0$ there exist a finite number $\delta > 0$ such that

$$|S_n - L| < \epsilon \tag{3.51}$$

for any choice of the points $P_1, P_2, P_3, \ldots P_{n-1}$ (where n need not be fixed) for which the largest line segment is less than δ, then L is called the length of the curve Γ between P_A and P_B. If the curve Γ has the length L between P_A and P_B, it is called a *rectifiable curve* between those points.

Unless otherwise stated, we shall be considering rectifiable curves throughout.

In addition to the rectifiability of a curve, we shall deal with another fundamental property of curves, the *smoothness* of a curve.

If we consider the space curve Γ shown in Fig. 3.10, we see that $|d\mathbf{l}|$, the magnitude of an element of Γ, is given by

$$|d\mathbf{l}| = [(dx)^2 + (dy)^2 + (dz)^2]^{\frac{1}{2}}$$
$$= \left[1 + \left(\frac{dy}{dx}\right)^2 + \left(\frac{dz}{dx}\right)^2\right]^{\frac{1}{2}} dx \tag{3.52}$$

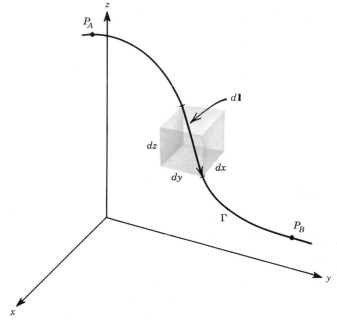

Figure 3.10   An element of a space curve.

It follows then that L, the length of Γ from the points P_A to P_B, is given by

$$L = \int_P^{P_B} [1 + (y')^2 + (z')^2]^{\frac{1}{2}} \, dx \qquad (3.53)$$

If L, the length of the arc from P_A to P_B, is given by Eq. (3.53) which presumes the existence of y' and z', the arc is said to be *regular*. As we move from one point to another between P_A and P_B, the tangent to Γ turns continuously, and we call this length of arc *smooth*. The predominant number of space curves encountered in the study of fields will be regular or will be composed of a finite number of regular arcs as shown in Fig. 3.11. We see in this figure that such a curve, called a regular curve, may not have a continuously turning tangent, but it is *piecewise smooth*. Thus the regular curve shown in Fig. 3.11 consists of regular arcs which extend from P_A to P_B, P_B to P_C, P_C to P_D, and P_D to P_E, and the curve has a tangent that turns continuously except at P_A, P_B, P_C, P_D, and P_E.

By analogy with a smooth or regular arc, we can consider a *regular* or *smooth* surface element. Such an element, when projected on the coordinate surfaces of a coordinate system, yields a surface which is the

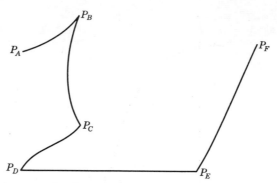

Figure 3.11   An example of a regular curve which does not have a continuously turning tangent.

interior of a regular closed curve (see Fig. 3.12). A point which is interior to a regular surface element is called a regular point of the surface. Surfaces consisting of regular surface elements are called regular and are the only ones considered.

The nature of the volumes or regions of space in which a field exists is also very important. A region of space is either simply (or singly) connected or multiply connected. Sometimes the former class of spaces is called acyclic and the latter cyclic.

If, in a region of space, all closed regular curves are reducible, that is, they can, by continuous shrinking, be reduced to a point without passing outside that region, then that region is *simply connected*. A region in which this cannot be done is called *multiply connected*. The dough in a doughnut is a multiply connected region (see Fig. 3.13). In this figure we see that it is possible to draw a closed curve completely encircling the hole of the

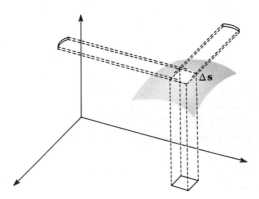

Figure 3.12   A regular surface element.

Figure 3.13   An example of a multiply connected region.

doughnut which cannot be shrunk to a point without passing out of the dough.

Now if we cut through the doughnut with a very thin knife, the two sides of the cut can then be considered as part of the surface of the doughnut. We now cannot have a closed regular curve within the doughnut which is not reducible, so that by the introduction of a suitable barrier we are able to convert a multiply connected region of space to a simply connected region (see Fig. 3.14). We shall deal with singly connected regions or multiply connected regions which can be converted to singly connected regions by the introduction of a barrier.

To facilitate our discussion of line, surface, and volume integration, let us now consider the three general categories of integrals involving vector quantities which depend on several independent variables.

1. The integrand is a scalar function and the differential is a vector. Both the integrand and the differential are functions of the n independent scalar variables $q_1, q_2, q_3, \ldots q_n$, that is,

$$\int f(q_1, q_2, \ldots q_n) \, d\mathbf{F}(q_1, q_2, \ldots q_n) \tag{3.54}$$

Figure 3.14   Illustration of the use of a barrier to convert a multiply connected region to a simply connected region.

Now $d\mathbf{F}$ can be written in the form

$$d\mathbf{F} = \mathbf{u}_x \, dF_x + \mathbf{u}_y \, dF_y + \mathbf{u}_z \, dF_z \tag{3.55}$$

Equation (3.54) may be resolved into its components as in the following:

$$\mathbf{u}_x \int f(q_1, q_2, \ldots q_n) \, dF_x + \mathbf{u}_y \int f(q_1, q_2, \ldots q_n) \, dF_y$$

$$+ \mathbf{u}_z \int f(q_1, q_2, \ldots q_n) \, dF_z \tag{3.56}$$

If F_x, F_y, and F_z are differentiable with respect to the scalar variables, we may write

$$dF_x = \frac{\partial F_x}{\partial q_1} \, dq_1 + \frac{\partial F_x}{\partial q_2} \, dq_2 + \cdots + \frac{\partial F_x}{\partial q_n} \, dq_n$$

$$= \sum_{j=1}^{n} \frac{\partial F_x}{\partial q_j} dq_j \tag{3.57}$$

Similarly,

$$dF_y = \sum_{j=1}^{n} \frac{\partial F_y}{\partial q_j} \, dq_j \quad \text{and} \quad dF_z = \sum_{j=1}^{n} \frac{\partial F_z}{\partial q_j} \, dq_j \tag{3.58}$$

so that the x-component of Eq. (3.56) becomes

$$\mathbf{u}_x \sum_{j=1}^{n} \int f(q_1, q_2, \ldots, q_n) \frac{\partial F_x}{\partial q_j} \, dq_j \tag{3.59}$$

Similar expressions can be written for the y- and z-components of Eq. (3.56).

2. The integrand is a vector function and the differential a scalar function of the independent scalar variables $q_1, q_2, \ldots, q_n$, that is,

$$\int_{q_1} \int_{q_2} \cdots \int_{q_n} \mathbf{G}(q_1, q_2, \ldots, q_n) \, dq_1 \, dq_2 \cdots dq_n \tag{3.60}$$

The symbol $\mathbf{G}$ can be written

$$\mathbf{G} = \mathbf{u}_x G_x(q_1, q_2, \ldots, q_n) + \mathbf{u}_y G_y(q_1, q_2, \ldots, q_n)$$

$$+ \mathbf{u}_z G_z(q_1, q_2, \ldots, q_n) \tag{3.61}$$

so that Eq. (3.60) may be resolved into its components and the magnitude of each component dealt with as a scalar integral.

3. The integrand and differential are vector functions of the independent scalar variables $q_1, q_2, \ldots, q_n$:

(a) When the integrand and differential form a scalar product,

$$\int \mathbf{G} \cdot d\mathbf{F} = \int G_x \, dF_x + \int G_y \, dF_y + \int G_z \, dF_z \tag{3.62}$$

In light of Eqs. (3.57) and (3.58), these integrals may be written

$$\sum_{j=1}^{n} \int \left(G_x \frac{\partial F_x}{\partial q_j} + G_y \frac{\partial F_y}{\partial q_j} + G_z \frac{\partial F_z}{\partial q_j} \right) dq_j \tag{3.63}$$

(b) When the integrand and differential form a vector product, as,

$$\int \mathbf{G} \times d\mathbf{F} = \mathbf{u}_x \int (G_y \, dF_z - G_z \, dF_y)$$

$$+ \mathbf{u}_y \int (G_z \, dF_x - G_x \, dF_z)$$

$$+ \mathbf{u}_z \int (G_x \, dF_y - G_y \, dF_x)$$

$$= \mathbf{u}_x \sum_{j=1}^{n} \int \left(G_y \frac{\partial F_z}{\partial q_j} - G_z \frac{\partial F_y}{\partial q_j} \right) dq_j$$

$$+ \mathbf{u}_y \sum_{j=1}^{n} \int \left(G_z \frac{\partial F_x}{\partial q_j} - G_x \frac{\partial F_z}{\partial q_j} \right) dq_j$$

$$+ \mathbf{u}_z \sum_{j=1}^{n} \int \left(G_x \frac{\partial F_y}{\partial q_j} - G_y \frac{\partial F_x}{\partial q_j} \right) dq_j \tag{3.64}$$

We shall now extend our discussion of these three categories of integrals, but, since we are interested in scalar and vector fields, we shall consider only scalar and vector functions of position.

Line Integrals. Integrals involving $d\mathbf{l}$ are

$$\int_{P_1 \Gamma}^{P_2} f(x, y, z) \, d\mathbf{l} \tag{3.65}$$

$$\int_{P_1 \Gamma}^{P_2} \mathbf{F} \cdot d\mathbf{l} \tag{3.66}$$

and

$$\int_{P_1 \Gamma}^{P_2} \mathbf{F} \times d\mathbf{l} \tag{3.67}$$

The first of these line integrals [Eq. (3.65)] represents a vector that is the vector sum of $f \, d\mathbf{l}$ along the curve Γ between the points P_1 and P_2. $f(x, y, z)$ is a scalar field in the region of space where the curve Γ exists (see Fig. 3.15). The length of the curve Γ between P_1 and P_2 can be divided into element lengths $\Delta \mathbf{l}_1, \Delta \mathbf{l}_2, \ldots, \Delta \mathbf{l}_j, \ldots, \Delta \mathbf{l}_N$ such that the total length of the curve Γ between P_1 and P_2 is

$$\sum_{j=1}^{N} |\Delta \mathbf{l}_j|$$

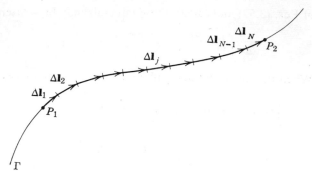

Figure 3.15   Illustration for the discussion of line integral involving a scalar field.

These $\Delta \mathbf{l}$'s are small enough that the value of the scalar field over the length of $\Delta \mathbf{l}_j$ is assigned a single value f_j which represents a sort of average value of f over $\Delta \mathbf{l}_j$. Then the sum of the vectors $f_j \, \Delta \mathbf{l}_j$ for all N $\Delta \mathbf{l}$'s is written

$$\sum_{j=1}^{N} f_j \, \Delta \mathbf{l}_j$$

In the limit as N approaches infinity in such a way that all the $\Delta \mathbf{l}$'s approach zero,

$$\lim_{N \to \infty} \sum_{j=1}^{N} f_j \, \Delta \mathbf{l}$$

is denoted by the symbol

$$\int_{P_1 \Gamma}^{P_2} f \, d\mathbf{l} \tag{3.68}$$

As an example of a two-dimensional integral of this type, let us consider a curve Γ specified by $y = x^2$ which exists in a region of space where a scalar field $f = x^3 y + 2y$ also exists. Then between the points $x = 1$, $y = 1$ to $x = 2$, $y = 4$, the value of the line integral can be computed as follows: the element of length is given by

$$d\mathbf{l} = \mathbf{u}_x \, dx + \mathbf{u}_y \, dy$$

However, since $dy = 2x \, dx = 2y^{1/2} \, dx$, we may write

$$d\mathbf{l} = \mathbf{u}_x \, dx + \mathbf{u}_y \, 2x \, dx = (\mathbf{u}_x + 2x\mathbf{u}_y) \, dx$$

or

$$= (\tfrac{1}{2}\mathbf{u}_x y^{-1/2} + \mathbf{u}_y) \, dy$$

Then

$$\int_{P_1}^{P_2} f \, d\mathbf{l} = \int_{1,1}^{2,4} (x^3 y + 2y) \, d\mathbf{l}$$

$$= \int_1^2 (x^5 + 2x^2)(\mathbf{u}_x + 2x\mathbf{u}_y) \, dx$$

$$= \mathbf{u}_x \left(\frac{x^6}{6} + \frac{2}{3} x^3 \right)_1^2$$

$$+ \mathbf{u}_y \left(\frac{2x^7}{7} + x^4 \right)_1^2$$

$$= \mathbf{u}_x(\tfrac{91}{6}) + \mathbf{u}_y(\tfrac{359}{7}) \tag{3.69}$$

or

$$= \int_1^4 [y^{5/2} + 2y][\mathbf{u}_x(\tfrac{1}{2})y^{-1/2} + \mathbf{u}_y] \, dy$$

$$= \mathbf{u}_x \int_1^4 (\tfrac{1}{2}y^2 + y^{1/2}) \, dy$$

$$+ \mathbf{u}_y \int_1^4 (y^{5/2} + 2y) \, dy = (\tfrac{91}{6})\mathbf{u}_x + (\tfrac{359}{7})\mathbf{u}_y$$

That the value of integrals of this type do, in general, depend on the path from P_1 to P_2 can be seen by evaluating the integral in our example when Γ is a straight line between 1, 1 and 2, 4. Such a curve has the equation

$$y = 3x - 2 \qquad \text{or} \quad dy = 3 \, dx$$

Then Eq. (3.69) becomes

$$\int_{1,1}^{2,4} [x^3 y + 2y] \, d\mathbf{l} = \mathbf{u}_x \int_{1,1}^{2,4} [x^3 y + 2y] \, dx$$

$$+ \mathbf{u}_y \int_{1,1}^{2,4} (x^3 y + 2y) \, dy$$

$$= \mathbf{u}_x \int_1^2 [x^3(3x - 2) + 2(3x - 2)] \, dx$$

$$+ \mathbf{u}_y \int_1^2 3[x^3(3x - 2) + 2(3x - 2)] \, dx$$

$$= \tfrac{143}{10} \mathbf{u}_x + \tfrac{429}{10} \mathbf{u}_y \tag{3.70}$$

which is not the same result as obtained when the curve is $y = x^2$.

When the space curve Γ forms a closed path, for example, a circle or ellipse, this type of line integral is written

$$\oint_\Gamma f \, d\mathbf{l} \tag{3.71}$$

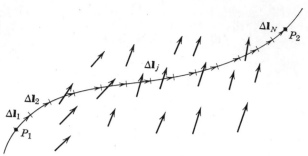

Figure 3.16   Illustration for the discussion of line integrals involving a vector field.

The line integral given by Eq. (3.66) may be interpreted as the sum of the magnitude of the components of the vector field **F** which are tangent to the space curve Γ. To see this, let us consider Fig. 3.16. As before, let the curve Γ from P_1 to P_2 be subdivided into N elements of length $\Delta \mathbf{l}_1, \Delta \mathbf{l}_2, \ldots \Delta \mathbf{l}_j \ldots, \Delta \mathbf{l}_N$. $\mathbf{F}_j \cdot \Delta \mathbf{l}_j$ is the magnitude of the component of $\mathbf{F}_j$ along $\Delta \mathbf{l}_j$ multiplied by $|\Delta \mathbf{l}_j|$. (We assume here that $\Delta \mathbf{l}_j$ is so small that **F** can be represented by $\mathbf{F}_j$ which represents a sort of average value of **F** over $\Delta \mathbf{l}_j$.) The sum of $\mathbf{F}_j \cdot \Delta \mathbf{l}_j$ as $\Delta \mathbf{l}_j$ moves from P_1 to P_2 is

$$\sum_{j=1}^{N} \mathbf{F}_j \cdot \Delta \mathbf{l}_j$$

If we divide Γ into smaller and smaller elements of length, that is, N approaches infinity, the result is Eq. (3.66),

$$\lim_{N \to \infty} \sum_{j=1}^{N} \mathbf{F}_j \cdot \Delta \mathbf{l}_j = \int_{P_1 \Gamma}^{P_2} \mathbf{F} \cdot d\mathbf{l} \tag{3.72}$$

A physical example of this type of line integral is the work done in moving a rock of mass m to the top of a mountain. To idealize the

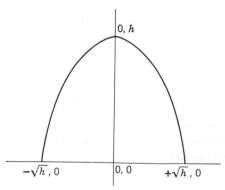

Figure 3.17   A physical example of a line integral of a scalar product.

problem, let us assume that the two-dimensional path taken can be described by $y = -x^2 + h$, $-h^{\frac{1}{2}} \leq x \leq h^{\frac{1}{2}}$ (see Fig. 3.17) and the rock is carried from the base of the mountain at $x = h^{\frac{1}{2}}$, $y = 0$ to the top $x = 0$, $y = h$. The force on the rock is $-mg\mathbf{u}_y$; then

$$-\int_{h^{\frac{1}{2}},0}^{0,h} (mg\mathbf{u}_y) \cdot d\mathbf{l} = -\int_0^h mg\, dy = -mgh \qquad (3.73)$$

Line integrals $\int_{P_1}^{P_2}{}_\Gamma \mathbf{F} \cdot d\mathbf{l}$ usually depend on the path Γ between P_1 and P_2, but there is a certain type of vector field for which such line integrals are independent of the path. For example, if

$$\mathbf{F} = \mathbf{u}_x 2xy^2 + \mathbf{u}_y 2(x^2y + y)$$

the value of $\int_{P_1}^{P_2}{}_\Gamma \mathbf{F} \cdot d\mathbf{l}$ is the same regardless of the path taken between P_1 and P_2 and depends only on the end points. To show that this is possible, consider Γ to be the straight line $y = 2x$ from 0, 0 to 2, 4; then Eq. (3.66) becomes

$$\int_{0,0}^{2,4} \mathbf{F} \cdot d\mathbf{l} = \int_{0,0}^{2,4} 2xy^2\, dx + 2\int_{0,0}^{2,4} (x^2y + y)\, dy$$

$$= 8\int_0^2 x^3\, dx + 8\int_0^2 (x^3 + x)\, dx$$

$$= 80 \qquad (3.74)$$

If Γ is a parabola $y = x^2$, then

$$\int_{0,0}^{2,4} \mathbf{F} \cdot d\mathbf{l} = 2\int_0^2 x^5\, dx + 4\int_0^2 (x^5 + x^3)\, dx$$

$$= 80$$

Thus we see that it is possible that the value of line integrals can be independent of the path for certain vector fields. We shall return to this important type of vector field in Chapter 5. A line integral $\int_{P_1}^{P_2}{}_\Gamma \mathbf{F} \cdot d\mathbf{l}$ whose value is independent of the path is usually written without the subscript Γ.

When the line integral of any vector field is taken around a closed path, for example, Γ is a circle or ellipse, the line integral is written

$$\oint_\Gamma \mathbf{F} \cdot d\mathbf{l} \qquad (3.75)$$

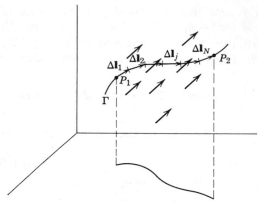

Figure 3.18   Illustration for the discussion of a line integral of a vector product.

The third line integral to be considered, $\int_{P_1 \Gamma}^{P_2} \mathbf{F} \times d\mathbf{l}$, represents a vector

that is the vector sum of $\mathbf{F} \times d\mathbf{l}$ along the curve Γ between the points P_1
to P_2. In Fig. 3.18 we see that Γ is divided into N elements of length
$\Delta l_1, \Delta l_2, \ldots, \Delta l_j, \ldots, \Delta l_N$; then if over Δl_j the average value of the
field is $\mathbf{F}_j$, the sum of the cross products $\mathbf{F}_j \times \Delta l_j$, is $\sum_{j=1}^{N} \mathbf{F}_j \times \Delta l_j$. If the
curve Γ is divided into more elements of length so that all elements
of length approach zero, the sum becomes

$$\lim_{N \to \infty} \sum_{j=1}^{N} \mathbf{F}_j \times \Delta l_j = \int_{P_1 \Gamma}^{P_2} \mathbf{F} \times d\mathbf{l} \tag{3.76}$$

As an example of integrals of this type, consider a two-dimensional
field

$$\mathbf{F} = \mathbf{u}_x y + \mathbf{u}_y x$$

in a region of space where a space curve Γ is given by

$$y = \frac{x^3}{3}$$

Then the value of the line integral $\int \mathbf{F} \times d\mathbf{l}$ between the points $(0, 0)$
and $(3, 9)$ on Γ is

$$\mathbf{u}_z \left\{ \int_0^3 \int_0^9 [y \, dy - x \, dx] \right\} = \mathbf{u}_z \left\{ \int_0^3 \left[\frac{x^5}{3} - x \right] dx \right\} = 36\mathbf{u}_z$$

Thus when Γ and $\mathbf{F}$ are in the same plane, the line integral of $\mathbf{F} \times d\mathbf{l}$
represents a vector perpendicular to that plane.

Surface Integrals. We shall consider surface integrals of the form

$$\iint_A f \, d\mathbf{s} = \iint_A f \mathbf{u}_n \, |d\mathbf{s}| \tag{3.77}$$

$$\iint_A \mathbf{F} \cdot d\mathbf{s} = \iint_A \mathbf{F} \cdot \mathbf{u}_n \, |d\mathbf{s}| \tag{3.78}$$

$$\iint_A \mathbf{F} \times d\mathbf{s} = \iint_A \mathbf{F} \times \mathbf{u}_n \, |d\mathbf{s}| \tag{3.79}$$

where $\mathbf{u}_n$ is a unit vector normal to the surface differential $|d\mathbf{s}|$.

To understand the significance of these equations, let us recall that a regular surface is composed of regular surface elements $d\mathbf{s}$, each of which can be considered as an almost plane surface (see Fig. 3.19). A plane containing this surface element is the tangent to the surface at $d\mathbf{s}$. In Fig. 3.19 we see that

$$dx \, dy = d\mathbf{s} \cdot \mathbf{u}_z = |d\mathbf{s}| \cos \psi(x, y)$$

Then the total area of A is

$$\iint_A |d\mathbf{s}| = \iint_A \frac{dx \, dy}{\cos \psi(x, y)} = \iint_A \sec \psi(x, y) \, dx \, dy \tag{3.80}$$

where the integral on the right represents the double integration which extends over the x and y extent of the projection of $d\mathbf{s}$ on the plane $z = 0$.

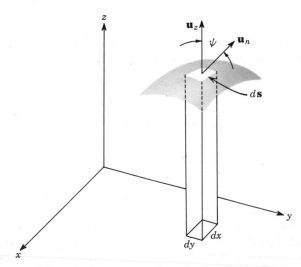

Figure 3.19 For discussion of surface integrals.

If f is a scalar function defined on A, the integral over A

$$\iint_A f\,|d\mathbf{s}|$$

may also be written as the double integral

$$\iint_{A_z} f \sec \psi(x, y)\,dx\,dy$$

over A_z, the projection of A on the plane $z = 0$.

Surface integrals of the form of (3.77) can be considered as the vector sum of vector quantities $f\,\Delta\mathbf{s}$ over the surface A. If the surface shown in Fig. 3.19 occupies a region of space where a scalar field exists and if this surface is divided into N small areas $\Delta\mathbf{s}_1, \Delta\mathbf{s}_2, \ldots, \Delta\mathbf{s}_j, \ldots, \Delta\mathbf{s}_N$, and if f_j is the value of the scalar field at $\Delta\mathbf{s}_j$, the vector sum of products $f_j\,\Delta\mathbf{s}_j$, that is, $\sum_{j=1}^{N} f_j\,\Delta\mathbf{s}_j$ as N approaches infinity so that all the $\Delta\mathbf{s}$'s approach zero, is

$$\lim_{N\to\infty} \sum_{j=1}^{N} f_j\,\Delta\mathbf{s}_j = \iint_A f\,d\mathbf{s} \qquad (3.81)$$

Here $\Delta\mathbf{s}_j$ is assumed sufficiently small that the scalar field at $\Delta\mathbf{s}_j$ may be considered to be the value f_j over it.

As an example of a surface integral of this type, let us consider the scalar field

$$f = r \cos \theta + \cos \phi$$

integrated over a hemisphere (see Fig. 3.20). We shall see in Chapter 4 that an element of area on a sphere of radius r is

$$d\mathbf{s} = r^2 \cos \phi \, d\theta \, d\phi \mathbf{u}_r$$

Then

$$\mathbf{u}_r \int_{\theta=0}^{2\pi} \int_{\phi=0}^{\pi/2} (r \cos \theta + \cos \phi)(r^2 \cos \phi)\,d\phi\,d\theta$$

$$= \mathbf{u}_r\, 2\pi r^2 \int_{\phi=0}^{\pi/2} \cos^2 \phi \, d\phi = \mathbf{u}_r \frac{(\pi r)^2}{2}$$

Surface integrals of the form of (3.78) are the sum of the products of the components of the vector field $\mathbf{F}$ which are normal to the surface and the surface element. If the surface A shown in Fig. 3.21 is divided into N small surface elements $\Delta\mathbf{s}_1, \Delta\mathbf{s}_2, \ldots, \Delta\mathbf{s}_j, \ldots, \Delta\mathbf{s}_N$, and if the value of the vector field over the surface $\Delta\mathbf{s}_j$ is $\mathbf{F}_j$, the product $\mathbf{F}_j \cdot \mathbf{u}_{n_j}$ is the component of $\mathbf{F}$ which is normal to $\Delta\mathbf{s}_j$. The sum of these products as N

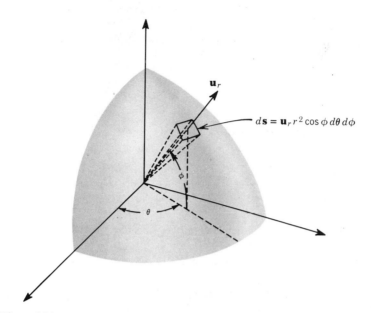

Figure 3.20   For example concerning the surface integration of a scalar field.

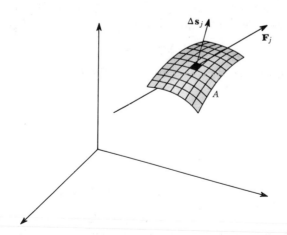

Figure 3.21   Illustration for discussion of surface integration involving vector fields.

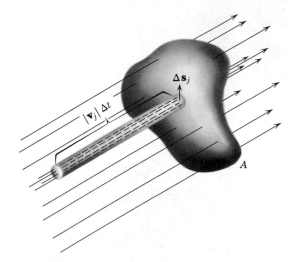

Figure 3.22   Illustration for example of surface integrals involving a scalar product.

approaches infinity in such a way that all Δs's approach zero is

$$\lim_{N\to\infty} \sum_{j=1}^{\infty} \mathbf{F}_j \cdot \Delta \mathbf{s}_j = \iint_A \mathbf{F} \cdot d\mathbf{s} = \iint_A \mathbf{F} \cdot \mathbf{u}_n \, |ds| \qquad (3.82)$$

A physical example of this surface integral is provided if we wish to determine the volume rate at which a fluid flows across a surface A (see Fig. 3.22). The surface A is divided into N small areas Δs_j at each of which the fluid velocity is $\mathbf{v}_j$. The volume of water through Δs_j in a time Δt is the cylinder shown in Fig. 3.22. The volume of this cylinder is $|\Delta \mathbf{s}_j| \, |\mathbf{v}_j| \, \Delta t \cos [\mathbf{u}_{n_j}, \mathbf{v}_j]$, which is just

$$\Delta t(\Delta \mathbf{s}_j \cdot \mathbf{v}_j) \qquad (3.83)$$

The total volume ΔV flowing across A in the time Δt is the sum of the volume of these cylinders:

$$\Delta V = \sum_{j=1}^{N} \mathbf{v}_j \cdot \Delta \mathbf{s}_j \, \Delta t \quad \text{or} \quad \frac{\Delta V}{\Delta t} = \sum_{j=1}^{N} \mathbf{v}_j \cdot \Delta \mathbf{s}_j \qquad (3.84)$$

The limit of this as N becomes infinite and Δt approaches zero is

$$\frac{dV}{dt} = \lim_{N\to\infty} \sum_{j=1}^{N} \mathbf{v}_j \cdot \Delta \mathbf{s}_j = \iint_A \mathbf{v} \cdot d\mathbf{s} \qquad (3.85)$$

the instantaneous net volumetric flow rate across the surface A.

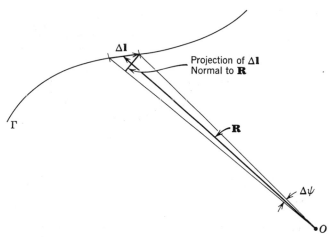

Figure 3.23 Illustration for discussion of plane angles.

Surface integrals of the type involving the scalar product of a vector and an element of a surface also arise when considering solid angles. Before discussing solid angles, however, let us first review some ideas concerning plane angles. From Fig. 3.23 we see that the element of plane angle $d\psi$ subtended at 0 by dl, an element of the curve Γ, is defined to be the ratio of the magnitude of the projection of dl normal to the vector $\mathbf{R}$, drawn from 0 to dl, to the magnitude of $\mathbf{R}$, namely,

$$d\psi = \frac{|\text{the projection of } dl \text{ normal to } \mathbf{R}|}{|\mathbf{R}|} \tag{3.86}$$

Similarly, (see Fig. 3.24) we can define $d\Omega$, an element of solid angle subtended at 0 by $d\mathbf{s}$, an element of the surface A, to be the ratio of the magnitude of the projection of $d\mathbf{s}$ normal to the vector $\mathbf{R}$ drawn from 0 to $d\mathbf{s}$ to the square of the magnitude of $\mathbf{R}$, so that

$$d\Omega = \frac{|\text{projection of } d\mathbf{s} \text{ normal to } \mathbf{R}|}{R^2}$$

$$= \frac{|d\mathbf{s}|}{R^2} \cos [\mathbf{u}_R, \mathbf{u}_n]$$

$$= \frac{\mathbf{u}_R \cdot d\mathbf{s}}{R^2} \quad \text{where} \quad \mathbf{R} = \mathbf{u}_R |\mathbf{R}| \tag{3.87}$$

Then Ω, the total solid angle subtended by the area A, is

$$\Omega = \iint\limits_{A} \frac{\mathbf{u}_R \cdot d\mathbf{s}}{R^2} \tag{3.88}$$

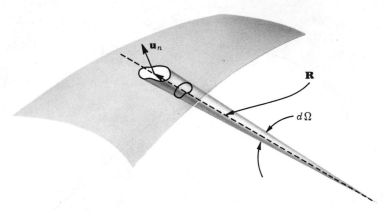

Figure 3.24   Illustration for discussion of solid angles.

Integrals of the form $\iint\limits_{A} \mathbf{F} \times d\mathbf{s}$ define a vector which is the vector sum of vectors of the form $\mathbf{F}_j \times \mathbf{u}_{n_j}$. Then

$$\lim_{N \to \infty} \sum_{j=1}^{N} \mathbf{F}_j \times \Delta \mathbf{s}_j = \iint\limits_{A} \mathbf{F} \times \mathbf{u}_n \, |d\mathbf{s}|$$

$$= \iint\limits_{A} \mathbf{F} \times d\mathbf{s} \qquad (3.89)$$

In a manner similar to that used when considering line integrals, these surface integrals are designated as

$$\oiint\limits_{A} \mathbf{F} \times d\mathbf{s} \qquad (3.90)$$

when A is a closed surface, for example, a complete sphere or ellipsoid of revolution.

Volume Integrals.   Since elements of volume are scalars, we consider two volume integrals:

$$\iiint\limits_{V} f \, dV \qquad (3.91)$$

and

$$\iiint\limits_{V} \mathbf{F} \, dV \qquad (3.92)$$

The first is just a scalar integral which is evaluated by the methods used in scalar calculus. It represents the sum of quantities of the form $f_j \, \Delta V_j$ where ΔV_j is an element of the volume V.

The second integral may be resolved into its components,

$$\iiint_V \mathbf{F} \, dV = \mathbf{u}_x \iiint_V F_x \, dV + \mathbf{u}_y \iiint_V F_y \, dV + \mathbf{u}_z \iiint_V F_z \, dV \quad (3.93)$$

and the magnitude of each component evaluated as in scalar calculus.

PROBLEMS

1. A car moves around a circular race track which can be described by $x^2 + y^2 = 100$ with a constant linear speed of 88 ft/sec. Find the speed of the car in the x- and in the y-direction at the point 6, 8 and graphically determine the linear velocity of that point.

2. $\mathbf{R}(t)$, the position of a particle at time t, is described by

$$\mathbf{R}(t) = \mathbf{C}_1 \sin \omega t + \mathbf{C}_2 \cos \omega t$$

where $\mathbf{C}_1$, $\mathbf{C}_2$, and ω are constants.

   (a) Determine $\mathbf{v}(t)$, the velocity, as a function of time.

   (b) Show that $\mathbf{v} \times \mathbf{R} = $ a constant.

   (c) Determine $\mathbf{a}(|\mathbf{R}|)$, the acceleration, as a function of $|\mathbf{R}|$, the distance from the origin.

3. Show that

$$d\mathbf{u}_R = -\mathbf{u}_R \times \frac{[\mathbf{R} \times d\mathbf{R}]}{|\mathbf{R}|^2}$$

4. If $\mathbf{A}(t)$ is a vector which has a constant magnitude, why is $\mathbf{A} \cdot d\mathbf{A}/dt$ zero?

5. Determine the value of

$$\oint_\Gamma \mathbf{F} \cdot d\mathbf{l}$$

where the path Γ is taken in the clockwise direction around the square formed by the lines $x = 0$, $x = a$, $y = 0$, $y = b$, when $\mathbf{F} = \mathbf{u}_x(xy) + \mathbf{u}_y(3x^2 - y)$.

6. Determine the value of

$$\iint_A \mathbf{F} \cdot d\mathbf{s}$$

where $\mathbf{F} = \mathbf{u}_x F_x + \mathbf{u}_y F_y + \mathbf{u}_z F_z$, and A is the area of a sphere of radius b.

4

Vector Field Representation and Coordinate Transformations

4.1 Introduction

In this chapter we shall first consider coordinate systems and their utility in locating a point in space. We shall discuss two two-dimensional coordinate systems: Cartesian (or rectangular) and polar; and three three-dimensional coordinate systems: Cartesian (or rectangular), circular cylindrical or just cylindrical, and spherical. These systems are the ones most commonly encountered in science and engineering. The relationships between the specifications of the location of a point P in these coordinate systems will also be discussed.

We shall also discuss the representation of a vector field in these coordinate systems. It must be emphasized again that the concept of a vector is fundamental and independent of the coordinate system used to represent it. For example, even though it is possible to describe a vector, representing the displacement of a particle from one point in space to another, in terms of six scalars necessary to specify its initial and final position, the idea involved in the sense, direction, and distance that a particle moves is unique and does not depend on the means we employ to describe it. The primary purpose of a coordinate system, then, is to provide means by which a point in space can be located in an unambiguous manner. The fact that we can use the same coordinate systems to describe vectors and vector fields is fortunate but not fundamental to the concept of a vector.

We shall also discuss the transformation of the representation of a vector field from one coordinate system to another. After treating this topic, we shall return to the subjects of the orthogonality and right-handedness of coordinate systems.

78

4.2 Coordinate Systems

The Cartesian or rectangular coordinate system is the one with which the reader is probably most familiar, and thus it is the one in which he prefers to attack field problems. However, a judicious choice of the coordinate system can simplify the mathematical work necessary to solve a problem, and such a choice can serve to facilitate the understanding of a physical concept or phenomenon. The choice of a coordinate system is usually predicated on whatever symmetry exists in the physical situation to be described. For example, it is much simpler to describe the electric field around a single point charge in terms of spherical coordinates. In this case the field can be completely specified in terms of the radial component alone. The description of this situation in other coordinate systems such as rectangular and cylindrical systems would require two or three independent coordinate variables.

TWO-DIMENSIONAL SYSTEMS

To describe the position of a point on a plane, we must specify two scalars. A discussion follows of the two most commonly employed coordinate systems which are used to specify these numbers.

Cartesian or Rectangular Coordinates. A two-dimensional rectangular coordinate system may be formed by the intersection of two lines, which are perpendicular to each other (see Fig. 4.1). These lines are called the

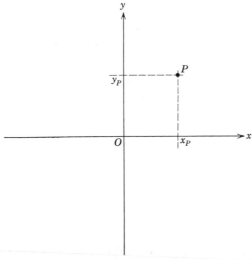

Figure 4.1   Location of a point in a two-dimensional Cartesian coordinate system.

x- and y-axes of the system, and the arbitrary point O at which they intersect is the origin. To locate any point P in such a frame of reference, we must pass through P two additional lines which are perpendicular to the axes. The distance from the origin to the positions where each of the lines through P intersects an axis are called the coordinates x_P and y_P of the point P. These numbers, x_P and y_P, serve to specify the position of P uniquely.

The magnitude of the element of length $d\mathbf{l}_x$ in the x-direction, that is, normal to the y-direction, is given by

$$dl_x = dx \tag{4.1}$$

Similarly, dl_y, the magnitude of an element of length in the y-direction, is

$$dl_y = dy \tag{4.2}$$

The magnitude of the element of length dl at P along an arbitrary direction is (see Fig. 4.2)

$$dl = [(dx)^2 + (dy)^2]^{1/2} \tag{4.3}$$

Polar coordinates. To form a polar coordinate system, we must first arbitrarily choose an origin O. Through this point we then pass a straight line. We choose one sense of this reference line as positive (see direction of arrowhead on reference line in Fig. 4.3). A point P is then specified by passing a line through O and P and by drawing a circle, whose center is

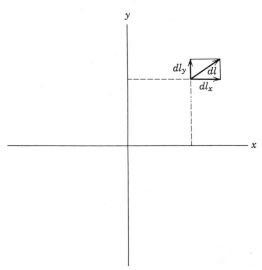

Figure 4.2 An elementary line segment of arbitrary orientation in a two-dimensional Cartesian coordinate system.

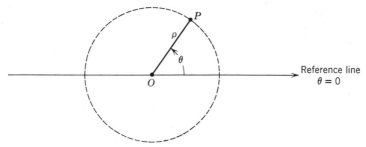

Figure 4.3   Location of a point in a polar coordinate system.

at O, through the point P. The radius of this circle ρ specifies the radial coordinate of the point P; the angle θ, between that portion of the reference line on the "positive" side of the origin and the line from O to P as measured in a counterclockwise direction, is the polar coordinate of P. Thus ρ and θ uniquely specify the position of P.

At a point P, dl_ρ, the magnitude of the element of length in the radial direction, that is, normal to the circle $\rho = $ a constant, is given by (see Fig. 4.4)

$$dl_\rho = d\rho \tag{4.4}$$

and dl_θ, the magnitude of the element of length at P in the polar direction, that is, normal to the line $\theta = $ a constant, is (see Fig. 4.4)

$$dl_\theta = \rho \, d\theta \tag{4.5}$$

Therefore the magnitude of the element of length at P in an arbitrary direction is

$$dl = [(d\rho)^2 + \rho^2(d\theta)^2]^{\frac{1}{2}} \tag{4.6}$$

From Fig. 4.5 we see that if the position of P is given in terms of ρ and θ, the x and y coordinates of P are

$$x = \rho \cos \theta, \qquad y = \rho \sin \theta \tag{4.7}$$

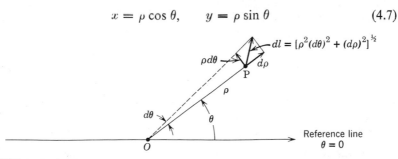

Figure 4.4   An elementary line segment of arbitrary orientation in a polar coordinate system.

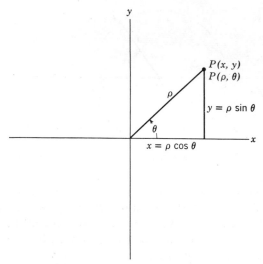

Figure 4.5   Relationship among Cartesian and polar coordinate variables.

Conversely, if the position of P is specified in terms of x and y, and we wish to state the position of P in polar coordinates, then from Fig. 4.5

$$\rho = [x^2 + y^2]^{1/2}, \qquad \theta = \arctan \frac{y^*}{x} \tag{4.8}$$

THREE-DIMENSIONAL COORDINATE SYSTEMS

If we desire to locate a point P in a three-dimensional space, then we must use a three-dimensional coordinate system.

Cartesian or Rectangular Coordinate System. A three-dimensional Cartesian coordinate system may be formed by first choosing an origin. Through the origin we pass three mutually perpendicular planes called *reference planes* (see Fig. 4.6). These planes are designated as the $x = 0$, $y = 0$, and $z = 0$ planes. The lines formed by the intersection of these planes are also mutually orthogonal and are called the x-, y-, and z-axes. A coordinate system of the type illustrated in Fig. 4.6 is called a right-handed system. A right-handed rectangular system may at this time be thought of as any rectangular system which, when rotated, can be brought into congruence with the one shown in Fig. 4.6. Such a system can be characterized as one in which a rotation of the $+x$-axis about the

---

* Care must be taken that θ is in the correct quadrant. For example, if $x = -1$ and $y = -1$, then $\theta = \arctan(1) \neq \pi/4$ but rather $5\pi/4$; that is, the point is in the third quadrant.

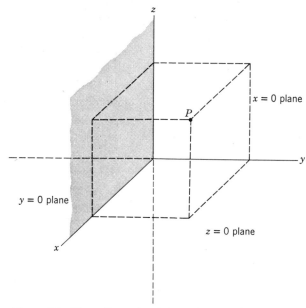

Figure 4.6   Three-dimensional Cartesian coordinate system.

z-axis, through the smaller angle toward the $+y$-axis, causes the z-axis to rotate in the direction taken by a right-hand screw as it moves in the direction of the $+z$-axis. A more profound property of right-handed systems will be discussed in Section 4.5. These systems are the only ones we shall consider because of the conventions that have been adopted in the mathematical treatment of scalar and vector fields.

To locate a point P in a rectangular coordinate system, we must pass through P three mutually orthogonal planes which are normal to the reference planes (see Fig. 4.6). The distances from the origin to the points where each of the planes through P intersects an axis are called the coordinates, x, y, and z of the point P. In such a system the point P is designated $P(x, y, z)$.

In Fig. 4.7 we see that the magnitude of the element of length dl_x, normal to the plane $x = $ a constant, is

$$dl_x = dx \tag{4.9}$$

Similarly, the magnitude of the element of length dl_y, normal to the plane $y = $ a constant, is

$$dl_y = dy \tag{4.10}$$

and utilizing the same notation

$$dl_z = dz \tag{4.11}$$

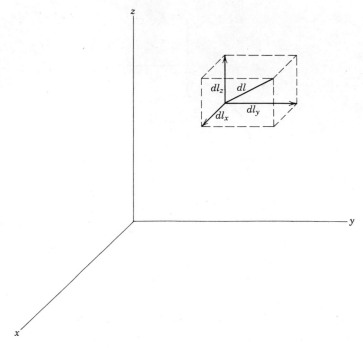

Figure 4.7   Elemental line segment of arbitrary orientation in Cartesian coordinates.

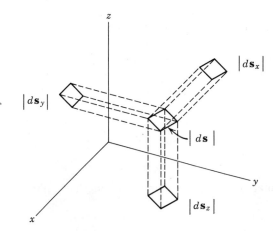

Figure 4.8   Projection of a surface element onto reference planes in a Cartesian co-ordinate system.

so that the magnitude of the element of length in an arbitrary direction is

$$dl = (dl^2 + dl_y^2 + dl_z^2)^{1/2} = [(dx)^2 + (dy)^2 + (dz)^2]^{1/2} \qquad (4.12)$$

From Fig. 4.8 we see that the magnitudes of elements of area may be written

$$ds_x = ds \cos \alpha \qquad (4.13)$$

$$ds_y = ds \cos \beta \qquad (4.14)$$

$$ds_z = ds \cos \gamma \qquad (4.15)$$

or

$$ds = \frac{ds_x}{\cos \alpha} = \frac{ds_y}{\cos \beta} = \frac{ds_z}{\cos \gamma} \qquad (4.16)$$

where α, β, and γ are the angles between a line drawn from ds to the origin and the x-, y-, and z-axes, respectively.

An element of volume dV is seen from Fig. 4.9 to be

$$dV = dx\, dy\, dz$$

Cylindrical Coordinate Systems.   The specification of the position of a point P can also be accomplished through utilizing another coordinate system called the circular cylindrical, or more commonly, the cylindrical coordinate system.   To construct such a system, we arbitrarily choose an origin and through it pass a reference plane; on the plane we pass a

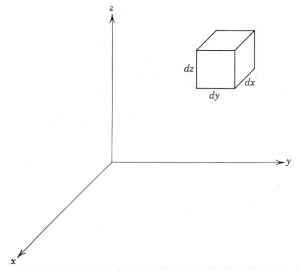

Figure 4.9   Element of volume in Cartesian coordinates.

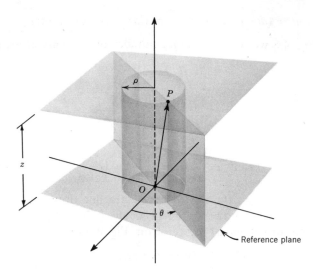

Figure 4.10   A cylindrical coordinate system.

reference line one sense of which is chosen as positive (see arrowhead on
reference line on reference plane in Fig. 4.10). The three coordinates
necessary to specify the location of P can now be determined by passing
through P three surfaces; a plane parallel to the reference plane (the
surface $z = $ a constant); a plane through O and P normal to the reference
plane (the surface $\theta = $ a constant); and a right circular cylinder whose
axis is normal to the reference plane and contains the origin (the surface
$\rho = $ a constant). The radius of the cylinder ρ is the radial coordinate of P;
the angle θ is the angle between that portion of the reference line on the
positive side of the origin and the plane through P and the origin normal
to the reference plane as measured in a counterclockwise direction.
θ is the polar coordinate* of point P. The shortest distance from P to the
reference plane is the z coordinate of P.

The magnitude of the element of length $d\mathbf{l}_\rho$ at P normal to the cylinder
$\rho = $ a constant, that is, in the planes $\theta = $ a constant and $z = a$ constant,
is (see Fig. 4.11)

$$dl_\rho = d\rho \qquad\qquad (4.17)$$

The magnitude of the element of length $d\mathbf{l}_\theta$ at P normal to the plane
$\theta = $ a constant, that is, on the cylinder $\rho = $ a constant and the plane

---

* θ is chosen as the polar angle because it is reasonable for the notation used in the
cylindrical system to agree with its two-dimensional counterpart, polar coordinates.

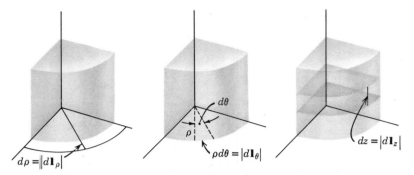

Figure 4.11   Line segments in a cylindrical coordinate system.

$z = $ a constant, is

$$dl_\theta = \rho\, d\theta \qquad (4.18)$$

and the magnitude of $d\mathbf{l}_z$, an element of length at P normal to the plane $z = $ a constant, that is, on the cylinder $\rho = $ a constant and the plane $\theta = $ a constant, is

$$dl_z = dz \qquad (4.19)$$

The magnitude of an element of area ds_ρ on the surface $\rho = $ a constant (see Fig. 4.12), that is, ds_ρ is normal to the planes $z = $ a constant and $\theta = $ a constant, is given by

$$ds_\rho = \rho\, d\theta\, dz \qquad (4.20)$$

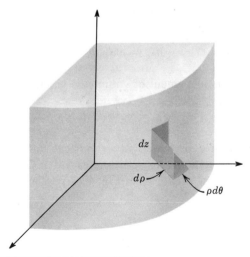

Figure 4.12   Elemental areas in a cylindrical coordinate system.

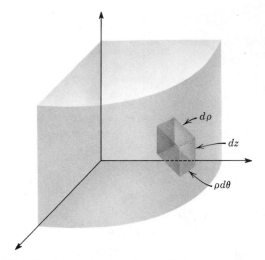

Figure 4.13   An elemental volume in a cylindrical coordinate system.

where ρ is the radial coordinate of ds_ρ. ds_θ, the magnitude of an element of area in the plane $\theta =$ a constant, that is, normal to the surfaces $\rho =$ a constant and $z =$ a constant, is

$$ds_\theta = d\rho \, dz \tag{4.21}$$

and the magnitude of the elemental area ds_z, which is in the plane $z =$ a constant, that is, normal to the plane $\theta =$ a constant and the cylinder $\rho =$ a constant, is written

$$ds_z = \rho \, d\rho \, d\theta \tag{4.22}$$

dV (see Fig. 4.13), an element of volume, is given by

$$dV = \rho \, d\rho \, d\theta \, dz \tag{4.23}$$

If the position of P is stated in cylindrical coordinates, $P(\rho, \theta, z)$, and we wish to determine its coordinates in a Cartesian coordinate system having the same origin, from Fig. 4.14 we see that

$$x = \rho \cos \theta \tag{4.24}$$

$$y = \rho \sin \theta \tag{4.25}$$

$$z = z \tag{4.26}$$

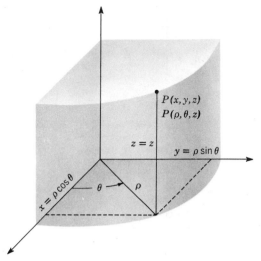

Figure 4.14   Relationships among Cartesian and cylindrical coordinate variables.

Conversely, if P is given in rectangular coordinates, its cylindrical coordinates are given by

$$\rho = (x^2 + y^2)^{1/2} \tag{4.27}$$

$$\theta = \arctan \frac{y^*}{x} \tag{4.28}$$

$$z = z \tag{4.29}$$

Spherical Coordinates.   Another three-dimensional coordinate system may also be formed by choosing an origin through which we pass a reference plane; we pass two mutually perpendicular lines through the origin, one lying in the reference plane, and choose a sense for each line which is considered positive (see arrowheads in Fig. 4.15). To locate a point P in such a system we pass through P and the origin.

1. A sphere of radius r whose center is at the origin, where r is the distance from the origin to P.

2. A plane $\theta =$ a constant, where θ is an angle measured in the counterclockwise direction from that portion of the reference line lying in the reference plane which lies on the "positive" side of the origin.

3. A cone of half-angle $(\pi/2 - \phi)$ whose apex is at the origin and whose axis is that portion of the reference line normal to the reference plane which lies on the "positive" side of the origin; ϕ is measured in the plane $\theta =$ a constant from the reference plane.

* Again, care must be taken that θ lies in the correct quadrant.

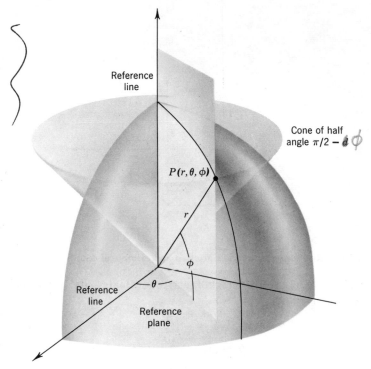

Figure 4.15   Location of a point in a spherical coordinate system

The stipulation of r, θ, and ϕ describe the position of P in a spherical coordinate system.

The magnitude of the element of length $d\mathbf{l}_r$ in the radial direction which is normal to the sphere $r =$ a constant is (see Fig. 4.16)

$$dl_r = dr \tag{4.30}$$

The magnitude of an element of length $d\mathbf{l}_\theta$, in the azimuthal direction, normal to the plane $\theta =$ a constant, is

$$dl_\theta = r \cos \phi \, d\theta \tag{4.31}$$

and dl_ϕ is

$$dl_\phi = r \, d\phi \tag{4.32}$$

The magnitude of an element of length $d\mathbf{l}$ in any direction is then

$$dl = [(dr)^2 + r^2 \cos^2 \phi (d\theta)^2 + r^2(d\phi)^2]^{1/2} \tag{4.33}$$

The magnitude of the elements of area $d\mathbf{s}_r$, $d\mathbf{s}_\theta$, and $d\mathbf{s}_\phi$ at P which are

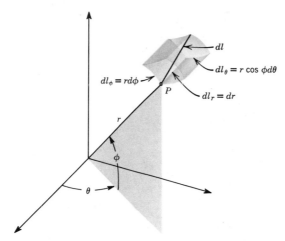

Figure 4.16   An arbitrary element of length in a spherical coordinate system.

on the sphere of radius r, the plane $\theta =$ a constant and the cone whose half-angle $(\pi/2 - \phi) =$ a constant, respectively, are given by (see Fig. 4.17)

$$ds_r = r^2 \cos \phi \, d\theta \, d\phi \tag{4.34}$$

$$ds_\theta = r \, dr \, d\phi \tag{4.35}$$

$$ds_\phi = r \cos \phi \, dr \, d\theta \tag{4.36}$$

We see in Fig. 4.18 that the volume element dV is given by

$$dV = r^2 \cos \phi \, dr \, d\theta \, d\phi \tag{4.37}$$

If P is given in terms of its spherical coordinates, $P(r, \theta, \phi)$, and we

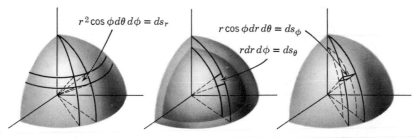

Figure 4.17   Elements of area in a spherical coordinate system.

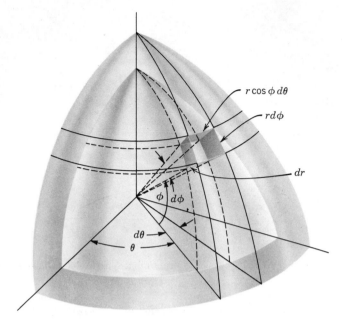

Figure 4.18   Volume element in a spherical coordinate system.

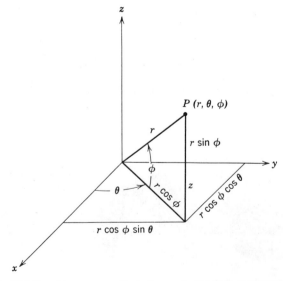

Figure 4.19   Relationships among Cartesian and spherical coordinate variables.

wish to give the position of P in Cartesian coordinates, then (see Fig. 4.19)

$$x = r \cos \phi \cos \theta \tag{4.38}$$
$$y = r \cos \phi \sin \theta \tag{4.39}$$
$$z = r \sin \phi \tag{4.40}$$

If we wish to determine the coordinates of P in spherical coordinates when P is given in Cartesian coordinates, we see from Eqs. (4.38), (4.39), and (4.40) that

$$r = (x^2 + y^2 + z^2)^{\frac{1}{2}} \tag{4.41}$$

$$\theta = \arctan \frac{y}{x} \tag{4.42}$$

$$\phi = \arcsin \frac{z}{(x^2 + y^2 + z^2)^{\frac{1}{2}}} \tag{4.43}$$

If the cylindrical coordinates of P are

$$\rho = r \cos \phi \tag{4.44}$$
$$\theta = \theta \tag{4.45}$$
$$z = r \sin \phi \tag{4.46}$$

where r, θ, and ϕ are the spherical coordinates of P, $P(\rho, \theta, z)$ may be transformed to $P(r, \theta, \phi)$ by

$$r = (\rho^2 + z^2)^{\frac{1}{2}} \tag{4.47}$$
$$\theta = \theta \tag{4.48}$$

$$\phi = \arctan \left(\frac{z}{\rho} \right)$$

$$= \arcsin \left[\frac{z}{(\rho^2 + z^2)^{\frac{1}{2}}} \right] \tag{4.49}$$

4.3   Vector Field Representation

We have discussed those coordinate systems which are commonly used in the study of scalar and vector fields. In this section we shall treat the representation of vector fields in these coordinate systems.

Vector Field Representation in Cartesian Coordinates.   In Chapter 2 we have seen that a vector field $\mathbf{A}$ may be represented in a Cartesian coordinate system as

$$\mathbf{A}(x, y, z) = \mathbf{u}_x A_x(x, y, z) + \mathbf{u}_y A_y(x, y, z) + \mathbf{u}_z A_z(x, y, z) \tag{2.24}$$
$$\tag{4.50}$$

where $\mathbf{u}_x$, $\mathbf{u}_y$, and $\mathbf{u}_z$ are unit vectors, and $A_x(x, y, z)$, $A_y(x, y, z)$, and $A_z(x, y, z)$ are the magnitudes of the components of $\mathbf{A}(x, y, z)$ along the x-, y-, and z-axes respectively. By the scalar multiplication of Eq. (4.50) with $\mathbf{u}_x$, we see again that

$$\mathbf{u}_x \cdot \mathbf{A} = |A_x| = A \cos [\mathbf{u}_x, \mathbf{A}] \tag{4.51}$$

In other words, since $[\mathbf{u}_x, \mathbf{A}]$ is the angle between the vector field $\mathbf{A}$ and the unit vector $\mathbf{u}_x$, then A_x is the magnitude of the projection of $\mathbf{A}$ along the x-axis.

As an example of a two-dimensional vector field, consider

$$\mathbf{A} = \mathbf{u}_y x \tag{4.52}$$

Here $A_x = 0$ and $A_y = x$. Figure 4.20 is the graphical representation of Eq. (4.52). We see that the y-component of $\mathbf{A}$ varies with x.

Another two-dimensional field is

$$\mathbf{A} = \mathbf{u}_x \frac{x}{\sqrt{x^2 + y^2}} + \mathbf{u}_y \frac{y}{\sqrt{x^2 + y^2}} \tag{4.53}$$

Here $A_x = x/\sqrt{x^2 + y^2}$ and $A_y = y/\sqrt{x^2 + y^2}$. Figure 4.21 shows Eq. (4.53) graphically, and we see it is a radial field.

As a further aid in the visualization and understanding of vector fields let us explore further the field lines discussed in Chapter 1. The reader

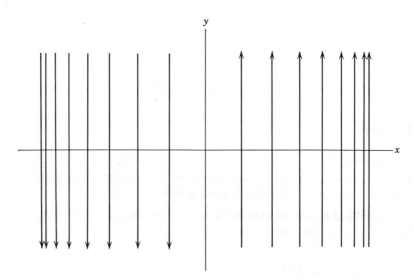

Figure 4.20   Representation of the two-dimensional field $\mathbf{A} = \mathbf{u}_y x$.

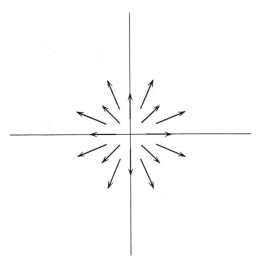

Figure 4.21   A radial vector field.

will recall that these field lines have the same direction as the vector field at every point; that is, the tangents to the field lines are in the same direction as the field. A displacement dx, the magnitude of the x-component of a displacement $d\mathbf{l}$ along a field line, has the same direction as $\mathbf{A}_x$, the component of $\mathbf{A}$ in the x-direction; in other words, they are both in the x-direction. If they are both in the same direction, we may write

$$d\mathbf{x} = k\mathbf{A}_x \qquad (4.54)$$

where k is a scale factor to make the equation possible. Similarly,

$$d\mathbf{y} = k\mathbf{A}_y \qquad (4.55)$$

Here we have assumed that the scale factor is the same for the x- and y-components.

Referring to Fig. 4.22, we see that at any point P the slope of the field line is dy/dx; since it is also A_y/A_x, we may write

$$\frac{dy}{dx} = \frac{A_y}{A_x} \qquad (4.56)$$

When A_x and A_y are given in terms of x and y, the resulting differential equation may be solved for families of curves which are the field lines. As an example of these ideas, consider the vector field

$$\mathbf{A} = \mathbf{u}_x 6y - \mathbf{u}_y 3x \qquad (4.57)$$

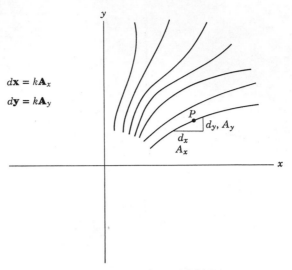

$$dx = k\mathbf{A}_x$$
$$dy = k\mathbf{A}_y$$

Figure 4.22   Equations of field lines.

Here (4.56) becomes

$$\frac{dy}{dx} = \frac{A_y}{A_x} = \frac{-3x}{6y} \tag{4.58}$$

or

$$6y\,dy = -3x\,dx$$

Integrating both sides yields

$$3y^2 = -\frac{3x^2}{2} + \text{a constant} \tag{4.59}$$

or

$$\frac{x^2}{2} + y^2 = \text{a constant} = C^2 \tag{4.60}$$

Here the field lines are a family of ellipses whose centers are at the origin (see Fig. 4.23).

As an example of a three-dimensional vector field, consider

$$\mathbf{A} = \mathbf{u}_x(6) + \mathbf{u}_y z + \mathbf{u}_z(4xy) \tag{4.61}$$

Here the magnitude of the x-component is 6 everywhere; the magnitude of the y-component varies with z and the magnitude of the z-component varies four times faster than the product xy. It is difficult to represent graphically such a vector field. To aid in visualizing such three-dimensional fields, it is sometimes instructive to construct the associated field lines. To do so, we recall that at any point the field line has the same direction

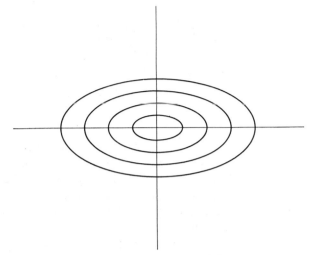

Figure 4.23   Elliptical field lines.

as the vector field. Therefore at any point an element $d\mathbf{l}$ of a field line is in the same direction as the vector field,

$$d\mathbf{l} = k\mathbf{A} \qquad (4.62)$$

where k is a scale factor by which $\mathbf{A}$ must be multiplied to make it equal to $d\mathbf{l}$,

$$d\mathbf{l} = \mathbf{u}_x\, dx + \mathbf{u}_y\, dy + \mathbf{u}_z\, dz = \mathbf{u}_x(kA_x) + \mathbf{u}_y(kA_y) + \mathbf{u}_z(kA_z) \qquad (4.63)$$

where dx, dy, and dz are the magnitudes of the components of $d\mathbf{l}$. Equating the components of Eq. (4.63) yields three scalar equations:

$$dx = kA_x, \qquad dy = kA_y, \qquad \text{and} \quad dz = kA_z$$

or

$$\frac{dx}{A_x} = k = \frac{dy}{A_y} = \frac{dz}{A_z} \qquad (4.64)$$

Equations (4.64) describe the fact that at any point in space the ratios of the magnitudes of the components of the two vector quantities $d\mathbf{l}$ and $\mathbf{A}$ along the x-, y-, and z-axes are constant. The solution of any two differential equations resulting from Eq. (4.64) are two families of surfaces and the intersection of these surfaces are the direction lines.

To illustrate these ideas, consider the vector field

$$\mathbf{A} = \mathbf{u}_x \frac{x}{(x^2 + y^2 + z^2)^{\frac{1}{2}}} + \mathbf{u}_y \frac{y}{(x^2 + y^2 + z^2)^{\frac{1}{2}}} + \mathbf{u}_z \frac{z}{(x^2 + y^2 + z^2)^{\frac{1}{2}}}$$

$$(4.65)$$

Then

$$\frac{dx}{dy} = \frac{x}{y} \quad \text{and} \quad \frac{dx}{dz} = \frac{x}{z} \tag{4.66}$$

These equations may be integrated to

$$\ln c_1 + \ln x = \ln y \qquad \text{or} \quad c_1 x = y \tag{4.67}$$

and

$$\ln c_2 + \ln x = \ln z \qquad \text{or} \quad c_2 x = z \tag{4.68}$$

These two equations represent families of planes through the origin; Eqs. (4.67) are planes normal to the plane $z = 0$ and Eqs. (4.68) are planes normal to the plane $y = 0$ (see Fig. 4.24). The field lines are the intersections of these families of planes, that is, they are straight lines which proceed radially and whose density (number of lines per unit area normal to field lines) is everywhere unity.

In order to facilitate our understanding of the representation of a vector field in cylindrical and spherical coordinate systems, it is best to consider the location of a point in any of the coordinate systems we have discussed as the intersection of three mutually orthogonal surfaces representing constant values of the coordinate variables. In a Cartesian coordinate system these surfaces are the three mutually orthogonal planes through the point.

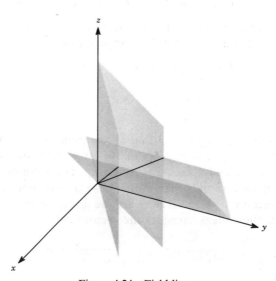

Figure 4.24   Field lines.

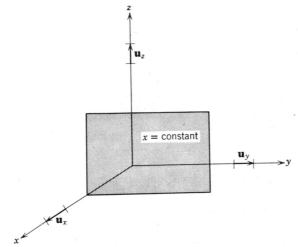

Figure 4.25   Unit vectors in a Cartesian coordinate system.

Vector Representation in a Cylindrical Coordinate System.   In many field problems such as the fluid flow in a pipe or the electric field around a line of charge, the cylindrical symmetry of the situation suggests that a cylindrical coordinate system be used.   In this system of coordinates, a vector **A** may be written in terms of its radial, azimuthal, and z components. To do so, three unit vectors must be defined.   However, in contradistinction to Cartesian coordinates, we no longer direct these unit vectors along the coordinate axes, for such "axes" do not exist for cylindrical or spherical coordinate systems.   Instead, we adopt a more fundamental concept of the unit vector, namely that it points in the direction of increasing values of the coordinate with which it is associated and, in addition, that a unit vector is normal to the surface on which its coordinate is a constant.   For example, referring to Fig. 4.25, we see that $\mathbf{u}_x$ points toward larger values of x and is normal to planes $x =$ a constant; $\mathbf{u}_y$ and $\mathbf{u}_z$ are thought of in similar terms.

In an analogous manner we may define three unit vectors $\mathbf{u}_\rho$, $\mathbf{u}_\theta$, and $\mathbf{u}_z$ which can be used to represent a vector in a cylindrical coordinate system. $\mathbf{u}_\rho$ is a unit vector at a point $P(\rho, \theta, z)$ which is normal to the surface $\rho =$ a constant; that is, $\mathbf{u}_\rho$ is normal to the cylinder $\rho =$ a constant, which passes through P; $\mathbf{u}_\rho$ is in the direction and sense in which ρ is increasing (see Fig. 4.26a). $\mathbf{u}_\theta$ is a unit vector at P normal to the plane $\theta =$ a constant and in the cylindrical surface $\rho =$ a constant, and the plane $z =$ a constant (see Fig. 4.26b).   Similarly, $\mathbf{u}_z$ is defined to be a unit vector at P on the cylinder $\rho =$ a constant and in the plane $\theta =$ a constant but normal to the plane $z =$ a constant (see Fig. 4.26c).

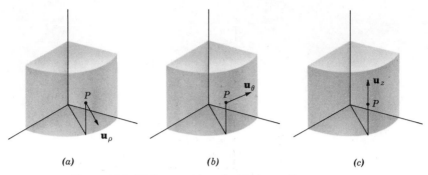

Figure 4.26   Unit vectors in cylindrical coordinate system.

The unit vectors $\mathbf{u}_\rho$ and $\mathbf{u}_\theta$ may be thought of in several ways. Sometimes it is convenient to think of them as always pointing in the same "direction" where, according to the ideas just presented, "direction" indicates the way toward which a coordinate variable increases. Considered thus, $\mathbf{u}_\rho$ and $\mathbf{u}_\theta$ do not change "direction" since they always point toward increasing values of ρ and θ, respectively. We may also view $\mathbf{u}_\rho$ and $\mathbf{u}_\theta$ in another manner. Since the direction of $\mathbf{u}_\rho$ and $\mathbf{u}_\theta$ depend on their position in space, we may consider them as particularly convenient vector fields.

We may now write for a vector $\mathbf{A}$ in a cylindrical coordinate system

$$\mathbf{A}(\rho, \theta, z) = \mathbf{u}_\rho A_\rho(\rho, \theta, z) + \mathbf{u}_\theta A_\theta(\rho, \theta, z) + \mathbf{u}_z A_z(\rho, \theta, z) \quad (4.69)$$

where the magnitude of a component may be found by dotting Eq. (4.69) with a unit vector in the component direction as

$$A_\rho = \mathbf{u}_\rho \cdot \mathbf{A} = \mathbf{u}_\rho \cdot (\mathbf{u}_\rho A_\rho + \mathbf{u}_\theta A_\theta + \mathbf{u}_z A_z) \quad (4.70)$$

since $\mathbf{u}_\rho \cdot \mathbf{u}_\rho = 1$ and $\mathbf{u}_\rho \cdot \mathbf{u}_\theta = \mathbf{u}_\rho \cdot \mathbf{u}_z = 0$ because the unit vectors are orthogonal.

Similarly,

$$A_\theta = \mathbf{u}_\theta \cdot \mathbf{A} \quad (4.71)$$

and

$$A_z = \mathbf{u}_z \cdot \mathbf{A} \quad (4.72)$$

As an example of a two-dimensional vector field which is represented in polar coordinates, consider

$$\mathbf{A} = \mathbf{u}_\rho \rho \quad (4.73)$$

Figure 4.27 shows that this vector field contains a radial component only; the magnitude of this radial component increases with distance from the origin.

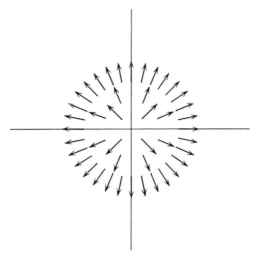

Figure 4.27 A radial field whose magnitude is proportional to the distance from the origin.

The mapping of the field lines associated with a vector field represented in a cylindrical coordinate system may be accomplished in a mannar similar to that discussed for Cartesian coordinate systems. Here an element of a field line $d\mathbf{l}$ may be written

$$d\mathbf{l} = \mathbf{u}_\rho \, dl_\rho + \mathbf{u}_\theta \, dl_\theta + \mathbf{u}_z \, dl_z$$

but from Eqs. (4.17), (4.18), and (4.19) this becomes

$$d\mathbf{l} = \mathbf{u}_\rho \, d\rho + \mathbf{u}_\theta \rho \, d\theta + \mathbf{u}_z \, dz \qquad (4.74)$$

Since this has the same direction and sense as the field,

$$\mathbf{A} = \mathbf{u}_\rho A_\rho + \mathbf{u}_\theta A_\theta + \mathbf{u}_z A_z$$

we can write

$$d\mathbf{l} - m\mathbf{A} = m(\mathbf{u}_\rho A_\rho + \mathbf{u}_\theta A_\theta + \mathbf{u}_z A_z) \qquad (4.75)$$

where m is a constant scalar, so that by equating the magnitudes of the components, we obtain

$$d\rho = mA_\rho \qquad (4.76)$$
$$\rho \, d\theta = mA_\theta \qquad (4.77)$$
$$dz = mA_z \qquad (4.78)$$

Solving each of these equations for m yields

$$m = \frac{d\rho}{A_\rho} = \frac{\rho \, d\theta}{A_\theta} = \frac{dz}{A_z} \qquad (4.79)$$

The differential equations resulting from any two of these equalities may be solved to give two families of surfaces. As in Cartesian coordinates, the intersections of these surfaces form the field lines.

Vector Field Representation in a Spherical Coordinate System. Let us now look at the representation of a vector field in a spherical coordinate system, the system whose coordinate variables are a length and two angles. Spherical coordinate systems arise quite naturally in such physical situations as orbit calculations—the flow of a fluid in the neighborhood of a source or sink.

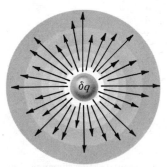

By analogy with the representation of a vector in the two previously discussed coordinate systems, we may write for the value of a vector quantity **A** at a point $P(r, \theta, \phi)$

Figure 4.28 The electric field surrounding a charge δq.

$$\mathbf{A}(r, \theta, \phi) = \mathbf{u}_r A_r + \mathbf{u}_\theta A_\theta + \mathbf{u}_\phi A_\phi \quad (4.80)$$

where $\mathbf{u}_r$ is a unit vector at P normal to the sphere $r =$ a constant, $\mathbf{u}_\theta$ is a unit vector at P normal to the plane $\theta =$ a constant, and $\mathbf{u}_\phi$ is a unit vector at P normal to the surface of a cone whose half-angle is $[\pi/2 - \phi]$. These three unit vectors are orthogonal to each other. The magnitude of the component $\mathbf{A}_r$ may be found by the scalar product of **A** with $\mathbf{u}_r$,

$$A_r = \mathbf{u}_r \cdot \mathbf{A} = \mathbf{u}_r \cdot (\mathbf{u}_r A_r + \mathbf{u}_\theta A_\theta + \mathbf{u}_\phi A_\phi) \quad (4.81)$$

However, $\mathbf{u}_r \cdot \mathbf{u}_r = 1$ and $\mathbf{u}_r \cdot \mathbf{u}_\theta = \mathbf{u}_r \cdot \mathbf{u}_\phi = 0$, because the unit vectors are normal to each other. Similarly,

$$A_\theta = \mathbf{u}_\theta \cdot \mathbf{A} \quad (4.82)$$

$$A_\phi = \mathbf{u}_\phi \cdot \mathbf{A} \quad (4.83)$$

A simple example of a three-dimensional vector field is the electric field **E** in free space surrounding a small charge δq located at the origin. It is given by (see Fig. 4.28)

$$\mathbf{E} = \frac{\delta q}{4\pi\epsilon_0 r^2} \mathbf{u}_r \quad \text{(MKS units)} \quad (4.84)$$

where ϵ_0 is the permittivity of free space.

The field lines of a vector field $\mathbf{A}(r, \theta, \phi)$ written in spherical coordinates are the intersections of families of surfaces determined as follows.

As before, an element $d\mathbf{l}$ of a field line at any point will be tangent to the field, $\mathbf{A} = \mathbf{u}_r A_r + \mathbf{u}_\theta A_\theta + \mathbf{u}_\phi A_\phi$, so that

$$d\mathbf{l} = m\mathbf{A} \tag{4.85}$$

From Eqs. (4.30), (4.31), and (4.32), we see that

$$
\begin{aligned}
d\mathbf{l} &= \mathbf{u}_r \, dl_r + \mathbf{u}_\theta \, dl_\theta + \mathbf{u}_\phi \, dl_\phi \\
&= \mathbf{u}_r \, dr + \mathbf{u}_\theta r \cos \phi \, d\theta + \mathbf{u}_\phi r \, d\phi
\end{aligned} \tag{4.86}
$$

Substituting Eq. (4.86) into (4.85) and equating components yields

$$dr = mA_r \tag{4.87}$$
$$r \cos \phi \, d\theta = mA_\theta \tag{4.88}$$
$$r \, d\phi = mA_\phi \tag{4.89}$$

or, solving these for m, we see that

$$m = \frac{dr}{A_r} = \frac{r \cos \phi \, d\theta}{A_\theta} = \frac{r \, d\phi}{A_\phi} \tag{4.90}$$

The solutions of the two differential equations resulting from any two of these equalities will be two families of surfaces whose intersections will form the field lines.

4.4 The Transformation of the Representation of a Vector Field from One Coordinate System to Another

To understand many field problems, it is of great value to be able to change the representation of a vector field from one coordinate system to another. In this section we shall discuss the graphical and analytic aspects of such transformations.

CYLINDRICAL TO CARTESIAN AND VICE VERSA

If a vector field $\mathbf{A}$ is expressed in cylindrical coordinates and we wish to represent it in Cartesian coordinates, we proceed as follows.

The desired transformation, as well as similar coordinate transformations, may be best accomplished by a process involving two steps: (a) changing the variables and (b) changing the magnitudes of the components from one coordinate system to another; that is, we have a vector $\mathbf{A}(\rho, \theta, z)$ given by

$$\mathbf{A}(\rho, \theta, z) = \mathbf{u}_\rho A_\rho(\rho, \theta, z) + \mathbf{u}_\theta A_\theta(\rho, \theta, z) + \mathbf{u}_z A_z(\rho, \theta, z) \tag{4.91}$$

Scalar and Vector Fields

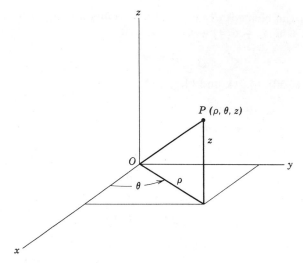

Figure 4.29   Transformation from cylindrical to Cartesian coordinates.

and we wish to change **A** to a vector represented in Cartesian coordinates thus:

$$\mathbf{A}(x, y, z) = \mathbf{u}_x A_x(x, y, z) + \mathbf{u}_y A_y(x, y, z) + \mathbf{u}_z A_z(x, y, z) \quad (4.92)$$

The order in which we undertake these two steps is immaterial. Equations (4.24), (4.25), and (4.26) are used to change the variables ρ, θ, and z to x, y, and z. To illustrate this step in the transformation, consider the vector field

$$\mathbf{B}(\rho, \theta, z) = \mathbf{u}_\rho z \cos \theta + \mathbf{u}_\theta \rho \sin \theta + \mathbf{u}_z z \rho \quad (4.93)$$

By utilizing Eqs. (4.24), (4.25), (4.26), (4.27), (4.28), and (4.29), Eq. (4.93) becomes

$$\mathbf{B}(x, y, z) = \mathbf{u}_\rho \frac{zx}{(x^2 + y^2)^{1/2}} + \mathbf{u}_\theta y + \mathbf{u}_z z(x^2 + y^2)^{1/2} \quad (4.94)$$

The final step in the transformation is to change the components $\mathbf{B}_\rho = \mathbf{u}_\rho [zx/(x^2 + y^2)^{1/2}]$, $\mathbf{B}_\theta = \mathbf{u}_\theta y$, and $\mathbf{B}_z = \mathbf{u}_z z(x^2 + y^2)^{1/2}$ to the Cartesian components, $\mathbf{B}_x$, $\mathbf{B}_y$, and $\mathbf{B}_z$. To find the magnitude of the x-component $\mathbf{B}_x$, we must recall from Section 2.3 that the magnitude of the component of a vector in a particular direction is obtained by taking the dot product of the vector with a unit vector in that particular direction, for example,

$$A_x = \mathbf{A} \cdot \mathbf{u}_x \quad (4.95)$$

For any vector **A** expressed in cylindrical coordinates, we may write

$$A_x = (\mathbf{u}_\rho A_\rho + \mathbf{u}_\theta A_\theta + \mathbf{u}_z A_z) \cdot \mathbf{u}_x$$
$$= A_\rho[\mathbf{u}_\rho \cdot \mathbf{u}_x] + A_\theta[\mathbf{u}_\theta \cdot \mathbf{u}_x] + A_z[\mathbf{u}_z \cdot \mathbf{u}_x] \tag{4.96}$$

$$A_y = \mathbf{A} \cdot \mathbf{u}_y = A_\rho[\mathbf{u}_\rho \cdot \mathbf{u}_y] + A_\theta[\mathbf{u}_\theta \cdot \mathbf{u}_y] + A_z[\mathbf{u}_z \cdot \mathbf{u}_y] \tag{4.97}$$

$$A_z = \mathbf{A} \cdot \mathbf{u}_z = A_\rho[\mathbf{u}_\rho \cdot \mathbf{u}_z] + A_\theta[\mathbf{u}_\theta \cdot \mathbf{u}_z] + A_z[\mathbf{u}_z \cdot \mathbf{u}_z] \tag{4.98}$$

Thus we see that the problem of transforming components reduces to one of determining the dot products of the unit vectors of the coordinate systems involved.

By referring to Fig. 4.29, we see that in the transformation from cylindrical to Cartesian coordinates we are concerned with the angle θ so that

$$\mathbf{u}_\rho \cdot \mathbf{u}_x = \cos \theta = \frac{x}{(x^2 + y^2)^{1/2}} \tag{4.99a}$$

$$\mathbf{u}_\rho \cdot \mathbf{u}_y = \sin \theta = \frac{y}{(x^2 + y^2)^{1/2}} \tag{4.99b}$$

$$\mathbf{u}_\rho \cdot \mathbf{u}_z = 0 \tag{4.99c}$$

$$\mathbf{u}_\theta \cdot \mathbf{u}_x = -\sin \theta = -\frac{y}{(x^2 + y^2)^{1/2}} \tag{4.99d}$$

$$\mathbf{u}_\theta \cdot \mathbf{u}_y = \cos \theta = \frac{x}{(x^2 + y^2)^{1/2}} \tag{4.99e}$$

$$\mathbf{u}_\theta \cdot \mathbf{u}_z = 0 \tag{4.99f}$$

$$\mathbf{u}_z \cdot \mathbf{u}_x = 0 \tag{4.99g}$$

$$\mathbf{u}_z \cdot \mathbf{u}_y = 0 \tag{4.99h}$$

$$\mathbf{u}_z \cdot \mathbf{u}_z - 1 \tag{4.99i}$$

These equations constitute the projections of one unit vector on another.

Substituting the results of Eqs. (4.99) into Eqs. (4.96), (4.97), and (4.98) yields

$$A_x = \frac{A_\rho x}{(x^2 + y^2)^{1/2}} - \frac{A_\theta y}{(x^2 + y^2)^{1/2}} \tag{4.100}$$

$$A_y = \frac{A_\rho y}{(x^2 + y^2)^{1/2}} + \frac{A_\theta x}{(x^2 + y^2)^{1/2}} \tag{4.101}$$

and obviously,

$$A_z = A_z \tag{4.102}$$

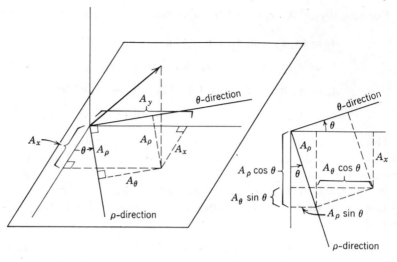

Figure 4.30 For discussion of transformations between Cartesian and cylindrical coordinate systems.

Therefore

$$\mathbf{A} = \mathbf{u}_x\left[\frac{A_\rho x}{(x^2 + y^2)^{1/2}} - \frac{A_\theta y}{(x^2 + y^2)^{1/2}}\right]$$

$$+ \mathbf{u}_y\left[\frac{A_\rho y}{(x^2 + y^2)^{1/2}} + \frac{A_\theta x}{(x^2 + y^2)^{1/2}}\right]$$

$$+ \mathbf{u}_z A_z \qquad (4.103)$$

Figure 4.30 shows these results in graphical form. Applying this result to our example expressed in Eqs. (4.93) and (4.94), we see that

$$\mathbf{B} = \mathbf{u}_x\left[\frac{zx^2}{(x^2 + y^2)} - \frac{y^2}{(x^2 + y^2)^{1/2}}\right]$$

$$+ \mathbf{u}_y\left[\frac{zxy}{(x^2 + y^2)} + \frac{xy}{(x^2 + y^2)}\right]$$

$$+ \mathbf{u}_z[z(x^2 + y^2)^{1/2}] \qquad (4.104)$$

The same approach may be used to transform from Cartesian to cylindrical coordinates.

The general results of these vector transformations as well as their inverse, that is, the transformation from Cartesian to cylindrical coordinates and vice versa, are summarized in Table 4.1.

SPHERICAL TO CARTESIAN AND VICE VERSA

If a vector $\mathbf{A}$ is represented in a spherical coordinate system, and we wish to express it in Cartesian coordinates, we proceed as before by transforming the spherical coordinate variables to Cartesian and then transforming the components from spherical to Cartesian. The coordinate transformation can be effected by Eqs. (4.38), (4.39), and (4.40). The components A_x, A_y, and A_z may be determined by

$$A_x = \mathbf{u}_x \cdot \mathbf{A} = \mathbf{u}_x \cdot (\mathbf{u}_r A_r + \mathbf{u}_\theta A_\theta + \mathbf{u}_\phi A_\phi)$$

$$= A_r[\mathbf{u}_x \cdot \mathbf{u}_r] + A_\theta[\mathbf{u}_x \cdot \mathbf{u}_\theta] + A_\phi[\mathbf{u}_x \cdot \mathbf{u}_\phi] \tag{4.105}$$

$$A_y = \mathbf{u}_y \cdot \mathbf{A} = A_r[\mathbf{u}_y \cdot \mathbf{u}_\theta] + A_\theta[\mathbf{u}_y \cdot \mathbf{u}_\theta] + A_\phi[\mathbf{u}_y \cdot \mathbf{u}_\phi] \tag{4.106}$$

and

$$A_z = A_r[\mathbf{u}_z \cdot \mathbf{u}_r] + A_\theta[\mathbf{u}_z \cdot \mathbf{u}_\theta] + A_\phi[\mathbf{u}_z \cdot \mathbf{u}_\phi] \tag{4.107}$$

By referring to Fig. 4.31, we see that the scalar products involving $\mathbf{u}_x$ and $\mathbf{u}_y$ are determined by first projecting $\mathbf{u}_r$, $\mathbf{u}_0$, and $\mathbf{u}_\phi$ on the xy-plane and then determining the components of these projections on the x- and y-axes.

Table 4.1

Relations among the coordinate variables and components in transformations involving Cartesian and cylindrical coordinate systems

Coordinate Variable Change		Component Change	
Cartesian to Cylindrical	Cylindrical to Cartesian	Cylindrical to Cartesian	Cartesian to Cylindrical
$\rho = (x^2 + y^2)^{1/2}$	$x = \rho \cos \theta$	$A_x = A_\rho \dfrac{x}{(x^2 + y^2)^{1/2}}$	$A_\rho = A_x \cos \theta$
		$\qquad - A_\theta \dfrac{y}{(x^2 + y^2)^{1/2}}$	$\qquad + A_y \sin \theta$
$\theta = \arctan \dfrac{y}{x}$	$y = \rho \sin \theta$	$A_y = A_\rho \dfrac{y}{(x^2 + y^2)^{1/2}}$	$A_\theta = -A_x \sin \theta$
		$\qquad + A_\theta \dfrac{x}{(x^2 + y^2)^{1/2}}$	$\qquad + A_y \cos \theta$
$z = z$	$z = z$	$A_z = A_z$	$A_z = A_z$

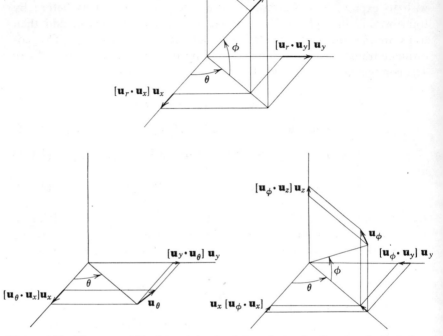

Figure 4.31   Figures to aid in determining the dot products of unit vectors in Cartesian and spherical coordinate systems.

The scalar products involving $\mathbf{u}_z$ involve only the angle ϕ.   Therefore

$$\mathbf{u}_x \cdot \mathbf{u}_r = \cos \phi \cos \theta = \frac{x}{(x^2 + y^2 + z^2)^{\frac{1}{2}}} \qquad (4.108a)$$

$$\mathbf{u}_x \cdot \mathbf{u}_\theta = -\sin \theta = -\frac{y}{(x^2 + y^2)^{\frac{1}{2}}} \qquad (4.108b)$$

$$\mathbf{u}_x \cdot \mathbf{u}_\phi = -\sin \phi \cos \theta = -\frac{x}{(x^2 + y^2)^{\frac{1}{2}}} \frac{z}{(x^2 + y^2 + z^2)^{\frac{1}{2}}} \qquad (4.108c)$$

$$\mathbf{u}_y \cdot \mathbf{u}_r = \cos \phi \sin \theta = \frac{y}{(x^2 + y^2 + z^2)^{\frac{1}{2}}} \qquad (4.108d)$$

$$\mathbf{u}_y \cdot \mathbf{u}_\theta = \cos \theta = \frac{x}{(x^2 + y^2)^{\frac{1}{2}}} \qquad (4.108e)$$

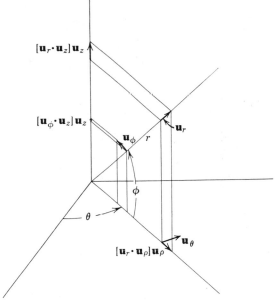

Figure 4.32   Transforming a vector expressed in cylindrical coordinates to one expressed in spherical coordinates and vice versa.

$$\mathbf{u}_y \cdot \mathbf{u}_\phi = -\sin\phi\sin\theta = \frac{-yz}{(x^2+y^2)^{\frac{1}{2}}(x^2+y^2+z^2)^{\frac{1}{2}}} \tag{4.108f}$$

$$\mathbf{u}_z \cdot \mathbf{u}_r = \sin\phi = \frac{z}{(x^2+y^2+z^2)^{\frac{1}{2}}} \tag{4.108g}$$

$$\mathbf{u}_z \cdot \mathbf{u}_\theta = 0 \tag{4.108h}$$

$$\mathbf{u}_z \cdot \mathbf{u}_\phi = \cos\phi = \frac{(x^2+y^2)^{\frac{1}{2}}}{(x^2+y^2+z^2)^{\frac{1}{2}}} \tag{4.108i}$$

The resulting magnitudes of the components for the transformation of a vector from spherical to Cartesian coordinates as well as the inverse transformation from Cartesian to spherical are presented in Table 4.2.

SPHERICAL TO CYLINDRICAL AND VICE VERSA

The transformation of a vector field from spherical coordinates to cylindrical or vice versa involves the following dot products which the reader can determine from Fig. 4.32.

$$\mathbf{u}_r \cdot \mathbf{u}_\rho = \cos\phi = \frac{\rho}{(\rho^2+z^2)^{\frac{1}{2}}} \tag{4.109a}$$

Table 4.2

Relations among the coordinate variables and the components in transformations involving Cartesian and spherical coordinate systems

Coordinate Variable Change

Cartesian to Spherical	Spherical to Cartesian
$r = (x^2 + y^2 + z^2)^{1/2}$	$x = r\cos\theta\cos\phi$
$\theta = \arctan \dfrac{y}{x}$	$y = r\sin\theta\cos\phi$
$\phi = \arcsin \dfrac{z}{(x^2 + y^2 + z^2)^{1/2}}$	$z = r\sin\phi$

Component Change

Cartesian to Spherical	Spherical to Cartesian
$A_r = A_x\cos\theta\cos\phi + A_y\sin\theta\cos\phi + A_z\sin\phi$	$A_x = \dfrac{A_r x}{(x^2 + y^2 + z^2)^{1/2}} - \dfrac{A_\theta y}{(x^2 + y^2)^{1/2}} - \dfrac{A_\phi xz}{(x^2 + y^2)^{1/2}(x^2 + y^2 + z^2)^{1/2}}$
$A_\theta = -A_x\sin\theta + A_y\cos\theta$	$A_y = \dfrac{A_r y}{(x^2 + y^2 + z^2)^{1/2}} + \dfrac{A_\theta x}{(x^2 + y^2)^{1/2}} - \dfrac{A_\phi yz}{(x^2 + y^2)^{1/2}(x^2 + y^2 + z^2)^{1/2}}$
$A_\phi = -A_x\cos\theta\sin\phi - A_y\sin\theta\sin\phi + A_z\cos\phi$	$A_z = \dfrac{A_r z}{(x^2 + y^2 + z^2)^{1/2}} + \dfrac{A_\phi (x^2 + y^2)^{1/2}}{(x^2 + y^2 + z^2)^{1/2}}$

$$\mathbf{u}_r \cdot \mathbf{u}_\theta = 0 \tag{4.109b}$$

$$\mathbf{u}_r \cdot \mathbf{u}_z = \sin \phi = \frac{z}{(\rho^2 + z^2)^{\frac{1}{2}}} \tag{4.109c}$$

$$\mathbf{u}_\theta \cdot \mathbf{u}_\rho = 0 \tag{4.109d}$$

$$\mathbf{u}_\theta \cdot \mathbf{u}_\theta = 1 \tag{4.109e}$$

$$\mathbf{u}_\theta \cdot \mathbf{u}_z = 0 \tag{4.109f}$$

$$\mathbf{u}_\phi \cdot \mathbf{u}_\rho = -\sin \phi = \frac{-z}{(\rho^2 + z^2)^{\frac{1}{2}}} \tag{4.109g}$$

$$\mathbf{u}_\phi \cdot \mathbf{u}_\theta = 0 \tag{4.109h}$$

$$\mathbf{u}_\phi \cdot \mathbf{u}_z = \cos \phi = \frac{\rho}{(\rho^2 + z^2)^{\frac{1}{2}}} \tag{4.109i}$$

and the pertinent coordinate variable transformations are given in Eqs. (4.44), (4.45), (4.46), (4.47), (4.48), and (4.49).

Table 4.3 contains the transformations necessary to change the representation of a vector field from spherical to cylindrical coordinates and vice versa.

MATRIX FORMULATION OF VECTOR FIELD TRANSFORMATIONS

The coordinate transformations just discussed can be stated very succinctly if we employ matrix notation. We shall now treat this method

Table 4.3

Relations among the coordinate variables and the components in transformations involving spherical and cylindrical coordinate systems

Coordinate Variable Change		Component Change	
Spherical to Cylindrical	Cylindrical to Spherical	Spherical to Cylindrical	Cylindrical to Spherical
$\rho = r \cos \phi$	$r = (\rho^2 + z^2)^{\frac{1}{2}}$	$A_\rho = A_r \dfrac{\rho}{(\rho^2 + z^2)^{\frac{1}{2}}}$ $\quad - A_\phi \dfrac{z}{(\rho^2 + z^2)^{\frac{1}{2}}}$	$A_r = A_\rho \cos \phi$ $\quad + A_z \sin \phi$
$\theta = \theta$	$\theta = \theta$	$A_\theta = A_\theta$	$A_\theta = A_\theta$
$z = r \sin \phi$	$\phi = \arcsin$ $\dfrac{z}{(\rho^2 + z^2)^{\frac{1}{2}}}$	$A_z = A_r \dfrac{z}{(\rho^2 + z^2)^{\frac{1}{2}}}$ $\quad + A_\phi \dfrac{\rho}{(\rho^2 + z^2)^{\frac{1}{2}}}$	$A_\phi = -A_\rho \sin \phi$ $\quad + A_z \cos \phi$

of representing the transformation of an expression for a vector field from one coordinate system to another.

The equations describing the transformation of the magnitudes of the components of a vector field **A** from Cartesian to cylindrical coordinates are given in Table 4.1:

$$A_\rho = A_x \cos \theta + A_y \sin \theta + A_z(0) \tag{4.110}$$

$$A_\theta = -A_x \sin \theta + A_y \cos \theta + A_z(0) \tag{4.111}$$

$$A_z = A_x(0) + A_y(0) + A_z \tag{4.112}$$

We see that these equations form a system of simultaneous algebraic equations. For treating such sets of equations, a systematic technique has been developed involving matrices. To see how matrices can be useful in solving a system of simultaneous algebraic equations, consider the following example. Suppose we are given a set of simultaneous algebraic equations involving the dependent variables y_1, y_2, and y_3 and the independent variables x_1, x_2, and x_3:

$$y_1 = a_{11}x_1 + a_{12}x_2 + a_{13}x_3 \tag{4.113}$$

$$y_2 = a_{21}x_1 + a_{22}x_2 + a_{23}x_3 \tag{4.114}$$

$$y_3 = a_{31}x_1 + a_{32}x_2 + a_{33}x_3 \tag{4.115}$$

The equations may be written in the matrix form

$$
\begin{pmatrix} y_1 \\ y_2 \\ y_3 \end{pmatrix} = \begin{bmatrix} a_{11} & a_{12} & a_{13} \\ a_{21} & a_{22} & a_{23} \\ a_{31} & a_{32} & a_{33} \end{bmatrix} \begin{pmatrix} x_1 \\ x_2 \\ x_3 \end{pmatrix} \tag{4.116}
$$

In Eqs. (4.113), (4.114), and (4.115), the a_{ij}'s are intermixed with the x's, whereas in the form of Eq. (4.116), the column matrix containing the x's is distinct from the square matrix containing the a's. The multiplication of the matrices in (4.116) is simply that procedure which makes Eq. (4.116) equivalent to (4.113), (4.114), and (4.115); in other words, the elements of the first row of the square matrix are multiplied with the corresponding terms in the column matrix and the results are summed and set equal to the first element of the y column matrix; the second and third rows are similarly multiplied and summed.

In general, the product of two matrices is defined only when they are conformable, that is, when the number of columns of one equals the number of rows of the second. For example,

$$
\begin{bmatrix} a_{11} & a_{12} \\ a_{21} & a_{22} \\ a_{31} & a_{33} \end{bmatrix} \begin{bmatrix} b_{11} & b_{12} & b_{13} \\ b_{21} & b_{22} & b_{23} \end{bmatrix} = \begin{vmatrix} c_{11} & c_{12} & c_{13} \\ c_{21} & c_{22} & c_{23} \\ c_{31} & c_{32} & c_{33} \end{vmatrix} \tag{4.117}
$$

where

$$c_{11} = a_{11}b_{11} + a_{12}b_{21}$$
$$c_{12} = a_{11}b_{12} + a_{12}b_{22}$$

.

.   (4.118)

.

.

$$c_{33} = a_{31}b_{13} + a_{33}b_{23}$$

In general, c_{ij} results from the multiplication of the ith row of the first matrix by the jth column of the second matrix.

Applying this short matrix notation to Eqs. (4.110), (4.111), and (4.112) results in

$$\begin{Bmatrix} A_\rho \\ A_\theta \\ A_z \end{Bmatrix} = \begin{bmatrix} \cos\theta & \sin\theta & 0 \\ -\sin\theta & \cos\theta & 0 \\ 0 & 0 & 1 \end{bmatrix} \begin{Bmatrix} A_x \\ A_y \\ A_z \end{Bmatrix} \qquad (4.119)$$

The equations represented by (4.119) may be written in a simpler form,

$$\{A_{\text{cyl}}\} = [\Theta(\theta)_{\text{rot}}]\{A_{\text{Cart}}\} \qquad (4.120)$$

where

$$[\Theta(\theta)_{\text{rot}}] = \begin{vmatrix} \cos\theta & \sin\theta & 0 \\ -\sin\theta & \cos\theta & 0 \\ 0 & 0 & 1 \end{vmatrix}$$

By referring to Fig. 4.30, we see that a transformation from a Cartesian to a cylindrical coordinate system is merely a rotation of the Cartesian coordinate system about the z-axis through an angle θ. It is therefore reasonable that the square matrix $[\Theta(\theta)_{\text{rot}}]$ is a function of θ only.

Suppose now we wish to solve Eqs. (4.110), (4.111), and (4.112) for A_x, A_y, and A_z in terms of A_ρ, A_θ, and A_z, that is, we wish to determine the relations (4.100), (4.101), and (4.102) by which $\mathbf{A} = \mathbf{u}_\rho A_\rho + \mathbf{u}_\theta A_\theta + \mathbf{u}_z A_z$ can be expressed in Cartesian coordinates. By using the concept of determinants and Cramer's rule, we can solve Eqs. (4.110), (4.111), and (4.112) for A_x, A_y, and A_z, thus:

$$A_x = \dfrac{\begin{vmatrix} A_\rho & \sin\theta & 0 \\ A_\theta & \cos\theta & 0 \\ A_z & 0 & 1 \end{vmatrix}}{\begin{vmatrix} \cos\theta & \sin\theta & 0 \\ -\sin\theta & \cos\theta & 0 \\ 0 & 0 & 1 \end{vmatrix}} = \dfrac{A_\rho\cos\theta - A_\theta\sin\theta}{1} \qquad (4.121)$$

Similarly,

$$A_y = \frac{\begin{vmatrix} \cos\theta & A_\rho & 0 \\ -\sin\theta & A_\theta & 0 \\ 0 & A_z & 1 \\ \cos\theta & \sin\theta & 0 \\ -\sin\theta & \cos\theta & 0 \\ 0 & 0 & 1 \end{vmatrix}}{} = \frac{A_\theta\cos\theta + A_\rho\sin\theta}{1} \qquad (4.122)$$

and

$$A_z = A_z \qquad (4.123)$$

which are essentially Eqs. (4.100), (4.101), and (4.102). Equations (4.121), (4.122), and (4.123) may be written in matrix form

$$\begin{Bmatrix} A_x \\ A_y \\ A_z \end{Bmatrix} = \begin{bmatrix} \cos\theta & -\sin\theta & 0 \\ \sin\theta & \cos\theta & 0 \\ 0 & 0 & 1 \end{bmatrix} \begin{Bmatrix} A_\rho \\ A_\theta \\ A_z \end{Bmatrix} \qquad (4.124)$$

We may have anticipated this result by dividing Eq. (4.120) by $[\Theta(\theta)_{rot}]$ but remembering that we are not dealing with simple factors but with matrices or arrays of quantities. To accomplish this, let us define a matrix $[\Theta(\theta)_{rot}]^{-1}$ called the inverse of $[\Theta(\theta)_{rot}]$ such that

$$[\Theta(\theta)_{rot}][\Theta(\theta)_{rot}]^{-1} = I \qquad (4.125)$$

where

$$I = \begin{vmatrix} 1 & 0 & 0 \\ 0 & 1 & 0 \\ 0 & 0 & 1 \end{vmatrix}$$

is called the unit matrix. If we multiply (4.120) by $[\Theta(\theta)_{rot}]^{-1}$,

$$[\Theta(\theta)_{rot}]^{-1}\{\mathbf{A}_{cyl}\} = [\Theta(\theta)_{rot}]^{-1}[\Theta(\theta)_{rot}]\{\mathbf{A}_{Cart}\} = \{\mathbf{A}_{Cart}\} \qquad (4.126)$$

Comparing (4.126) with (4.124), we see that

$$[\Theta(\theta)_{rot}]^{-1} = \begin{vmatrix} \cos\theta & -\sin\theta & 0 \\ \sin\theta & \cos\theta & 0 \\ 0 & 0 & 1 \end{vmatrix} \qquad (4.127)$$

Thus for transformations between Cartesian and cylindrical coordinate systems, involving a simple rotation, the inverse matrix $[\Theta(\theta)_{rot}]^{-1}$ is simply the original transformation matrix $[\Theta(\theta)_{rot}]$ with corresponding terms transposed across the main matrix diagonal. In this case $[\Theta(\theta)_{rot}]^{-1}$

is called the transpose of $[\Theta(\theta)_{rot}]$ and may be obtained by interchanging the rows and columns of $[\Theta(\theta)_{rot}]$.

These concepts may be extended to transformations involving spherical and cylindrical coordinates. For example, from Table 4.3 we may write

$$\begin{Bmatrix} A_r \\ A_\theta \\ A_\phi \end{Bmatrix} = \begin{bmatrix} \cos\phi & 0 & \sin\phi \\ 0 & 1 & 0 \\ -\sin\phi & 0 & \cos\phi \end{bmatrix} \begin{Bmatrix} A_\rho \\ A_\theta \\ A_z \end{Bmatrix} \tag{4.128}$$

or

$$\{A_{sph}\} = [\Phi(\phi)_{rot}]\{A_{cyl}\} \tag{4.129}$$

This illustrates the fact that a transformation from a cylindrical system to a spherical coordinate system is a rotation through an angle ϕ about an axis normal to the plane $\theta = a$ constant that is, it is rotated about the θ-direction (see Fig. 4.32). By analogy with Eqs. (4.125), (4.126), and (4.127), we may multiply (4.128) by $[\Phi(\phi)_{rot}]^{-1}$ and obtain

$$[\Phi(\phi)_{rot}]^{-1}\{\mathbf{A}_{sph}\} = \{\mathbf{A}_{cyl}\} \tag{4.130}$$

where

$$[\Phi(\phi)_{rot}]^{-1}[\Phi(\phi)_{rot}] = I$$

and

$$[\Phi(\phi)_{rot}]^{-1} = \begin{vmatrix} \cos\phi & 0 & -\sin\phi \\ 0 & 1 & 0 \\ \sin\phi & 0 & \cos\phi \end{vmatrix}$$

which is also the transposition $[\Phi(\phi)_{rot}]$.

Transformations between spherical and Cartesian coordinate systems can also be formulated in terms of matrices. Substituting (4.120) into (4.129), we see that

$$\{A_{sph}\} = [\Phi(\phi)_{rot}][\Theta(\theta)_{rot}]\{A_{Cart}\} \tag{4.131}$$

where

$$[\Phi(\phi)_{rot}][\Theta(\theta)_{rot}] = \begin{vmatrix} \cos\phi & 0 & \sin\phi \\ 0 & 1 & 0 \\ -\sin\phi & 0 & \cos\phi \end{vmatrix} \begin{vmatrix} \cos\theta & \sin\theta & 0 \\ -\sin\theta & \cos\theta & 0 \\ 0 & 0 & 1 \end{vmatrix}$$

$$= \begin{vmatrix} \cos\phi\cos\theta & \cos\phi\sin\theta & \sin\phi \\ -\sin\theta & \cos\theta & 0 \\ -\sin\phi\cos\theta & -\sin\phi\sin\theta & \cos\phi \end{vmatrix} \tag{4.132}$$

This indicates that the spherical coordinate system can be considered as a Cartesian coordinate system which has been rotated through an angle θ

about the z-axis together with a rotation through an angle ϕ in the plane θ equals a constant. When multiplying these matrices we see that the element of the product matrix in the ith row and jth column is obtained by summing the products of the elements of the jth column of the second matrix by the corresponding elements in the ith row of the first matrix.

4.5   The Orthogonality and Right-Handedness of Coordinate Systems

The three coordinate systems discussed previously are orthogonal and right handed. In the foregoing sections, we stated that an orthogonal coordinate system is one in which the surfaces, representing constant values of the coordinate variables, which located a point P intersected each other at right angles, that is, were mutually orthogonal at P. In such a system

$$\mathbf{u}_1 \cdot \mathbf{u}_2 = 0 \tag{4.133}$$

$$\mathbf{u}_2 \cdot \mathbf{u}_3 = 0 \tag{4.134}$$

$$\mathbf{u}_3 \cdot \mathbf{u}_1 = 0 \tag{4.135}$$

where 1, 2, and 3 can, for example, represent x, y, and z or ρ, θ, and z or r, θ, and ϕ. For such coordinate systems, the magnitude of a vector is given by the square root of the sum of the squares of its components, thus

$$
\begin{aligned}
A^2 = \mathbf{A} \cdot \mathbf{A} &= (\mathbf{u}_1 A_1 + \mathbf{u}_2 A_2 + \mathbf{u}_3 A_3) \cdot (\mathbf{u}_1 A_1 + \mathbf{u}_2 A_2 + \mathbf{u}_3 A_3) \\
&= (\mathbf{u}_1 \cdot \mathbf{u}_1) A_1^2 + (\mathbf{u}_1 \cdot \mathbf{u}_2) A_1 A_2 + (\mathbf{u}_1 \cdot \mathbf{u}_3) A_1 A_3 \\
&\quad (\mathbf{u}_2 \cdot \mathbf{u}_1) A_2 A_1 + (\mathbf{u}_2 \cdot \mathbf{u}_2) A_2^2 + (\mathbf{u}_2 \cdot \mathbf{u}_3) A_2 A_3 \\
&\quad (\mathbf{u}_3 \cdot \mathbf{u}_1) A_3 A_1 + (\mathbf{u}_3 \cdot \mathbf{u}_2) A_3 A_2 + (\mathbf{u}_3 \cdot \mathbf{u}_3) A_3^2
\end{aligned}
\tag{4.136}
$$

Then

$$A = \sqrt{A_1^2 + A_2^2 + A_3^2} \tag{4.137}$$

As an example of a system not orthogonal, consider the coordinate system shown in Fig. 4.33. For such a system the angles between the unit vectors is not $90°$; since they are not orthogonal,

$$\mathbf{u}_1 \cdot \mathbf{u}_2 \neq 0$$
$$\mathbf{u}_2 \cdot \mathbf{u}_3 \neq 0 \tag{4.138}$$
$$\mathbf{u}_3 \cdot \mathbf{u}_1 \neq 0$$

and Eq. (4.137) does not follow from (4.136).

Since in an orthogonal system the vector product of any two unit vectors is a vector in the same direction of the other unit vector (although its sense may be different), any unit vector is determined by the cross

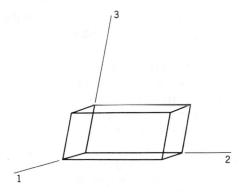

Figure 4.33 A nonorthogonal coordinate system.

product of the other two vectors. This brings us to the subject of the right-handedness of coordinate systems. Consider the right-handed coordinate system shown in Fig. 4.34. The indicated set of unit vectors represents the directions of the increasing values of the coordinate variables, that is, they may represent Cartesian, cylindrical, or spherical unit vectors. A rotation of $\mathbf{u}_1$ about the $\mathbf{u}_3$-direction through 90° so that $\mathbf{u}_1$ assumes the position initially occupied by $\mathbf{u}_2$ results in the advance of a right-hand screw whose axis is coincident with $\mathbf{u}_3$. If $\mathbf{u}_2$ is rotated 90° about the $\mathbf{u}_1$-direction so that it assumes the position initially occupied by $\mathbf{u}_3$, $\mathbf{u}_1$ will rotate in the same direction as a right-handed screw advancing in the direction and sense of $\mathbf{u}_1$. Similarly, if $\mathbf{u}_3$ assumes the position of $\mathbf{u}_1$ by rotating 90° about $\mathbf{u}_2$, $\mathbf{u}_2$ will rotate in the direction

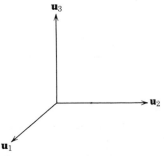

Figure 4.34 A right-handed set of unit vectors.

that a right-handed screw would rotate if it were advancing in the direction and sense of $\mathbf{u}_2$. Consequently, we may write

$$\mathbf{u}_1 \times \mathbf{u}_2 = \mathbf{u}_3 \qquad (4.139)$$

$$\mathbf{u}_2 \times \mathbf{u}_3 = \mathbf{u}_1 \qquad (4.140)$$

$$\mathbf{u}_3 \times \mathbf{u}_1 = \mathbf{u}_2 \qquad (4.141)$$

These relations may be summarized by

$$\mathbf{u}_i \times \mathbf{u}_j = \mathbf{u}_k \qquad (4.142)$$

where i, j, and k are in cyclic order, that is, they are in the order 123, 231, or 312. For the three systems we have discussed,

i corresponds to x in the Cartesian system
ρ in the cylindrical system
r in the spherical system
j corresponds to y in the Cartesian system
θ in the cylindrical system
θ in the spherical system
k corresponds to z in the Cartesian system
z in the cylindrical system
ϕ in the spherical system.

Under this permutation rule we can construct a left-handed coordinate system (see Fig. 4.35). For such a set of unit vectors, Eqs. (4.139), (4.140), and (4.141) would contain a minus sign as follows:

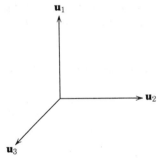

$$\mathbf{u}_1 \times \mathbf{u}_2 = -\mathbf{u}_3 \qquad (4.143)$$

$$\mathbf{u}_2 \times \mathbf{u}_3 = -\mathbf{u}_1 \qquad (4.144)$$

$$\mathbf{u}_3 \times \mathbf{u}_1 = -\mathbf{u}_2 \qquad (4.145)$$

Figure 4.35 A left-handed set of unit vectors.

However, notice that there is nothing unique about the coordinates but only in the order in which we place them. For example, the system shown in Fig. 4.35 could be made right handed merely by specifying the proper order by a cyclic permutation of jik, and not ijk as above. We see then that for such a convention we may write

$$\mathbf{u}_2 \times \mathbf{u}_1 = \mathbf{u}_3 \qquad (4.146)$$

$$\mathbf{u}_1 \times \mathbf{u}_3 = \mathbf{u}_2 \qquad (4.147)$$

$$\mathbf{u}_3 \times \mathbf{u}_2 = \mathbf{u}_1 \qquad (4.148)$$

Conversely, we can change the coordinate system shown in Fig. 4.34 into a left-handed system by taking the coordinates in the order ikj or cyclic permutation of that order.

We shall always choose that order of the coordinates which gives a right-handed system or more specifically, for the three coordinate systems we have discussed, we shall always choose the system such that

$$\mathbf{u}_x \times \mathbf{u}_y = \mathbf{u}_z$$

$$\mathbf{u}_y \times \mathbf{u}_z = \mathbf{u}_x$$

$$\mathbf{u}_z \times \mathbf{u}_x = \mathbf{u}_y$$

$$\mathbf{u}_\rho \times \mathbf{u}_\theta = \mathbf{u}_z$$

$$\mathbf{u}_\theta \times \mathbf{u}_z = \mathbf{u}_\rho \qquad (4.149)$$

$$\mathbf{u}_z \times \mathbf{u}_\rho = \mathbf{u}_\theta$$

$$\mathbf{u}_r \times \mathbf{u}_\theta = \mathbf{u}_\phi$$

$$\mathbf{u}_\theta \times \mathbf{u}_\phi = \mathbf{u}_r$$

$$\mathbf{u}_\phi \times \mathbf{u}_r = \mathbf{u}_\theta$$

4.6 Angular Displacements—Finite and Infinitesimal

In Section 1.2 we discussed the finite angular displacement and concluded that although it may be characterized by a direction, sense, and magnitude, an angular displacement is not a vector quantity. We now intend to demonstrate that this conclusion is correct.

We assumed without proof, in Section 1.2, that an infinitesimal angular displacement is a vector quantity. We shall show here that such an assumption is correct.

To show that a finite angular displacement is not a vector quantity, it is necessary to demonstrate that the orientation of a coordinate system which has undergone two finite angular displacements depends on the order the two angular displacements are executed. If this contention is true, that finite angular displacements do not commute, then such quantities cannot be classified as vector quantities (see Eq. 2.3).

Before attempting to establish these facts, let us recall that when discussing the matrix formulation of the transformation of the components of a vector from Cartesian to cylindrical coordinates (see Section 4.4, p. 115), we concluded that this transformation is equivalent to the rotation of the Cartesian coordinate system through an angle θ about the z-direction. This transformation can be written

$$\begin{pmatrix} A_\rho \\ A_\theta \\ A_z \end{pmatrix} = [\Theta(\theta)_{\text{rot}}] \begin{pmatrix} A_x \\ A_y \\ A_z \end{pmatrix} \qquad \text{(see Eqs. 4.119 and 4.120)} \qquad (4.150)$$

where A_ρ, A_θ, and A_z are the components of $\mathbf{A} = \mathbf{u}_x A_x + \mathbf{u}_y A_y + \mathbf{u}_z A_z$ in cylindrical coordinates and

$$[\Theta(\theta)_{\text{rot}}] = \begin{vmatrix} \cos\theta & \sin\theta & 0 \\ -\sin\theta & \cos\theta & 0 \\ 0 & 0 & 1 \end{vmatrix} \qquad (4.151)$$

Conversely, the Cartesian coordinates of $\mathbf{A} = \mathbf{u}_\rho A_\rho + \mathbf{u}_\theta A_\theta + \mathbf{u}_z A_z$ can be determined by

$$\begin{Bmatrix} A_x \\ A_y \\ A_z \end{Bmatrix} = [\Theta(\theta)_{\text{rot}}]^{-1} \begin{Bmatrix} A_\rho \\ A_\theta \\ A_z \end{Bmatrix} \qquad (4.152)$$

where

$$[\Theta(\theta)_{\text{rot}}]^{-1} \equiv \begin{vmatrix} \cos\theta & -\sin\theta & 0 \\ \sin\theta & \cos\theta & 0 \\ 0 & 0 & 1 \end{vmatrix}$$

This equation can, of course, be interpreted as a rotation of a cylindrical coordinate system through an angle $(-\theta)$ about the z-direction.

If we now examine the components of a vector $\mathbf{A}$ before and after it is rotated by an angle θ about the z-direction, we find that

$$A_{x_f} = A_{x_i} \cos\theta - A_{y_i} \sin\theta + A_{z_i}(0) \qquad (4.153a)$$

$$A_{y_f} = A_{x_i} \sin\theta + A_{y_i} \cos\theta + A_{z_i}(0) \qquad (4.153b)$$

and

$$A_{z_f} = A_{x_i}(0) + A_{y_i}(0) + A_{z_i} \qquad (4.153c)$$

where A_{x_i}, A_{y_i}, and A_{z_i} are the magnitudes of the components of $\mathbf{A}$ before it is rotated and A_{x_f}, A_{y_f}, and A_{z_f} the components after rotation. Equations (4.153) may be written in matrix form as

$$\begin{Bmatrix} A_{x_f} \\ A_{y_f} \\ A_{z_f} \end{Bmatrix} = \begin{bmatrix} \cos\theta & -\sin\theta & 0 \\ \sin\theta & \cos\theta & 0 \\ 0 & 0 & 1 \end{bmatrix} \begin{Bmatrix} A_{x_i} \\ A_{y_i} \\ A_{z_i} \end{Bmatrix} \qquad (4.154)$$

Since Eqs. (4.152) and (4.154) are identical in form, it is reasonable to interpret the common transformation matrix in two ways; it can represent a rotation of the coordinate system through an angle of $(-\theta)$ about the z-direction for a fixed vector or it signifies a rotation of a vector through an angle θ about the z-direction of a fixed coordinate system.

To describe a three-dimensional coordinate system, we have seen that it is sufficient to specify three unit vectors which are not coplanar. The unit vectors $\mathbf{u}_1$, $\mathbf{u}_2$, and $\mathbf{u}_3$, which we shall assume to be attached to and to characterize the attitude of a rigid body, may be written (see Fig. 4.36)

$$\mathbf{u}_1 = \mathbf{u}_x \cos \psi_{x_1} + \mathbf{u}_y \cos \psi_{y_1} + \mathbf{u}_z \cos \psi_{z_1} \qquad (4.155a)$$

$$\mathbf{u}_2 = \mathbf{u}_x \cos \psi_{x_2} + \mathbf{u}_y \cos \psi_{y_2} + \mathbf{u}_z \cos \psi_{z_2} \qquad (4.155b)$$

$$\mathbf{u}_3 = \mathbf{u}_x \cos \psi_{x_3} + \mathbf{u}_y \cos \psi_{y_3} + \mathbf{u}_z \cos \psi_{z_3} \qquad (4.155c)$$

where $\mathbf{u}_x$, $\mathbf{u}_y$, and $\mathbf{u}_z$ are unit vectors of a Cartesian coordinate system and ψ_{x_1}, for example, is the angle between $\mathbf{u}_x$ and $\mathbf{u}_1$. If $\mathbf{u}_1$, $\mathbf{u}_2$, and $\mathbf{u}_3$ are initially coincident with $\mathbf{u}_x$, $\mathbf{u}_y$, and $\mathbf{u}_z$, respectively, the relationship between both sets of unit vectors may be described by the unit matrix

$$\begin{vmatrix} 1 & 0 & 0 \\ 0 & 1 & 0 \\ 0 & 0 & 1 \end{vmatrix}$$

A rotation of the rigid body whose attitude is specified by $\mathbf{u}_1$, $\mathbf{u}_2$, and $\mathbf{u}_3$ through an angle θ about the $\mathbf{u}_3$-direction can be described, by analogy

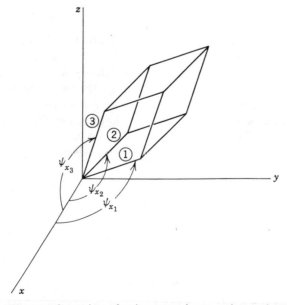

Figure 4.36   The transformation of unit vectors in an orthogonal system to a non-orthogonal system.

with Eq. (4.154), as

$$[\Theta(\theta)_{\mathrm{rot}}]^{-1} \begin{bmatrix} 1 & 0 & 0 \\ 0 & 1 & 0 \\ 0 & 0 & 1 \end{bmatrix} = \begin{bmatrix} \cos\theta & -\sin\theta & 0 \\ \sin\theta & \cos\theta & 0 \\ 0 & 0 & 1 \end{bmatrix} \qquad (4.156)$$

where that matrix on the right-hand side specifies the direction cosines of the rotated u_1, u_2, u_3 coordinate system relative to the u_x, u_y, u_z coordinate system. If we now rotate the u_1, u_2, u_3 system through an angle ϕ about the u_2-direction, we obtain

$$[\Theta(\phi)_{\mathrm{rot}}]^{-1} \begin{vmatrix} \cos\theta & -\sin\theta & 0 \\ \sin\theta & \cos\theta & 0 \\ 0 & 0 & 1 \end{vmatrix}$$

$$= \begin{vmatrix} \cos\phi & 0 & -\sin\phi \\ 0 & 1 & 0 \\ \sin\phi & 0 & \cos\phi \end{vmatrix} \begin{vmatrix} \cos\theta & -\sin\theta & 0 \\ \sin\theta & \cos\theta & 0 \\ 0 & 0 & 1 \end{vmatrix}$$

$$= \begin{vmatrix} \cos\phi\cos\theta & -\cos\phi\sin\theta & -\sin\phi \\ \sin\theta & \cos\theta & 0 \\ \sin\phi\cos\theta & -\sin\phi\sin\theta & \cos\phi \end{vmatrix} \qquad (4.157)$$

This last matrix describes completely the rotation of the u_1, u_2, u_3 system relative to the u_x, u_y, u_z coordinate system when the former has undergone a rotation θ about the u_3-direction and a rotation ϕ about the u_2-direction.

Let us now go back to the situation when the two coordinate systems are coincident. If we rotate the u_1, u_2, u_3 system through an angle ϕ about the u_2-direction and then about the u_3-direction for an angle θ, the direction cosines of the u_1, u_2, u_3 system would be

$$\begin{vmatrix} \cos\theta & -\sin\theta & 0 \\ \sin\theta & \cos\theta & 0 \\ 0 & 0 & 1 \end{vmatrix} \begin{vmatrix} \cos\phi & 0 & -\sin\phi \\ 0 & 1 & 0 \\ \sin\phi & 0 & \cos\phi \end{vmatrix} \begin{vmatrix} 1 & 0 & 0 \\ 0 & 1 & 0 \\ 0 & 0 & 1 \end{vmatrix}$$

$$= \begin{vmatrix} \cos\phi\cos\theta & -\sin\theta & -\sin\phi\cos\theta \\ \cos\phi\sin\theta & \cos\theta & -\sin\phi\sin\theta \\ \sin\phi & 0 & \cos\phi \end{vmatrix} \qquad (4.158)$$

Comparison of Eqs. (4.157) and (4.158) leads us to conclude that since the direction cosines of the rotated coordinate system depend on the order in which two separate rotations are executed, finite angular displacements are not commutative and hence cannot be vector quantities.

If, on the other hand, the angular displacement θ and ϕ are infinitesimal, that is, $\theta \to d\theta$ and $\phi \to d\phi$, then Eqs. (4.157) and (4.158) become identical and equal to

$$\begin{vmatrix} 1 & -d\theta & -d\phi \\ d\theta & 1 & 0 \\ d\phi & 0 & 1 \end{vmatrix}$$

where $\sin \theta = d\theta$, $\cos \theta = 1$, etc., and $d\theta \, d\phi$ is negligibly small.

We conclude therefore that an infinitesimal angular rotation is a commutative quantity and, since it can be characterized by a direction, sense, and magnitude, we are justified in classifying it as a vector quantity.

4.7   Frames of Reference

The foregoing discussion was predicated on the assumption that an origin could be chosen. Such an origin represents a point which is fixed in some *frame of reference*. This can be thought of as a coordinate system and a method of measuring time which permit us to describe position and time in a consistent quantitative manner. We may wish to postulate a preferred frame of reference which is considered as absolute in space and time. However, the arbitrariness of such an assumption and the fact that we are forced in many practical problems to consider one frame of reference whose relation to other frames is changing with time and space make it difficult to define such an absolute frame of reference. It follows then that, generally, the representation of vector and scalar quantities and the operations performed on them vary from one frame of reference to another. To be explicit, one must state the frame of reference in which a field is described and in which certain operations are performed on the fields.

It is often useful and instructive to consider and compare the rate of change of a vector quantity as seen by (1) an observer fixed in some coordinate system and by (2) an observer moving relative to that coordinate system. To accomplish this, let us first examine the motion of a rigid body (see Fig. 4.37). From this figure we see that $\mathbf{R}$ the position vector of point P from the fixed point O can be written as the sum of $\mathbf{R}_{OO'}$, the position of O' as seen from O and $\mathbf{R}_{O'P}$, the position vector locating P from O', that is,

$$\mathbf{R} = \mathbf{R}_{OO'} + \mathbf{R}_{O'P} \tag{4.159}$$

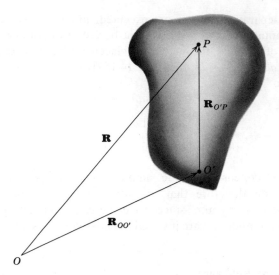

Figure 4.37   The position of a point P as seen from a fixed origin O from a moving origin O'.

Differentiating this vector equation with respect to time, we obtain

$$\frac{d\mathbf{R}}{dt} = \frac{d\mathbf{R}_{OO'}}{dt} + \frac{d\mathbf{R}_{O'P}}{dt} \qquad (4.160)$$

or

$$\mathbf{v} = \mathbf{v}_{OO'} + \mathbf{v}_{O'P} \qquad (4.161)$$

In words, this equation says that the velocity of P, a point of a rigid body as seen by a fixed observer, is the sum of the velocity of O' as seen from O plus the velocity of P as seen from O'.

In a rigid body the distance from O' to P cannot change, so that $\mathbf{R}_{O'P}$ can change in direction only. Consequently, an observer at O' moving along with O' can describe the motion of P in terms of an angular velocity about an axis through O'. If he represents this angular velocity by a vector $\boldsymbol{\omega}$, the velocity $\mathbf{v}_{O'P}$ can be written

$$\mathbf{v}_{O'P} = \boldsymbol{\omega} \times \mathbf{R}_{O'P} \qquad (4.162)$$

in which case Eq. (4.161) becomes

$$\mathbf{v} = \mathbf{v}_{OO'} + \boldsymbol{\omega} \times \mathbf{R}_{O'P} \qquad (4.163)$$

The acceleration of P as seen by the observer at O can be obtained by differentiating Eq. (4.163) with respect to time, that is,

$$\mathbf{a} \equiv \frac{d\mathbf{v}}{dt} = \frac{d\mathbf{v}_{OO'}}{dt} + \frac{d\boldsymbol{\omega}}{dt} \times \mathbf{R}_{O'P} + \boldsymbol{\omega} \times \mathbf{v}_{O'P}$$

$$= \mathbf{a}_{OO'} + \frac{d\boldsymbol{\omega}}{dt} \times \mathbf{R}_{O'P} + \boldsymbol{\omega} \times (\boldsymbol{\omega} \times \mathbf{R}_{O'P}) \qquad (4.164)$$

Here the last two terms on the right-hand side represent the acceleration of P as observed from O' and $\mathbf{a}_{OO'}$ is the linear acceleration of O' relative to O.

Let us now examine the motion of a point P as seen by a nonrotating observer at O and by an observer at O' rotating with an angular velocity $\boldsymbol{\omega}$ (see Fig. 4.38a). From Fig. 4.38a we see that

$$\mathbf{R}_{NR} = \mathbf{R}_R + \mathbf{R}_O \qquad (4.165)$$

where $\mathbf{R}_{NR}$ locates P from the nonrotating observer,

$\qquad \mathbf{R}_R$ locates P from the rotating observer, and

$\qquad \mathbf{R}_O$ locates the rotating observer from the nonrotating observer (this vector is a constant because the two observers are either stationary or are moving with the same linear velocity).

During the time Δt the point P will move to a new position P' (see Fig. 4.37b) so that $\mathbf{R}_{NR}$ will change by the amount $\Delta \mathbf{R}_{NR}$. During this

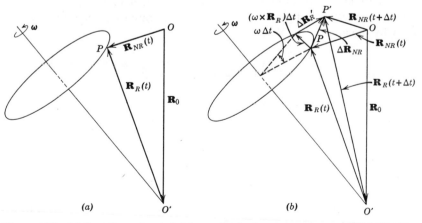

Figure 4.38   (a) Location of a point by a fixed observer and a rotating observer. (b) Description of motion by a fixed observer and a rotating observer.

period of time $\mathbf{R}_R$ changes by the amount $\Delta\mathbf{R}_R$, where

$$\Delta\mathbf{R}_R \equiv \mathbf{R}_R(t + \Delta t) - \mathbf{R}_R(t) = \Delta\mathbf{R}'_R + (\boldsymbol{\omega} \times \mathbf{R}_R)\,\Delta t \qquad (4.166)$$

that is, during the time Δt, $\mathbf{R}_R$ changes for two reasons: (1) P has moved ($\Delta\mathbf{R}'_R$ denotes the change in $\mathbf{R}_R$ because P has moved), and (2) the rotating observer has rotated an amount $(\boldsymbol{\omega} \times \mathbf{R}_R)\,\Delta t$. If, for example, P had not moved to P', $\mathbf{R}_R$ would have changed (direction) by the amount $(\boldsymbol{\omega} \times \mathbf{R}_R)\,\Delta t$. Since $\Delta\mathbf{R}_{NR} = \Delta\mathbf{R}_R$, we may write

$$\Delta\mathbf{R}_{NR} = \Delta\mathbf{R}_R = \Delta\mathbf{R}'_R + (\boldsymbol{\omega} \times \mathbf{R}_R)\,\Delta t \qquad (4.167)$$

$\Delta\mathbf{R}'_R$ can be viewed as the change in $\mathbf{R}_R$ as seen by the rotating observer when P moves to P'.

Dividing Eq. (4.167) by Δt and letting Δt approach zero, we obtain

$$\left(\frac{d\mathbf{R}_{NR}}{dt}\right)_{NR} = \left(\frac{d\mathbf{R}_R}{dt}\right)_{NR} = \left(\frac{d\mathbf{R}_R}{dt}\right)_R + \boldsymbol{\omega} \times \mathbf{R}_R \qquad (4.168)$$

where $(d\mathbf{R}_{NR}/dt)_{NR} = (d\mathbf{R}_R/dt)_{NR}$ is the velocity of P as seen by the nonrotating observer and $(d\mathbf{R}_R/dt)_R$ is the velocity of P as seen by the rotating observer.

The result stated in Eq. (4.168) is valid when two observers, one rotating and the other nonrotating, look at a position vector. Let us now consider the observations of these same two observers when they view any vector quantity $\mathbf{A}$ which is changing with time. Remembering that $\mathbf{A}$ can change by changing direction and by changing magnitude, we see that these observers will differ in opinion as to the rate of change of direction of $\mathbf{A}$ by the amount $\boldsymbol{\omega} \times \mathbf{A}$:

$$\left(\frac{d\mathbf{A}}{dt}\right)_{NR} = \left(\frac{d\mathbf{A}}{dt}\right)_R + \boldsymbol{\omega} \times \mathbf{A} \qquad (4.169)$$

The concept involved in this relation is usually called the theorem of Coriolis, and it states the transformation of the time derivative between the rotating and nonrotating coordinate systems.

We are now in a position to calculate the acceleration as observed in these two coordinate systems. Expressing Eq. (4.168) as

$$\mathbf{v}_{NR} = \mathbf{v}_R + \boldsymbol{\omega} \times \mathbf{R}_R \qquad (4.170)$$

we can calculate the rate of change of $\mathbf{v}_{NR}$ by utilizing Eq. (4.169), namely, by considering $\mathbf{v}_{NR}$ in Eq. (4.170) to be $\mathbf{A}$ in Eq. (4.169),

$$
\begin{aligned}
\mathbf{a}_{NR} &\equiv \left(\frac{d\mathbf{v}_{NR}}{dt}\right)_{NR} = \left(\frac{d\mathbf{v}_{NR}}{dt}\right)_{R} + \boldsymbol{\omega} \times \mathbf{v}_{NR} \\
&= \left(\frac{d\mathbf{v}_{R}}{dt}\right)_{NR} + \boldsymbol{\omega} \times \left(\frac{d\mathbf{R}_{R}}{dt}\right)_{NR} + \left(\frac{d\boldsymbol{\omega}}{dt}\right)_{NR} \times \mathbf{R}_{R} \\
&= \left(\frac{d\mathbf{v}_{R}}{dt}\right)_{R} + \boldsymbol{\omega} \times \mathbf{v}_{R} + \boldsymbol{\omega} \times \left\{\left(\frac{d\mathbf{R}_{R}}{dt}\right)_{R} + \boldsymbol{\omega} \times \mathbf{R}_{R}\right\} \\
&\quad + \left(\frac{d\boldsymbol{\omega}}{dt}\right)_{R} \times \mathbf{R}_{R} \\
&= \mathbf{a}_{R} + 2(\boldsymbol{\omega} \times \mathbf{v}_{R}) + \boldsymbol{\omega} \times (\boldsymbol{\omega} \times \mathbf{R}_{R}) + \left(\frac{d\boldsymbol{\omega}}{dt}\right)_{R} \times \mathbf{R}_{R} \quad (4.171)
\end{aligned}
$$

where we have utilized the fact that

$$
\left(\frac{d\boldsymbol{\omega}}{dt}\right)_{NR} = \left(\frac{d\boldsymbol{\omega}}{dt}\right)_{R} + \boldsymbol{\omega} \times \boldsymbol{\omega} = \left(\frac{d\boldsymbol{\omega}}{dt}\right)_{R} \quad (4.172)
$$

[See Eq. (4.169).]

Equation (4.171) relates the acceleration of P as seen by the non-rotating observer to the acceleration of P seen by the rotating observer.

4.8 Mathematical Generalizations—Vector and Function Spaces

Fundamental to the mathematical treatment of many aspects of fields is the eigenvalue problem and the expansion of certain classes of functions in terms of complete orthonormal sets of functions. A close analogy exists between these aspects of the expansion of a function and the representation of a vector in an orthogonal coordinate system. By examining this analogy, nothing new is uncovered, but we can consider the abstractions of the eigenfunction problem in a geometric way and, by so doing, facilitate their understanding. To formulate such a geometrical interpretation, let us recall a few of the basic characteristics of vectors and their representation.

We have seen that it is convenient to represent a vector $\mathbf{A}$ which exists in a three-dimensional space in terms of its Cartesian coordinates (see Eq. 2.24). We also saw in the preceding sections that this manner of representation can be extended to any orthogonal coordinate system as

$$
\begin{aligned}
\mathbf{A} &= \mathbf{u}_1 A_1 + \mathbf{u}_2 A_2 + \mathbf{u}_3 A_3 \\
&= \sum_{n=1}^{3} A_n \mathbf{u}_n \quad (4.173)
\end{aligned}
$$

where $\mathbf{u}_1$, $\mathbf{u}_2$, and $\mathbf{u}_3$ are the orthogonal unit vectors associated with the 1, 2, and 3 directions, respectively, and A_1, A_2, and A_3 are the magnitudes of the components of $\mathbf{A}$ in the 1, 2, and 3 directions, respectively; the quantities A_1, A_2, and A_3 can be thought of as the coefficients of the expansion of $\mathbf{A}$ in terms of the orthogonal unit vectors $\mathbf{u}_1$, $\mathbf{u}_2$, and $\mathbf{u}_3$. These coefficients can be found by taking the scalar product of Eq. (4.173) with a unit vector corresponding to the component whose value is desired, for example,

$$A_2 = \mathbf{u}_2 \cdot \mathbf{A} = \sum_{n=1}^{3} A_n \mathbf{u}_2 \cdot \mathbf{u}_n = A_2 \qquad (4.174)$$

Here we have utilized the fact that the unit vectors $\mathbf{u}_1$, $\mathbf{u}_2$, and $\mathbf{u}_3$ are orthogonal and normalized (in this regard the word "normalized" means that the magnitude of the unit vector is unity). In other words, we have taken advantage of the fact that

$$\begin{aligned} \mathbf{u}_m \cdot \mathbf{u}_n &= 0 \qquad m \neq n \qquad (m, n = 1, 2, 3) \\ &= 1 \qquad m = n \end{aligned} \qquad (4.175)$$

It is convenient to write this relationship

$$\mathbf{u}_m \cdot \mathbf{u}_n = \delta_{mn}$$

where δ_{mn}, the Kronecker delta, is defined by

$$\begin{aligned} \delta_{mn} &= 0 \qquad m \neq n \\ &= 1 \qquad m = n \end{aligned} \qquad (4.176)$$

For this reason we refer to the unit vectors $\mathbf{u}_m$ as forming an orthonormal set defining an orthogonal coordinate system or an orthogonal vector space.

The length or magnitude of $\mathbf{A}$ is then determined to be

$$\begin{aligned} A = |\mathbf{A}| &= \left\{ \left[\sum_{m=1}^{3} A_m \mathbf{u}_m \right] \cdot \left[\sum_{n=1}^{3} A_n \mathbf{u}_n \right] \right\}^{\frac{1}{2}} \\ &= \{A_1^2 + A_2^2 + A_3^2\}^{\frac{1}{2}} = \left\{ \sum_{n=1}^{3} A_n^2 \right\}^{\frac{1}{2}} \end{aligned} \qquad (4.177)$$

The foregoing ideas and notation can be generalized to an orthogonal vector space of N dimensions. By analogy with Eq. (4.173) we may write for a "vector" in such a space

$$\mathbf{A} = \sum_{n=1}^{N} A_n \mathbf{u}_n$$

where the A_n's are the components of $\mathbf{A}$ in the orthogonal "directions" along which the $\mathbf{u}_n$'s are unit vectors.

With certain reservations, which will be discussed momentarily, we may let N tend to infinity; in other words, we shall consider an infinite dimensional orthogonal vector space. A "vector" in such a space can be represented as

$$\mathbf{A} = \sum_{n=1}^{\infty} A_n \mathbf{u}_n \tag{4.178}$$

where the $\mathbf{u}_n$'s are unit vectors which are mutually orthogonal. The magnitude of the mth component of such a vector is then given by

$$A_m = \mathbf{u}_m \cdot \mathbf{A} = \sum_{n=1}^{\infty} A_n \mathbf{u}_m \cdot \mathbf{u}_n = \sum_{n=1}^{\infty} A_n \, \delta_{mn} = A_m \tag{4.179}$$

[Compare with Eq. (4.174).] The "length" or magnitude of such a vector is

$$A = |\mathbf{A}| = \left\{ \left[\sum_{m=1}^{\infty} A_m \mathbf{u}_m \right] \cdot \left[\sum_{n=1}^{\infty} A_n \mathbf{u}_n \right] \right\}^{\frac{1}{2}} = \left\{ \sum_{n=1}^{\infty} A_n^2 \right\}^{\frac{1}{2}} \tag{4.180}$$

[Compare with Eq. (4.177).]

When considering many of the differential equations encountered in science and engineering, it is often convenient to represent a more or less arbitrary function $f(x)$ by an infinite sum of eigenfunctions $\phi_n(x)$,

$$f(x) = \sum_{n=1}^{\infty} c_n \phi_n(x) \tag{4.181}$$

The Fourier representation of an odd function $g(x)$,

$$g(x) = \sum_{n=1}^{\infty} c_n \sin(\alpha_n x) \tag{4.182}$$

is an example of this type of expansion. In Eq. (4.182) α_n is an eigenvalue determined by the boundary conditions of the problem; for example, in the vibrating string problem $\phi_n = \sqrt{2/L} \sin(\alpha_n x)$, where $\alpha_n = n\pi/L$, where n is an integer and the ends of the string are at $x = 0$ and $x = L$.

The object of this section is to point out and explore the similarity between Eqs. (4.178) and (4.181). Because of the representational similarity shown in these two equations, we are led to think of $f(x)$ as a "vector" in an infinite dimensional space whose components c_n are the "magnitudes" of $f(x)$ in the "directions" along which the ϕ_n's are the "unit vectors." Such a space is called function space.

This somewhat superficial similarity between Eqs. (4.178) and (4.181) can be extended in many ways to aid in understanding and visualizing the expansion of functions in terms of eigenfunctions.

To calculate c_m, a typical expansion coefficient for Eq. (4.181), we proceed as follows:

$$\int_0^L \phi_m(x) f(x)\, dx = \int_0^L \phi_m(x) \sum_{n=1}^{\infty} c_n \phi_n(x)\, dx$$

$$= \sum_{n=1}^{\infty} c_n \int_0^L \phi_m(x)\phi_n(x)\, dx \qquad (4.183)$$

[Compare with Eq. (4.179).]

Now we can extend our concept of orthogonality to mean that

$$\int_0^L \phi_m(x)\phi_n(x)\, dx = \delta_{mn} \qquad (4.184)$$

Then Eq. (4.183) becomes

$$\int_0^L \phi_m(x)f(x)\, dx = \sum_{n=1}^{\infty} c_n \delta_{mn} = c_m \qquad (4.185)$$

More specifically, if the function to be expanded in the region 0 to L is an odd function of x which can be represented by a Fourier sine series (for example, the previously mentioned vibrating string problem), c_m, a typical expansion coefficient, is

$$\sqrt{\frac{2}{L}} \int_0^L f(x) \sin (\alpha_m x)\, dx = \frac{2}{L} \sum_{n=1}^{\infty} c_n \int_0^L \sin (\alpha_m x) \sin (\alpha_n x)\, dx$$

$$= \frac{2}{L} \sum_{n=1}^{\infty} c_n \delta_{mn} \left(\frac{L}{2}\right) = c_m \qquad (4.186)$$

Comparing this result with Eq. (4.179), we see that there is a further correspondence between the representation of a "vector" in an infinite dimensional space and the expansion of a function in an infinite dimensional function space. Furthermore, since it is physically reasonable to consider only vectors whose "length" or magnitude remains finite, in other words, where

$$A = |\mathbf{A}| = \left\{ \sum_{n=1}^{\infty} A_n^2 \right\}^{1/2} \qquad (4.187)$$

remains finite, it appears judicious to restrict the function $f(x)$ to that class of functions whose magnitude remains finite. To see what restrictions this places on $f(x)$, we first examine the nature of the restriction this places on the c_n's. By analogy with Eq. (4.187), we see that the magnitude of $f(x)$ is given by

$$|f(x)| = \left\{ \sum_{n=1}^{\infty} c_n^2 \right\}^{1/2} \qquad (4.188)$$

Thus if $|f(x)|$ remains finite, $\sum\limits_{n=1}^{\infty} c_n^2$ must also remain finite; but this leads to

$$
\begin{aligned}
\sum_{n=1}^{\infty} c_n^2 &= \sum_{m=1}^{\infty} \sum_{n=1}^{\infty} c_m c_n \, \delta_{mn} \\
&= \sum_{m=1}^{\infty} \sum_{n=1}^{\infty} c_m c_n \int_0^L \phi_m(x)\phi_n(x) \, dx \\
&= \int_0^L \left\{ \sum_{m=1}^{\infty} c_m\phi_m(x) \sum_{n=1}^{\infty} c_n\phi_n(x) \right\} dx \\
&= \int_0^L f^2(x) \, dx
\end{aligned}
\tag{4.189}
$$

That is, we have to restrict our discussion to those functions $f(x)$ for which $\int_0^L f^2(x) \, dx$ remains finite. This restriction is referred to as the condition of quadratic integrability. We conclude that we can expand $f(x)$ in an eigenfunction series only if $f(x)$ is quadratically integrable.

As indicated previously, we can define many coordinate systems in which to represent a vector; we must bear in mind, however, that the physically significant quantity is the vector itself. We need not restrict ourselves therefore to the representation of a vector in an orthogonal coordinate system. The vector **B** may be represented as a linear super-position of any three noncoplanar vectors $\mathbf{w}_1$, $\mathbf{w}_2$, and $\mathbf{w}_3$

$$
\mathbf{B} = B_1\mathbf{w}_1 + B_2\mathbf{w}_2 + B_3\mathbf{w}_3
\tag{4.190}
$$

where B_1, B_2, and B_3 are the magnitudes of **B** along the directions in which $\mathbf{w}_1$, $\mathbf{w}_2$, and $\mathbf{w}_3$ are vectors. Such a set of vectors is *complete*—there exists no vector which is orthogonal to all three. If there were such a vector **A**, which was orthogonal to $\mathbf{w}_1$, $\mathbf{w}_2$, and $\mathbf{w}_3$, it would not be possible to represent **A** completely in terms of $\mathbf{w}_1$, $\mathbf{w}_2$, and $\mathbf{w}_3$ because the components of **A** along $\mathbf{w}_1$, $\mathbf{w}_2$, and $\mathbf{w}_3$ would all be zero:

$$
A_n = \mathbf{A} \cdot \mathbf{w}_n = 0 \qquad (n = 1, 2, \text{ and } 3)
\tag{4.191}
$$

If $\mathbf{w}_1$, $\mathbf{w}_2$, and $\mathbf{w}_3$ were coplanar, they would be useless to describe a vector **A** in three-dimensional space because they could not be used to describe **A** or the component of any vector which is normal to all the vectors $\mathbf{w}_1$, $\mathbf{w}_2$, and $\mathbf{w}_3$. We cannot therefore utilize incomplete sets of vectors to characterize coordinate systems in which to represent vectors.

Fortunately, in the three-dimensional space with which we are intuitively familiar, any set of three noncoplanar vectors forms a complete set. In infinite dimensional vector space, however, it may not be so obvious that a set is complete.

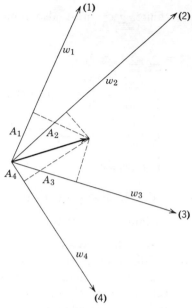

Figure 4.39   The resolution of a vector along four directions.

Corresponding to the fact that we must have a complete set of vectors to represent a vector, a complete set of eigenfunctions must exist if we are to expand a function in terms of them. By analogy with vector space, a set of eigenfunctions need not be orthogonal and normalized, but sets which are orthonormal are much more convenient with which to work.

Implicit in our previous discussion of vectors and vector fields is the idea that if a vector quantity is zero, each of its components must be zero. This is a consequence of the fact that we have been dealing with coordinate systems whose unit vectors are *linearly independent*; if a vector quantity is zero, then the relationship

$$\mathbf{u}_1 A_1 + \mathbf{u}_2 A_2 + \mathbf{u}_3 A_3 = 0 \tag{4.192}$$

is only possible if $A_1 = A_2 = A_3 = 0$. However, there are coordinate systems where this is not true. For example, suppose that a three-dimensional vector $\mathbf{A}$ were resolved into its components along the four directions associated with $\mathbf{w}_1$, $\mathbf{w}_2$, $\mathbf{w}_3$, and $\mathbf{w}_4$ (see Fig. 4.39) as in

$$\mathbf{A} = \mathbf{w}_1 A_1 + \mathbf{w}_2 A_2 + \mathbf{w}_3 A_3 + \mathbf{w}_4 A_4 \tag{4.193}$$

Now it is possible to conceive of a situation where a vector $\mathbf{A}$ is equal to zero but where its components A_1, A_2, A_3, and A_4 are all nonzero. In other words, it is possible that

$$\sum_{n=1}^{4} A_n \mathbf{w}_n = 0 \tag{4.194}$$

when some or all the A_n's are different from zero. Such a situation means that the magnitudes of these nonzero components are not uniquely defined. For example, if we multiply

$$\mathbf{w}_1 A_1 + \mathbf{w}_2 A_2 + \mathbf{w}_3 A_3 + \mathbf{w}_4 A_4 = 0 \tag{4.195}$$

by q,

$$\mathbf{w}_1 q A_1 + \mathbf{w}_2 q A_2 + \mathbf{w}_3 q A_3 + \mathbf{w}_4 q A_4 = 0 \tag{4.196}$$

and equate Eq. (4.195) with Eq. (4.196), we obtain

$$\mathbf{w}_1 q A_1 + \mathbf{w}_2 q A_2 + \mathbf{w}_3 q A_3 + \mathbf{w}_4 q A_4 = \mathbf{w}_1 A_1 + \mathbf{w}_2 A_2 + \mathbf{w}_3 A_3 + \mathbf{w}_4 A_4$$

Equating components, we see that

$$q A_1 = A_1$$

This cannot be true for arbitrary values of q.

We then say that the members of the set $\mathbf{w}_n$ are not linearly independent and the characteristics of this set are attributable to the fact that we do not really need four vectors to represent a three-dimensional vector—three are sufficient. It is clear that in a three-dimensional space, these $\mathbf{w}_n$'s cannot be mutually orthogonal. Vectors $N + 1$ cannot be mutually orthogonal in an N-dimensional space.

Similarly, we may provide too many eigenfunctions, that is, more eigenfunctions than are necessary for the expansion of a function. Redundancy of this nature, when it appears in eigenvalue problems, may lead to an ambiguous expansion of $f(x)$.

PROBLEMS

1. Consider a two-dimensional coordinate system in which a point $P(x, y)$ can be located by

$$x = a \cosh \psi \cos \eta$$
$$y = a \sinh \psi \sin \eta$$

where a is a constant. Such a coordinate system is called an ellipsoidal coordinate system. Curves of constant ψ are confocal ellipsoids and curves of constant η are confocal hyperbolas.

(a) Is this system orthogonal?

(b) Determine the expression for $\mathbf{A} = \mathbf{u}_x 3x + \mathbf{u}_y xy$ in this coordinate system.

2. Repeat Problem 1 for a coordinate system in which

$$x = aV + dW$$
$$y = aW - bV$$

where a, b, c and d are constants and V and W are the coordinate variables.

3. If the equations which transform the coordinates of a point from ellipsoidal to Cartesian coordinates are

$$x = a(V^2 - 1)^{1/2}(1 - W^2)^{1/2}\cos\psi$$
$$y = a(V^2 - 1)^{1/2}(1 - W^2)^{1/2}\sin\psi$$
$$z = aVW$$

determine the equations describing the coordinate surfaces $V = $ a constant, $W = $ a constant, and $\psi = $ a constant.

4. Determine the expression for the vector $\mathbf{A}$ in the ellipsoidal coordinates of Problem 3 when $\mathbf{A}$ is given by

$$\mathbf{A} = \mathbf{u}_x 6x + \mathbf{u}_y xy + \mathbf{u}_z yz$$

5. A radar station located at the origin in Fig. 4.40 is tracking an airplane whose instantaneous position is 6 miles east and 2 miles south of the radar station and whose instantaneous velocity is 600 miles per hour in a westerly direction. Determine its distance, azimuth, elevation angle and velocity in spherical coordinates relative to the radar station. Use matrix notation.

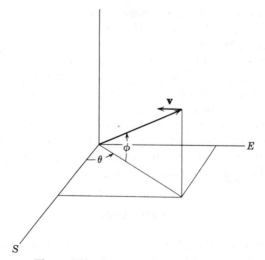

Figure 4.40   Geometry for Problem 4.5.

6. If the equations

$$\mathbf{u}_1 = a_{1A}\mathbf{u}_A + a_{1B}\mathbf{u}_B + a_{1C}\mathbf{u}_C$$
$$\mathbf{u}_2 = a_{2A}\mathbf{u}_A + a_{2B}\mathbf{u}_B + a_{2C}\mathbf{u}_C$$
$$\mathbf{u}_3 = a_{3A}\mathbf{u}_A + a_{3B}\mathbf{u}_B + a_{3C}\mathbf{u}_C$$

define the orthogonal coordinate transformation of one set of unit vectors $\mathbf{u}_A$, $\mathbf{u}_B$, and $\mathbf{u}_C$ to another set $\mathbf{u}_1$, $\mathbf{u}_2$, and $\mathbf{u}_3$, prove that

(a) $a_{nA}^2 + a_{nB}^2 + a_{nC}^2 = 1$ $n = 1, 2,$ or 3

(b) $a_{nA}a_{mA} + a_{nB}a_{mB} + a_{nC}a_{mC} = 0$ $n \neq m$

(c) Δ, the determinant of the transformation, is given by $\Delta^2 = 1$.

5

The Gradient of a Scalar Field

5.1 Introduction

Certain characteristics of scalar and vector fields are best understood in terms of properties that depend on the spatial rate of change of the fields. The most important of these properties, the gradient and Laplacian of a scalar field and the divergence and curl of a vector field, are fundamental properties of fields which can be utilized to characterize them and describe their influence.

In an attempt to provide the reader with a basis for visualizing these field properties, we shall discuss the gradient (this Chapter), the divergence (Chapter 6), and the curl (Chapter 7) from viewpoints which stress their physical significance.

5.2 The Gradient of a Scalar Field

It was stated in Section 1.3, p. 10 that a scalar field is defined for a region in space if a value of a scalar quantity can be associated with every point of that region. The value of the scalar quantity may, in general, change from point to point, and the magnitude of this change depends on the nature of the field, the distance between the points, and the direction of the displacement between the points. The subject of this chapter, the gradient, deals with the manner in which a scalar field varies from one position to another.

To understand the physical significance of the gradient of a scalar field, let us continue the discussion initiated in Section 1.3, p. 10. In that section we used $h(x, y)$, the elevation of the earth, as an example of a scalar field, that is, each position on the earth has associated with it a unique value of its height above a reference level, usually sea level. As a specific example of this idea, we discussed the shape of a mountain (see Fig. 5.1a). Let us now extend that example and inquire how the elevation of a mountain varies from point to point. We saw in Section

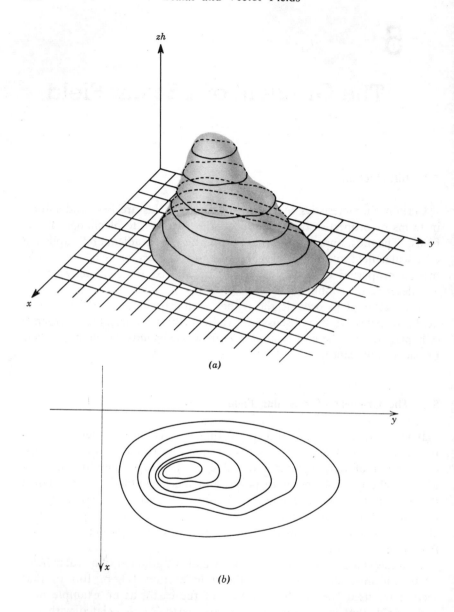

(a)

(b)

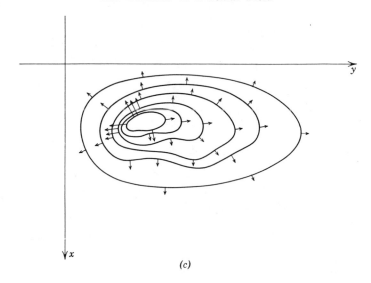

(c)

Figure 5.1   (a) An example of a scalar field. (b) Contour lines. (c) A vector field representing the acceleration of a ball on a mountain.

1.3, p. 10 that we can graphically represent the profile of a mountain by contour lines (see Fig. 5.1b) and these lines can be used to ascertain how the elevation varies with position. Another particularly instructive way we can determine how the elevation of a mountain varies with position is to place a ball at various places on the mountain side and examine the acceleration of the ball at these different locations. The ball, initially at rest, is acted on by gravity and rolls downhill with an acceleration vector along the surface of the mountain at those points forming the path taken by the ball. The sense direction and magnitude of the acceleration of the ball at every point on the mountain define a vector field (see Fig. 5.1c).

It is apparent from the foregoing discussion that there is a relationship between the scalar field representing the elevation and the vector field representing the acceleration of the ball. The association of the acceleration of a ball with the steepness of the slope of a mountain is an example of a relationship often occurring in science and engineering, namely, that a vector field may, in many instances, be derived from the spatial rate of change of a scalar field. Mathematically, the rate of change of a scalar field is similar to the ordinary derivative discussed in differential calculus. The situation is somewhat complicated by the necessity of finding the sense and direction of the resulting vector field. In other words, we must, in our example, determine at every point on the mountain the direction of the steepest slope if we are to ascertain the direction the ball is to roll down

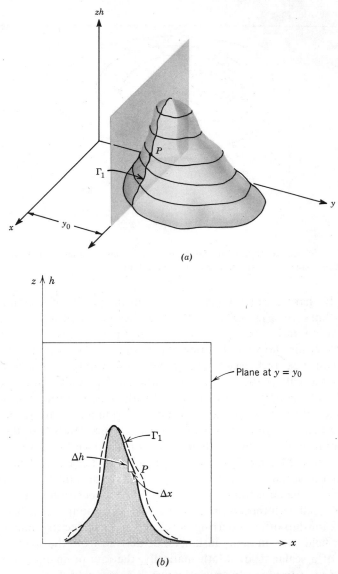

(a)

(b)

Figure 5.2   (a) For the discussion of the directional derivative. (b) For the discussion of the partial derivative.

the mountain. At any point on the mountain the sense direction and magnitude of the steepest slope are called the gradient or to state it in more general terms: the gradient of a scalar field is a vector field which represents, at every point, the direction, sense, and magnitude of the greatest spatial rate of change of the scalar field.

Before discussing the gradient of a scalar field in more quantitative terms, it is necessary to introduce the concept of the directional derivative. Consider again the situation when we measure the elevation of a mountain as a function of position on the earth. The elevation of the mountain may be represented by the scalar field $h(x, y)$, where x and y locate a particular position on the earth. We shall assume that h is single-valued, that given a particular x and y, h is determined uniquely. If we pass a plane, $y = y_0$ (where y_0 is a constant) through the point P, a curve Γ_1 is formed by the intersection of the plane with the surface $h(x, y)$ (see Fig. 5.2a). If we move along Γ_1, the rate at which h changes is given by (see Fig. 5.2b)

$$\lim_{\Delta x \to 0} \frac{\Delta h}{\Delta x}\bigg|_{y=y_0} = \frac{\partial h}{\partial x}\bigg|_{y=y_0} \qquad \text{at the point } P \qquad (5.1)$$

As we saw in Section 3.3, p. 58 this symbol is called the partial derivative of h with respect to x and it represents the slope of the curve Γ_1 on the plane $y = y_0$ at the point P.

Similarly, if we pass a plane $x = x_0$ (where x_0 is a constant) through the point P on the surface $h(x, y)$, the intersection of this plane with the surface $h(x, y)$ is a curve we shall call Γ_2. To determine the rate at which $h(x, y)$ changes with y on the curve Γ_2, we differentiate with respect to y and hold x constant at x_0,

$$\frac{\partial h}{\partial y}\bigg|_{x=x_0}$$

This represents the slope of Γ_2 on the plane $x = x_0$.

As an example of the foregoing ideas consider the surface

$$h = x^2 - xy + 6y^3$$

On the plane $y = 1$, the slope of the surface $h(x, y)$ in the x-direction is

$$\frac{\partial h}{\partial x}\bigg|_{y=1} = 2x - 1$$

and at the point $x = 2$, the rate at which h is changing in the x-direction is 3. The slope of the surface in the y-direction on the plane $x = 2$ is

$$\frac{\partial h}{\partial y}\bigg|_{x=2} = -2 + 18y^2$$

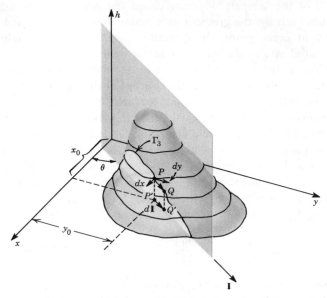

Figure 5.3   The rate of change of a scalar field.

so that the rate at which h changes in the y-direction at the point $y = 1$ is 16.

We have been able to determine the rate at which h changes with x on the curve Γ_1 which is the intersection of the surface h with a plane through any point P and perpendicular to the y-axis; and the rate of change of h with y along a curve Γ_2 formed by the intersection of h with a plane perpendicular to the x-axis. Now we ask what is the rate of change of h along Γ_3, the intersection of the surface h with a plane through a point P and normal to the x-y plane which makes an angle θ with the x-axis? (θ is measured relative to the positive x-axis in a counterclockwise direction.)

To answer this question, consider Fig. 5.3. As indicated in the figure, $\mathbf{l}$ is a vector locating any point along the straight line which is the projection of Γ_3 on the x-y plane. $\mathbf{l} = 0$ is at that point where the plane intersecting h (thereby creating Γ_3) crosses the x-axis. The points $P(x_0, y_0)$ and $Q(x, y)$ are on the curve Γ_3 and their projections on x-y plane are the points $P'(x_0, y_0)$ and $Q'(x, y)$ respectively. $\Delta\mathbf{l}$ is the small distance from $P'(x_0, y_0)$ to $Q'(x, y)$ on the projection of Γ_3 on the x-y plane. The coordinates of the point Q' are given by

$$x = x_0 + |\Delta\mathbf{l}| \cos \theta$$

$$y = y_0 + |\Delta\mathbf{l}| \cos \left(\frac{\pi}{2} - \theta\right) = y_0 + |\Delta\mathbf{l}| \sin \theta$$

or

$$\Delta x = |\Delta l| \cos \theta \qquad \text{where } \Delta x \equiv x - x_0 \qquad (5.2a)$$

$$\Delta y = |\Delta l| \sin \theta \qquad \text{where } \Delta y \equiv y - y_0 \qquad (5.2b)$$

Then, if we let Q approach P, the rate at which h changes as we move in the l direction, that is, as we move along Γ_3, is

$$\left.\frac{dh}{|dl|}\right|_P = \left.\frac{\partial h}{\partial x}\right|_P \frac{dx}{|dl|} + \left.\frac{\partial h}{\partial y}\right|_P \frac{dy}{|dl|}$$

which, when (5.2a) and (5.2b) are considered, becomes

$$\left.\frac{dh}{|dl|}\right|_P = \left.\frac{\partial h}{\partial x}\right|_P \cos\theta + \left.\frac{\partial h}{\partial y}\right|_P \cos\left(\frac{\pi}{2}-\theta\right) = \left.\frac{\partial h}{\partial x}\right|_P \cos\theta + \left.\frac{\partial h}{\partial y}\right|_P \sin\theta$$

$$(5.3)$$

This equation represents the slope of the mountain in the direction l at a point P. Stated in more general terms, it represents at the point P the rate of change of the scalar field h in the direction specified by θ.

To make this concept clearer, it is instructive to consider the following example: determine the directional derivative of the scalar field h at the point $x = 3$, $y = 2$ in the direction $\theta = \pi/4$ where

$$h = 5 + x^2 - xy^3 + \frac{1}{y}$$

Since

$$\left.\frac{\partial h}{\partial x}\right|_{\substack{x=3 \\ y=2}} = \left[2x - y^3\right]\Big|_{\substack{x=3 \\ y=2}} = -2$$

and

$$\left.\frac{\partial h}{\partial y}\right|_{\substack{x=3 \\ y=2}} = \left[-3xy^2 - \frac{1}{y^2}\right]\Big|_{\substack{x=3 \\ y=2}} = -\frac{145}{4}$$

Eq. (5.3) becomes

$$\frac{dh}{|dl|} = -2\cos\frac{\pi}{4} - \frac{145}{4}\sin\frac{\pi}{4}$$

$$= -\frac{153}{8}\sqrt{2}$$

This is the slope, at the point $(3, 2)$ of the curve formed by the intersection of $h(x, y)$ with a plane through the point $(3, 2)$ which is normal to the x-y plane and which makes an angle $\pi/4$ with the $+x$ axis.

Returning to our discussion of the motion of a ball on the side of the mountain, let us ask the question, "If we place the ball at a point P on the mountain, in what direction will it roll and what is the magnitude of the force acting on the ball to accelerate it in that particular direction?" Since the ball will roll in the direction along which the slope or rate of change of elevation is the greatest, and since the accelerating force is

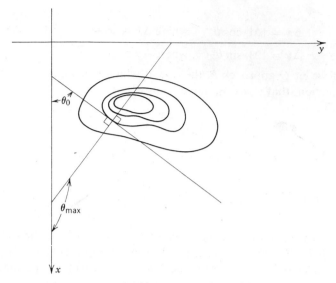

Figure 5.4   The minimum and maximum rate of change of a scalar field.

proportional to the slope in that direction, the foregoing question is equivalent to asking "What is the direction and magnitude of the greatest slope at P?" or in other words, "In what direction is the directional derivative a maximum and what is the maximum value of the directional derivative?"

To determine the direction in which the directional derivative is a maximum and its value in that direction, we take the derivative of Eq. (5.3) with respect to θ and set it equal to zero, thus:

$$\frac{\partial}{\partial \theta} \frac{dh}{|dl|}\bigg|_P = -\frac{\partial h}{\partial x}\bigg|_P \sin \theta + \frac{\partial h}{\partial y}\bigg|_P \cos \theta = 0 \qquad (5.4)$$

Then

$$\tan \theta_{\max}\bigg|_P = \frac{\dfrac{\partial h}{\partial y}\bigg|_P}{\dfrac{\partial h}{\partial x}\bigg|_P} \qquad 0 \le \theta \le \pi \qquad (5.5)$$

where $\theta_{\max}$ is the direction of the intersection plane through the point P, on which $h(x, y)$ changes more rapidly (see Fig. 5.4).

Then the maximum value of the directional derivative at P is

$$\frac{dh}{|dl|}\bigg|_P\bigg]_{\max} = \frac{\partial h}{\partial x}\bigg|_P \cos \theta_{\max} + \frac{\partial h}{\partial y}\bigg|_P \sin \theta_{\max} \qquad (5.6)$$

To obtain a clearer picture of the meaning of $\theta_{\max}$, let us consider its relationship to θ_0, the direction in which $dh/|d\mathbf{l}|$ is zero. [More specifically, θ_0 is the angle which a plane, perpendicular to the xy-plane and passing through the point P, makes with the $+x$-direction when its intersection with the surface $h(x, y)$ forms a curve on which the rate of change of $h(x, y)$ at the point P is zero.]

By solving Eq. (5.3) for the case when $dh/|d\mathbf{l}| = 0$, we find that

$$\tan \theta_0 \Big|_P = -\frac{\dfrac{\partial h}{\partial x}\Big|_P}{\dfrac{\partial h}{\partial y}\Big|_P} \tag{5.7}$$

which is the negative reciprocal of the $\tan \theta_{\max}$. Therefore, by comparing Eq. (5.7) with Eq. (5.5), we see that the direction in which the directional derivative is a maximum is normal to the direction in which the directional derivative is zero (see Fig. 5.4). Furthermore, the right-hand side of Eq. (5.7) is just $\dfrac{dy}{dx}\Big|_{P, h_0}$, that is, the rate of change of y with respect to x at the point P on a curve formed by the intersection of the surface $h(x, y)$ with a plane $h = h_0$ (a constant). To see this consider the following. In general, we can write for a small change in h at the point P

$$dh = \frac{\partial h}{\partial x}\Big|_P dx + \frac{\partial h}{\partial y}\Big|_P dy \tag{5.8}$$

On the plane $h = h_0$, h does not vary so that $dh = 0$ then Eq. (5.8) becomes

$$0 = \frac{\partial h}{\partial x}\Big|_{P, h_0} dx + \frac{\partial h}{\partial y}\Big|_{P, h_0} dy$$

or

$$\frac{dy}{dx}\Big|_{P, h_0} = -\frac{\dfrac{\partial h}{\partial x}\Big|_{P, h_0}}{\dfrac{\partial h}{\partial y}\Big|_{P, h_0}} \tag{5.9}$$

Therefore

$$\tan \theta_0 = \frac{dy}{dx}\Big|_{P, h_0}$$

or, in other words, the directional derivative at the point P can be made zero by choosing θ such that the intersecting plane (which is normal to the x-y plane and passes through P) is tangent at P to the curve representing the intersection of the surface $h(x, y)$ with the plane $h = h_0$. Obviously,

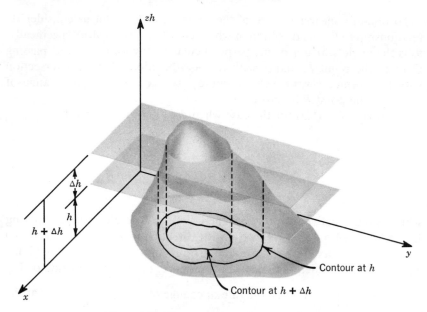

Figure 5.5   The generation of contour lines.

this requires the intersecting plane to be tangent to Γ_0 [the curve formed by the intersection of the plane $h = h_0$, through P and the surface $h(x, y)$] at the point P. This seems reasonable because we would expect that the rate at which $h(x, y)$ changes to be zero along the curve Γ_0 on which h is a constant.

The projection, on the x-y plane, of the intersection of the surface $h(x, y)$ with the planes representing constant values of h are called contour lines (see Fig. 5.5). It follows therefore that the direction θ_{max} in which the directional derivative at P is a maximum is normal to the direction θ_0, that is, it is normal to the contour line at the point P (see Fig. 5.4).

When the directional derivative is a maximum it can be written $dh/|d\mathbf{n}|$ to denote the fact that it is always in a direction normal to the contour lines, that is, $d\mathbf{n} = \mathbf{u}_n |d\mathbf{n}|$ is an element of length normal to the contour lines.

That the maximum spatial rate of change of the surface h is, in general, normal to the contour lines can also be seen from the following considerations. If we label one contour line h_0 and the next $h_0 + dh$, then we can see from Fig. 5.6 that the most rapid way to get from h_0 to $h_0 + dh$ is by moving normal to the contour lines. Then $dh/|d\mathbf{n}|$ is the magnitude of the greatest spatial rate of change of the elevation, $h(x, y)$, and the direction in which the directional derivative at P is a maximum we have shown to be

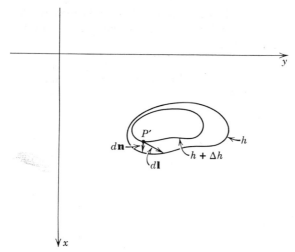

Figure 5.6   An infinitesimal displacement from one contour to another.

θ_{max}. We see therefore that for every point on the surface $h(x, y)$ we have determined a vector, in other words, we have determined a vector field, which represents the direction θ_{max} and the magnitude $dh/|d\mathbf{n}|$ of the greatest rate of change of $h(x, y)$. Let us now attempt to determine the components of this vector field—determine the components of each vector of which the field is composed.

From Fig. 5.6 we see that $d\mathbf{n}$, a displacement from the point P' normal to a contour line representing the intersection of the surface $h(x, y)$ with the plane h_0 is given by

$$d\mathbf{n} = \mathbf{u}_x |d\mathbf{n}|_x + \mathbf{u}_y |d\mathbf{n}|_y = \{\mathbf{u}_x[\mathbf{u}_n \cdot \mathbf{u}_x] + \mathbf{u}_y[\mathbf{u}_n \cdot \mathbf{u}_y]\} |d\mathbf{n}|$$
$$= \mathbf{u}_x \cos \theta \, |d\mathbf{n}| + \mathbf{u}_y \sin \theta \, |d\mathbf{n}|$$
$$= \mathbf{u}_x \, dx + \mathbf{u}_y \, dy \qquad (5.10)$$

where $\mathbf{u}_n \equiv d\mathbf{n}/|d\mathbf{n}|$ is a unit vector in the direction in which h changes most rapidly. To determine $\mathbf{u}_n$ in terms of θ_{max}, we see that Eq. (5.10) may be written

$$d\mathbf{n} = \mathbf{u}_x |d\mathbf{n}| \cos \theta_{max} + \mathbf{u}_y |d\mathbf{n}| \sin \theta_{max}$$

Then forming the ratio

$$\frac{d\mathbf{n}}{|d\mathbf{n}|} \equiv \mathbf{u}_n = \mathbf{u}_x \cos \theta_{max} + \mathbf{u}_y \sin \theta_{max}$$

we see how $\mathbf{u}_n$ is related to θ_{max}.

If we let the symbol $\mathbf{I} = \mathbf{u}_x I_x + \mathbf{u}_y I_y$ denote the vector which represents the sense, direction, and magnitude of the greatest rate of change of $h(x, y)$ at a point P, then

$$|\mathbf{I}| = \frac{dh}{|d\mathbf{n}|}\bigg|_P = \frac{\partial h}{\partial x}\bigg|_P \cos \theta_{\max} + \frac{\partial h}{\partial y}\bigg|_P \sin \theta_{\max} \qquad (5.11)$$

But the magnitude of $\mathbf{I}$ is just

$$\begin{aligned}
|\mathbf{I}| = \mathbf{I} \cdot \mathbf{u}_n &= (\mathbf{u}_x I_x + \mathbf{u}_y I_y) \cdot \mathbf{u}_n \\
&= (\mathbf{u}_n \cdot \mathbf{u}_x) I_x + (\mathbf{u}_n \cdot \mathbf{u}_y) I_y \\
&= I_x \cos \theta_{\max} + I_y \sin \theta_{\max} \qquad (5.12)
\end{aligned}$$

Comparing Eqs. (5.11) and (5.12) we see that

$$I_x = \frac{\partial h}{\partial x}\bigg|_P \qquad \text{and} \qquad I_y = \frac{\partial h}{\partial y}\bigg|_P$$

so that $\mathbf{I}$, which represents the sense, direction, and magnitude of the greatest rate of change of $h(x, y)$ at any point P, is given by

$$\mathbf{I} = \mathbf{u}_x \frac{\partial h}{\partial x}\bigg|_P + \mathbf{u}_y \frac{\partial h}{\partial y}\bigg|_P \qquad (5.13)$$

This, of course, is true for any point P where the derivatives exist, so that we shall drop the notation P. This vector $\mathbf{I}$, which gives the sense, direction, and magnitude of the greatest rate of change of the scalar field h, is of such great significance in the study of fields that it is given the unique symbol

$$\mathbf{I} \equiv \operatorname{grad} h(x, y) = \mathbf{u}_x \frac{\partial h}{\partial x} + \mathbf{u}_y \frac{\partial h}{\partial y}$$

and is called the gradient of the scalar field $h(x, y)$.

Sometimes the physical situations which the gradient describes require that a minus sign be used with it as,

$$\mathbf{I} = -\operatorname{grad} h(x, y)$$

The reason for the minus sign can be seen by considering again the ball on the mountainside. The sense of the acceleration of the ball is downward along the surface of the mountain and the positive sense of the gradient of the elevation of the mountain is upward along the surface of the mountain. To reconcile this difference, a minus sign is used. The presence of the minus sign in no way alters the previous discussion of the concepts involved in the gradient.

The foregoing two-dimensional example illustrating the physical significance of the gradient can be extended to include three-dimensional scalar fields. As an example, consider the temperature at every point in a room. Let us assume that the totality of all the data specifying the temperature as a function of position in the room can be represented in analytic form by

$$g = g(x, y, z)$$

Although $g(x, y, z)$ cannot be represented graphically, it is possible to connect all those points in a room which are at the same temperature by surfaces called isothermal surfaces. A surface connecting all those points at the temperature g_0 may be written

$$g_0 = g_0(x, y, z)$$

(see Fig. 5.7). These isothermal surfaces, since they represent a constant value of the dependent variable, are analogous to the contour lines in the discussion of two-dimensional scalar fields. The directional derivative of a three-dimensional scalar field is

$$\cdot \frac{dg}{|d\mathbf{l}|} = \frac{\partial g}{\partial x} \cos \alpha + \frac{\partial g}{\partial y} \cos \beta + \frac{\partial g}{\partial z} \cos \gamma$$

where α, β, and γ are the angles between the direction of $d\mathbf{l}$ and the

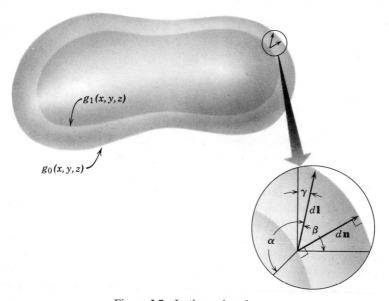

Figure 5.7   Isothermal surfaces.

x-, y-, and z-axes, respectively. Also by analogy with the two-dimensional case, the maximum value of directional derivative in three dimensions at any point P is normal to the isothermal surface passing through the point P. Equation (5.6) may then be extended to

$$\frac{dg}{|d\mathbf{l}|}\bigg]_{\max} = \frac{dg}{|d\mathbf{n}|}$$

$$= \frac{\partial g}{\partial x} \cos \alpha_{\max} + \frac{\partial g}{\partial y} \cos \beta_{\max} + \frac{\partial g}{\partial z} \cos \gamma_{\max} \qquad (5.14)$$

where $\alpha_{\max}$, $\beta_{\max}$, and $\gamma_{\max}$ are the angles between the direction of $\mathbf{u}_n$ (in which g changes most rapidly) and the x, y, z-directions, respectively, so that the cosines of $\alpha_{\max}$, $\beta_{\max}$, and $\gamma_{\max}$ are the direction cosines of the direction $\mathbf{u}_n$ (see Fig. 5.7). We can let $\mathbf{I}$ (x, y, z) represent the sense direction and the magnitude $dg/|d\mathbf{n}|$ of the greatest rate of change of g. The magnitude of $\mathbf{I}$ is given by

$$|\mathbf{I}| = \frac{dg}{|d\mathbf{n}|} = \mathbf{I} \cdot \mathbf{u}_n = [\mathbf{u}_n \cdot \mathbf{u}_x]I_x + [\mathbf{u}_n \cdot \mathbf{u}_y]I_y + [\mathbf{u}_n \cdot \mathbf{u}_z]I_z$$

$$= I_x \cos \alpha_{\max} + I_y \cos \beta_{\max} + I_z \cos \gamma_{\max} \qquad (5.15)$$

where $\mathbf{u}_n$ is a unit vector in the $\mathbf{n}$ direction, that is, the direction in which the temperature g changes most rapidly.

By comparing Eqs. (5.14) and (5.15) we see that

$$I_x = \frac{\partial g}{\partial x} \qquad (5.16a)$$

$$I_y = \frac{\partial g}{\partial y} \qquad (5.16b)$$

$$I_z = \frac{\partial g}{\partial z} \qquad (5.16c)$$

so that

$$\mathbf{I} = \mathbf{u}_x \frac{\partial g}{\partial x} + \mathbf{u}_y \frac{\partial g}{\partial y} + \mathbf{u}_z \frac{\partial g}{\partial z} = \text{grad } g \qquad (5.17)$$

if g is expressed in a three-dimensional Cartesian coordinate system.

Here $\mathbf{I}$ represents a vector field whose sense, direction, and magnitude at every point is the greatest rate of change of the scalar field g. As stated before, the physical situation described by Eq. (5.17) may require that a minus sign be associated with the right-hand side of this equation. For example, if g is the temperature distribution in a region of space, then $\mathbf{I}$ is a vector field proportional to the rate at which heat flows per unit area. However, the direction in which heat flows is opposite to that of the positive temperature gradient; in other words, heat flows from a region of higher temperature to a region of lower temperature, whereas the positive temperature gradient is from cold to hot. To reconcile this difference, a minus sign is used. We shall return to this point in Chapter 11, where scalar and vector potentials are discussed.

The foregoing discussion of the gradient is not the only way in which this operator may be introduced. We have chosen this mode of presentation to facilitate the visualization of the operation that the gradient represents. In Section 5.3 we shall see that there is a more fundamental definition of the gradient which can be used to transform integrals involving vector quantities.

We have discussed the gradient in two and three dimensions. The results we have obtained can also be generalized for an N-dimensional space, whose space coordinates are $x_1, x_2 \ldots x_j, \ldots x_N$. In such a case the gradient is defined by

$$\text{grad} \equiv \sum_{j=1}^{N} \mathbf{u}_j \frac{\partial}{\partial x_j} \tag{5.18}$$

where $\mathbf{u}_j$ is a unit vector in the x_j-direction.

An interesting property of $\mathbf{I}$ is that the magnitude of its projection in any direction is equal to the directional derivative of the scalar field, that is, the rate of change of the scalar field in that direction. To prove this, consider the magnitude of the projection of $\mathbf{I}$ in a general direction characterized by a unit vector $\mathbf{u}_l$, namely, $\mathbf{I} \cdot \mathbf{u}_l$, where $\mathbf{u}_l$ is given by

$$\mathbf{u}_l = \mathbf{u}_x[\mathbf{u}_x \cdot \mathbf{u}_l] + \mathbf{u}_y[\mathbf{u}_y \cdot \mathbf{u}_l] + \mathbf{u}_z[\mathbf{u}_z \cdot \mathbf{u}_l]$$
$$= \mathbf{u}_x \cos \alpha + \mathbf{u}_y \cos \beta + \mathbf{u}_z \cos \gamma \tag{5.19}$$

where α, β, and γ are the angles between the directional $d\mathbf{l}$, and the x-, y-, and z-axes, respectively. Then

$$\mathbf{I} \cdot \mathbf{u}_l = (\mathbf{u}_x I_x + \mathbf{u}_y I_y + \mathbf{u}_z I_z) \cdot (\mathbf{u}_x \cos \alpha + \mathbf{u}_y \cos \beta + \mathbf{u}_z \cos \gamma)$$
$$= I_x \cos \alpha + I_y \cos \beta + I_z \cos \gamma \tag{5.20}$$

However, because of Eq. 5.16a, b, c this becomes

$$\mathbf{I} \cdot \mathbf{u}_l = \frac{\partial g}{\partial x} \cos \alpha + \frac{\partial g}{\partial y} \cos \beta + \frac{\partial g}{\partial z} \cos \gamma \tag{5.21}$$

This is just the directional derivative of the scalar field g in the $\mathbf{u}_l$ direction: $dg/|d\mathbf{l}| = \mathbf{I} \cdot \mathbf{u}_l$.

It follows from this discussion that if we move an incremental distance $d\mathbf{l}$ in a scalar field g, the value of the field will change by an amount dg which is given by

$$dg = \text{grad}\, g \cdot d\mathbf{l} = \mathbf{I} \cdot d\mathbf{l} = \mathbf{I} \cdot \mathbf{u}_l \,|d\mathbf{l}| \tag{5.22}$$

In the preceding discussion we have assumed that the scalar field g is an explicit function of x, y, and z. Sometimes this is not the case; for example, g may be an explicit function of w, which in turn is a function of x, y, and z. We may then write the gradient as

$$\operatorname{grad} g(w) = \mathbf{u}_x \frac{\partial g}{\partial w} \frac{\partial w}{\partial x} + \mathbf{u}_y \frac{\partial g}{\partial w} \frac{\partial w}{\partial y} + \mathbf{u}_z \frac{\partial g}{\partial w} \frac{\partial w}{\partial z}$$

$$= \frac{\partial g}{\partial w} \left(\mathbf{u}_x \frac{\partial w}{\partial x} + \mathbf{u}_y \frac{\partial w}{\partial y} + \mathbf{u}_z \frac{\partial w}{\partial z} \right)$$

$$= \frac{\partial g}{\partial w} \operatorname{grad} w \qquad (5.23)$$

It may also occur that g is an explicit function of the scalar variables $w_1, w_2 \ldots w_n$, each of which is a function of x, y, and z. We may then write for the gradient of g

$$\operatorname{grad} g(w_1, w_2, \ldots w_n) = \mathbf{u}_x \frac{\partial g}{\partial x} + \mathbf{u}_y \frac{\partial g}{\partial y} + \mathbf{u}_z \frac{\partial g}{\partial z}$$

$$= \mathbf{u}_x \left(\frac{\partial g}{\partial w_1} \frac{\partial w_1}{\partial x} + \frac{\partial g}{\partial w_2} \frac{\partial w_2}{\partial x} + \cdots + \frac{\partial g}{\partial w_n} \frac{\partial w_n}{\partial x} \right)$$

$$+ \mathbf{u}_y \left(\frac{\partial g}{\partial w_1} \frac{\partial w_1}{\partial y} + \frac{\partial g}{\partial w_2} \frac{\partial w_2}{\partial y} + \cdots + \frac{\partial g}{\partial w_n} \frac{\partial w_n}{\partial y} \right)$$

$$+ \mathbf{u}_z \left(\frac{\partial g}{\partial w_1} \frac{\partial w_1}{\partial z} + \frac{\partial g}{\partial w_2} \frac{\partial w_2}{\partial z} + \cdots + \frac{\partial g}{\partial w_n} \frac{\partial w_n}{\partial z} \right)$$

$$= \frac{\partial g}{\partial w_1} \operatorname{grad} w_1 + \frac{\partial g}{\partial w_2} \operatorname{grad} w_2 + \cdots + \frac{\partial g}{\partial w_n} \operatorname{grad} w_n$$

$$(5.24)$$

Another interesting and useful property of a vector field $\mathbf{I}$ which is the gradient of a scalar field is that the line integral of $\mathbf{I} \cdot d\mathbf{l}$ along a path Γ (where $d\mathbf{l}$ is an increment of the path Γ) between any two points is independent of the path between those points. To see this, consider the line integral of $\mathbf{I}(x, y, z)$ on the path Γ between the points P_1 and P_2 (see Fig. 5.8)

$$\int_{P_1 \Gamma}^{P_2} \mathbf{I} \cdot d\mathbf{l} = \int_{P_1 \Gamma}^{P_2} \mathbf{I} \cdot \mathbf{u}_l \, |d\mathbf{l}| \qquad (5.25)$$

where $\mathbf{u}_l$ is a unit vector in the $d\mathbf{l}$ direction. Referring to Eq. (5.22) we may write

$$\mathbf{I} \cdot \mathbf{u}_l = \frac{dg}{|d\mathbf{l}|} = \operatorname{grad} g \cdot \mathbf{u}_l \qquad (5.26)$$

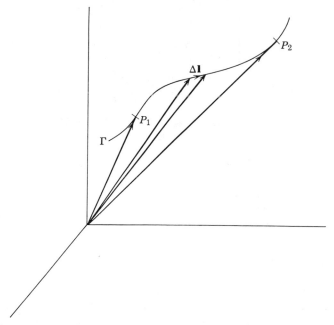

Figure 5.8   Geometrical interpretation of a line integral.

Then the integral in Eq. (5.25) becomes

$$\int_{P_1\Gamma}^{P_2} \operatorname{grad} g \cdot dl = \int_{P_1\Gamma}^{P_2} \frac{dg}{|dl|} |dl| = \int_{P_1}^{P_2} dg = g(P_2) - g(P_1)$$

and as stated previously, the result is independent of the path taken, so that the value of the line integral of the gradient of a scalar field is the same regardless of how we go from P_1 to P_2.

If the path Γ, considered previously, is a closed curve, then the integral of $I \cdot dl$ is zero. This is equivalent to letting $P_1 = P_2$, that is, the initial and the final points coincide. In this situation

$$\oint_\Gamma I \cdot dl = \oint_\Gamma (\operatorname{grad} g) \cdot dl = \oint dg$$

$$= \int_{P_1}^{P_1} dg = g(P_1) - g(P_1) = 0 \qquad (5.27)$$

so that we can say that the line integral of $I \cdot dl$ around a closed path is identically zero if the vector field I is the gradient of a scalar field. Conversely, if in a region in space the integral of $I \cdot dl$ around every closed path is zero, I must be the gradient of a scalar field. To prove this consider

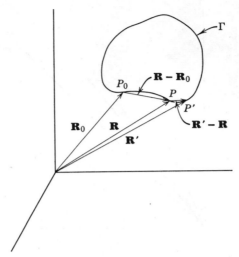

Figure 5.9   The closed line integral of the vector field I.

a closed curve Γ (see Fig. 5.9) in a region in space where a vector field $\mathbf{I}$ exists. Let the point P_0 (located by the vector $\mathbf{R}_0$) be fixed at some point on the curve Γ and let P (located by the vector $\mathbf{R}$) be a point whose position on Γ is not fixed. Since the integral completely around Γ is zero, we can write

$$\oint_\Gamma \mathbf{I} \cdot d\mathbf{l} = 0 = \int_{P_0 \atop \text{right}}^{P} \mathbf{I} \cdot d\mathbf{l} + \int_{P \atop \text{left}}^{P_0} \mathbf{I} \cdot d\mathbf{l} = \int_{P_0 \atop \text{right}}^{P} \mathbf{I} \cdot d\mathbf{l} - \int_{P_0 \atop \text{left}}^{P} \mathbf{I} \cdot d\mathbf{l} \quad (5.28)$$

where the indications of right and left refer to the side of Γ over which the integration is performed. This becomes

$$\int_{P_0 \Gamma \atop \text{right}}^{P} \mathbf{I} \cdot d\mathbf{l} = \int_{P_0 \Gamma \atop \text{left}}^{P} \mathbf{I} \cdot d\mathbf{l} \quad (5.29)$$

so that no matter how we go from $P_0(\mathbf{R}_0)$ to $P(\mathbf{R})$ the line integral of $\mathbf{I} \cdot d\mathbf{l}$ between these two points is the same; or in other words, the value of the line integral of $\mathbf{I} \cdot d\mathbf{l}$ in going from $P_0(\mathbf{R}_0)$ to $P(\mathbf{R})$ is independent of the path taken. Furthermore, we note that if $P_0(\mathbf{R}_0)$ is fixed, the value of the line integral of $\mathbf{I} \cdot d\mathbf{l}$ from $P_0(\mathbf{R}_0)$ to $P(\mathbf{R})$ depends only on the $P(\mathbf{R})$; that is, the integral is a scalar function of the position of P. Therefore we can say, in general, that the expression

$$\int_{P_{\text{ref}}}^{P} \mathbf{I} \cdot d\mathbf{l} + c = g[P(\mathbf{R})] = g(\mathbf{R}) \quad (5.30)$$

where c is an arbitrary constant representing the difference of the integral between P_0 and some reference point P_{ref}. Thus Eq. 5.30 can be used to define a scalar field $g(\mathbf{R})$.

If we move the position of P a distance $\Delta \mathbf{l}$ along Γ to a new position P', then

$$\int_{P_{\text{ref}}}^{P'} \mathbf{I} \cdot d\mathbf{l} + c = g[P'(\mathbf{R}')] = g(\mathbf{R}') \tag{5.31}$$

where $\mathbf{R}'$ locates the new point P' (see Fig. 5.9). Since the distance from P to P' is small; that is, $|\mathbf{R}' - \mathbf{R}| = |\Delta \mathbf{R}| = |\Delta \mathbf{l}|$ (see Section 3.2) is small, we may write

$$g(\mathbf{R}') = g(\mathbf{R}) + \frac{\partial g}{|\partial \mathbf{R}|} |\Delta \mathbf{R}| \tag{5.32}$$

This result is obtained from a Taylor series expansion of $g(\mathbf{R}')$ about the point P located by $\mathbf{R}$ and neglecting higher order terms in $|\Delta \mathbf{R}|$. If we now compute the difference in the line integrals given by Eqs. (5.30) and (5.31), we obtain

$$\int_{P_{\text{ref}}}^{P'} \mathbf{I} \cdot d\mathbf{l} - \int_{P_{\text{ref}}}^{P} \mathbf{I} \cdot d\mathbf{l} = \int_{P}^{P'} \mathbf{I} \cdot d\mathbf{l} \tag{5.33}$$

Using Eq. (5.32) the left-hand side of (5.33) becomes

$$g(\mathbf{R}') - g(\mathbf{R}) = g(\mathbf{R}) + \frac{\partial g}{|\partial \mathbf{R}|} |\Delta \mathbf{R}| - g(\mathbf{R})$$

$$= \frac{\partial g}{|\partial \mathbf{R}|} |\Delta \mathbf{R}|$$

$$= \Delta g \quad \text{(in the } \Delta \mathbf{R} \text{ or } \Delta \mathbf{l} \text{ direction)} \tag{5.34}$$

We know, however, that if we move a distance $|\Delta \mathbf{l}|$ in a scalar field g, the value of the scalar quantity will change by the amount Δg given by

$$\Delta g \quad \text{(in the direction } \Delta \mathbf{l}) = \text{grad } g \cdot \Delta \mathbf{l} \tag{5.35}$$

so that

$$g(\mathbf{R}') - g(\mathbf{R}) = \text{grad } g \cdot \Delta \mathbf{l} \tag{5.36}$$

In the incremental distance $\Delta \mathbf{l}$ from P to P', $\mathbf{I}$ does not change, so that the right-hand side of Eq. (5.33) becomes

$$\int_{P}^{P'} \mathbf{I} \cdot d\mathbf{l} = \mathbf{I} \cdot \Delta \mathbf{l} \tag{5.37}$$

Then
$$\text{grad } g \cdot \Delta \mathbf{l} = \mathbf{I} \cdot \Delta \mathbf{l} \qquad (5.38)$$
Thus
$$\text{grad } g = \mathbf{I}$$

We see that $\mathbf{I}$ must have been the gradient of a scalar field; therefore we have proved that if

$$\oint \mathbf{I} \cdot d\mathbf{l} = 0 \qquad (5.39)$$

for any closed path, $\mathbf{I}$ is the gradient of a scalar field. A vector field like $\mathbf{I}$, which is the gradient of a scalar field and therefore satisfies Eq. (5.39), is called *irrotational*. We shall return to this type of field in Chapter 9.

Let us summarize these results.

1. The gradient of a scalar field is the vector field representing the magnitude, sense, and direction of the maximum spatial rate of change of the scalar field.

2. When a displacement $d\mathbf{l}$ is made between two points in a scalar field g, the difference dg in the value of the scalar quantity at those two points is given by
$$dg = (\text{grad } g) \cdot d\mathbf{l} = \mathbf{I} \cdot d\mathbf{l}$$

3. The line integral of $\mathbf{I} \cdot d\mathbf{l}$ around a closed path is zero if $\mathbf{I}$ is the gradient of a scalar field.

4. If the value of the line integral of $\mathbf{I} \cdot d\mathbf{l}$ is zero around every closed path in a region of space, the vector field $\mathbf{I}$ must be the gradient of a scalar field.

5.3   Further Considerations Involving the Gradient

We shall again discuss the gradient of a scalar field, but from a different viewpoint. Additional expressions, representing the gradient, will be developed to illustrate further its physical significance and to lay the foundation for the discussion of the integral properties of fields given in Chapter 9.

We shall first show that the gradient of a scalar field at a point P may be represented in integral form by

$$\text{grad } h = \lim_{\Delta V \to 0} \frac{1}{\Delta V} \oiint_a \mathbf{u}_n h \, |d\mathbf{s}| \qquad (5.40)$$

where ΔV is a small volume surrounding the point P and a is the surface area of ΔV; an element of the surface a is designated $d\mathbf{s} = \mathbf{u}_n\,|d\mathbf{s}| = \mathbf{u}_n\,ds$. Here we assume that ΔV approaches zero in such a way that a, the surface of ΔV, is well-behaved; a, for example, does not approach infinity as ΔV approaches zero.

To prove this statement, consider the elemental volume ΔV surrounding a point P which is located in a region of space where a scalar field $h(x, y, z)$ exists (see Fig. 5.10a). The scalar field h, as well as its first derivatives, is assumed to be continuous at every point of this region of

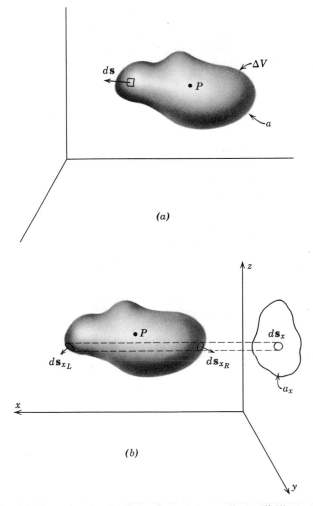

(a)

(b)

Figure 5.10 (a) Illustration for the discussion of the gradient. (b) Illustration for the discussion of the gradient.

space. By expanding Eq. (5.40) into component form, we may write

$$\text{grad } h = \lim_{\Delta V \to 0} \frac{1}{\Delta V} \oiint_a \{ \mathbf{u}_x [\mathbf{u}_x \cdot \mathbf{u}_n] h \, ds + \mathbf{u}_y [\mathbf{u}_y \cdot \mathbf{u}_n] h \, ds + \mathbf{u}_z [\mathbf{u}_z \cdot \mathbf{u}_n] h \, ds \}$$

$$= \mathbf{u}_x \lim_{\Delta V \to 0} \frac{1}{\Delta V} \oiint_a [\mathbf{u}_x \cdot \mathbf{u}_n] h \, ds + \mathbf{u}_y \lim_{\Delta V \to 0} \frac{1}{\Delta V} \oiint_a [\mathbf{u}_y \cdot \mathbf{u}_n] h \, ds$$

$$+ \mathbf{u}_z \lim_{\Delta V \to 0} \frac{1}{\Delta V} \oiint_a [\mathbf{u}_z \cdot \mathbf{u}_n] h \, ds \qquad (5.41)$$

We shall consider the x-component of this expression.

Parallel to the x-axis let us pass a cylinder of cross-sectional area ds_x through the volume ΔV (see Fig. 5.10b). This cylinder need not necessarily be a circular cylinder. The elements of area ds_{x_R} and ds_{x_L} intercepted by the cylinder on the right- and left-hand sides of ΔV are related to ds_x by

$$d\mathbf{s}_x = \mathbf{u}_x \, ds_x = -\mathbf{u}_x [\mathbf{u}_x \cdot d\mathbf{s}_{x_R}] = \mathbf{u}_x [\mathbf{u}_x \cdot d\mathbf{s}_{x_L}]$$

$$= -\mathbf{u}_x [\mathbf{u}_x \cdot \mathbf{u}_{n_R}] \, ds_{x_R} = \mathbf{u}_x [\mathbf{u}_x \cdot \mathbf{u}_{n_L}] \, ds_{x_L} \qquad (5.42)$$

where $\mathbf{u}_{n_R}$ and $\mathbf{u}_{n_L}$ are unit vectors normal to the areas ds_{x_R} and ds_{x_L}, respectively. The minus sign is necessary because the sense of that component of $\mathbf{u}_{n_R}$ parallel to the x-axis is always in the minus x-direction. Note also that $d\mathbf{s}_x$ is the projection of $d\mathbf{s}_{x_R}$ and $d\mathbf{s}_{x_L}$ on the plane $x = 0$. We may then write the x-component of Eq. (5.41) as

$$\mathbf{u}_x \lim_{\Delta V \to 0} \frac{1}{\Delta V} \oiint_a [\mathbf{u}_x \cdot \mathbf{u}_n] h \, ds = \mathbf{u}_x \lim_{\Delta V \to 0} \frac{1}{\Delta V} \iint_{\substack{\text{right side} \\ \text{of } \Delta V}} [\mathbf{u}_x \cdot \mathbf{u}_{n_R}] h_R \, ds_{x_R}$$

$$+ \mathbf{u}_x \lim_{\Delta V \to 0} \frac{1}{\Delta V} \iint_{\substack{\text{left side} \\ \text{of } \Delta V}} [\mathbf{u}_x \cdot \mathbf{u}_{n_L}] h_L \, ds_{x_L} \qquad (5.43)$$

where h_R and h_L are the values of the scalar field on ds_{x_R} and ds_{x_L} respectively.

In light of (5.42), we may write (5.43) as

$$\mathbf{u}_x \lim_{\Delta V \to 0} \frac{1}{\Delta V} \oiint_a [\mathbf{u}_x \cdot \mathbf{u}_n] h \, ds = \mathbf{u}_x \lim_{\Delta V \to 0} \frac{1}{\Delta V} \iint_{a_x} h_L \, ds_x$$

$$- \mathbf{u}_x \lim_{\Delta V \to 0} \frac{1}{\Delta V} \iint_{a_x} h_R \, ds_x$$

$$= \mathbf{u}_x \lim_{\Delta V \to 0} \frac{1}{\Delta V} \iint_{a_x} (h_L - h_R) \, ds_x \qquad (5.44)$$

Thus we see that we have transformed an integration over a, the surface of ΔV, to an integration over a_x, the projection of a, on the plane $x = 0$.

Since ΔV is small, the points on the surfaces ds_{x_R} and ds_{x_L} are close to the point P so that on ds_{x_R} the value of h, h_R, may be expressed in a Taylor series expansion about P.

$$h_R = h_P + \frac{\partial h}{\partial x}\bigg|_P \Delta x + \frac{\partial h}{\partial y}\bigg|_P \Delta y + \frac{\partial h}{\partial z}\bigg|_P \Delta z$$

$$+ \left\{ \begin{array}{l} \text{terms which are higher order in } \Delta x, \Delta y, \\ \text{and } \Delta z \text{ which are negligible as } \Delta V \text{ approaches} \\ \text{zero, that is, as the points on the surface of} \\ \Delta V \text{ approach } P. \end{array} \right\} \quad (5.45)$$

where h_P = value of h at P,

$\Delta x_R = x_R - x_P$, where x_R is the x-coordinate of ds_{x_R} and x_P is the x-coordinate of P,

$\Delta y_R = y_R - y_P$, where y_R is the y-coordinate of ds_{x_R} and y_P is the y-coordinate of P; since $y_P = y_R$, $\Delta y = 0$ for a cylinder which is parallel to the x-axis.

and $\Delta z_R = z_R - z_P = 0$.

Similarly, the value of h at ds_{x_L} is

$$h_L = h_P + \frac{\partial h}{\partial x}\bigg|_P \Delta x = h_P + \frac{\partial h}{\partial x}\bigg|_P (x_L - x_P) \quad (5.46)$$

Then Eq. (5.44) becomes

$$\mathbf{u}_x \lim_{\Delta V \to 0} \frac{1}{\Delta V} \oiint_a [\mathbf{u}_x \cdot \mathbf{u}_n] h \, ds = \mathbf{u}_x \lim_{\Delta V \to 0} \frac{1}{\Delta V} \frac{\partial h}{\partial x}\bigg|_P \iint_{a_x} (x_L - x_R) \, ds_x \quad (5.47)$$

but $(x_L - x_R) \, ds_x$ is just the element of volume common to the cylinder and ΔV, that is, it is that volume of ΔV which is cut out by the cylinder. The integration of $(x_L - x_R) \, ds_x$ over a_x is just the volume ΔV so that Eq. (5.47) becomes

$$\mathbf{u}_x \lim_{\Delta V \to 0} \frac{1}{\Delta V} \oiint_a [\mathbf{u}_x \cdot \mathbf{u}_n] h \, ds = \mathbf{u}_x \frac{\partial h}{\partial x}\bigg|_P \quad (5.48)$$

Similar results can be obtained for the y and z components of Eq. (5.41) by considering a cylinder passed through ΔV in the y- and z-directions, respectively. We may then write Eq. (5.41) as

$$\text{grad } h = \mathbf{u}_x \frac{\partial h}{\partial x} + \mathbf{u}_y \frac{\partial h}{\partial y} + \mathbf{u}_z \frac{\partial h}{\partial z} \quad (5.49)$$

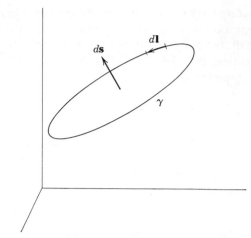

Figure 5.11   Illustration for the discussion of the gradient.

which, when compared to Eq. (5.17), established the fact that

$$\lim_{\Delta V \to 0} \frac{1}{\Delta V} \oiint_a \mathbf{u}_n h \, ds = \operatorname{grad} h \tag{5.50}$$

Equation (5.50) can also be written in the following approximate form.

$$\operatorname{grad} h = \frac{1}{dV} \oiint_a h \, ds \tag{5.51}$$

This approximation can be made arbitrarily exact by choosing dV as small as the limiting process requires.

Physically, Eqs. (5.50) and (5.51) may be interpreted in the following way. If we divide the surface of ΔV into elements of surface so small that h is essentially constant over each surface element, by multiplying each surface element by the value of the scalar field on it and summing these products as the number of surface elements increases in such a way that all the surface elements approach zero, then the result is the gradient of the scalar field.

To gain further insight into the physical significance of the gradient of a scalar field, let us consider an element of area, $d\mathbf{s} = \mathbf{u}_n \, |d\mathbf{s}|$, to be located in a region of space where h, a scalar field, exists. We shall show that (see Fig. 5.11)

$$\mathbf{u}_n \times \operatorname{grad} h = \frac{1}{|d\mathbf{s}|} \oint_\gamma h \, d\mathbf{l} \tag{5.52}$$

where $d\mathbf{l}$ is an element of length of γ, the periphery of $d\mathbf{s}$. The positive direction along γ is in accordance with the direction of $\mathbf{u}_n$ according to the right-hand rule.

To demonstrate that Eq. (5.52) is valid, we recall that Eq. (5.51) applies to any element of volume dV regardless of shape. For the purpose of this discussion, we shall take dV to be a right cylinder whose top $d\mathbf{s}_T = \mathbf{u}_{n_T}$ $|d\mathbf{s}_T|$ (see Fig. 5.12) is $d\mathbf{s}$ in Eq. (5.52), whose bottom $d\mathbf{s}_B$ is equal to $-d\mathbf{s}_T$, and whose altitude is ϵ. Therefore $\mathbf{u}_n$ in Eq. (5.52) is equal to $\mathbf{u}_{n_T} = -\mathbf{u}_{n_B}$. An element of the area of the sides of this cylinder will be designated $d\mathbf{s}_s = \mathbf{u}_{n_s} |d\mathbf{s}_s|$ (see Fig. 5.12). We may then write Eq. (5.52) as

$$\text{grad } h = \frac{1}{dV} \oiint_a h \, d\mathbf{s}$$
$$= \frac{1}{dV}\left\{ \iint_{\text{top}} h \, d\mathbf{s}_T + \iint_{\text{bottom}} h \, d\mathbf{s}_B + \iint_{\text{sides}} h \, d\mathbf{s}_S \right\} \tag{5.53}$$

If we take the vector product of $\mathbf{u}_n$ with Eq. (5.53), we obtain

$$\mathbf{u}_n \times \text{grad } h = \frac{1}{dV} \iint_{\text{sides}} h\mathbf{u}_n \times d\mathbf{s}_S \tag{5.54}$$

because $\mathbf{u}_n \times d\mathbf{s}_T$ and $\mathbf{u}_n \times d\mathbf{s}_B$ are zero since $\mathbf{u}_n$ and $\mathbf{u}_{n_T}$ have the same sense and direction and $\mathbf{u}_n$ and $\mathbf{u}_{n_B}$ are in the opposite direction. On the sides $|d\mathbf{s}_S| = \epsilon |d\mathbf{l}|$ so that Eq. (5.54) may be written

$$\mathbf{u}_n \times \text{grad } h = \frac{\epsilon}{dV} \oint_\gamma h\mathbf{u}_n \times \mathbf{u}_{n_S} |d\mathbf{l}| \tag{5.55}$$

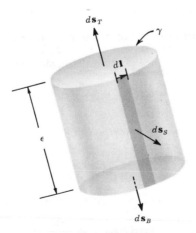

Figure 5.12   Illustration for the discussion of the gradient.

However, $\mathbf{u}_n \times \mathbf{u}_{n_s} = \mathbf{u}_l$, a unit vector in the direction $d\mathbf{l}$ and $\dfrac{\epsilon}{dV} =$ $|d\mathbf{s}_T| = |d\mathbf{s}|$ so that Eq. (5.55) becomes

$$\mathbf{u}_n \times \operatorname{grad} h = \frac{1}{|d\mathbf{s}|} \oint_\gamma h\mathbf{u}_l \, |d\mathbf{l}|$$

$$= \frac{1}{|d\mathbf{s}|} \oint_\gamma h \, d\mathbf{l} \tag{5.56}$$

and Eq. (5.52) is shown to be valid. This relationship is an important one to which we will return when discussing vector integral transformations.

In the discussion above we have considered the gradient of a scalar field in terms of its Cartesian coordinates. The reader will appreciate the fact that since no particular shape has been assumed for ΔV and the limit was taken in an arbitrary manner, this definition of the gradient is universal, quite independent of any coordinate system.

PROBLEMS

1. What is the value of the gradient of the scalar field h at the point 1, -1, 0 when h is given by
$$h = xyz + \ln x + e^z y?$$

2. At a point where the scalar field
$$g = g(x, y, z)$$
is continuously differentiable and has an extremum, show that its gradient is zero.

3. Determine the unit vector normal to the surface $xyz = 6$ at the point 2, -1, -3.

4. What is the angle between the normals to the surface $x^2 y = z$ at -2, 1, 4 and the normal to the surface $x^3 y^4 = z + 2$ at 2, -1, 6.

5. Determine the rate of change of the scalar field h in the direction
$$\mathbf{u}_l = \mathbf{u}_x(\tfrac{1}{2}) + \mathbf{u}_y(\tfrac{1}{2}) + \mathbf{u}_z \left(\frac{1}{\sqrt{2}} \right)$$
when h is given by
$$h = 3xy^3 + 6xz + 2y$$

6. If $\mathbf{C}$ is a constant vector, show that
$$\operatorname{grad} \mathbf{C} \cdot \mathbf{R} = \mathbf{C}$$

7. Show that for any differentiable scalar field $h(\mathbf{R})$
$$\operatorname{grad} h(\mathbf{R}) = \mathbf{u}_R \frac{dh}{|d\mathbf{R}|}$$

6

The Divergence

6.1 Introduction

The gradient discussed in the preceding section represents the direction and magnitude of the rate of change of a scalar field in the direction of its maximum spatial rate of change. A vector field may also change from point to point in space, but the mathematical description of the spatial rate at which a vector field changes is more complex. The reason for this is, of course, the fact that if we move from one point to another in a vector field, the vector quantity described by the field may change direction as well as magnitude. There are two field characteristics which describe the spatial rate of change of a vector field—the divergence and the curl. We shall discuss the divergence in this chapter and the curl in the following chapter. We shall see in Chapter 9 that a vector field is completely specified when its divergence and curl are given for every point in space. These two field properties are so important that, as we shall see in Chapters 6, 7, 11, and 12, for steady-state situations they may be considered as the "sources" or "sinks" of any vector field.

Two types of vector field "sources" (or "sinks", which are considered negative sources) exist: scalar and vector sources. We shall see that the divergence of a vector field is the scalar source density which gives rise to the irrotational portion of the vector field. The curl of a vector field is the vector source density which is responsible for the solenoidal portion of a vector field.

As in the treatment of the gradient given in Chapter 5, we shall first discuss the divergence operator in physical terms so that the reader may obtain an intuitive picture of its significance. Let us first discuss the meaning of the flux of a vector field through a surface.

6.2 The Flux of a Vector Field through a Surface

Consider a surface of area A located in a region of space in which a vector field $\mathbf{F}$ exists (see Fig. 6.1a).

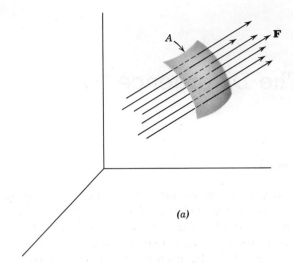

Figure 6.1   (a) The flux of a vector field through a surface.

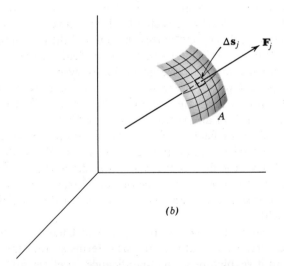

(b) The flux of a vector field through a surface.

Let us divide the surface into N elements of area $\Delta s_1, \Delta s_2 \ldots \Delta s_j \ldots$ Δs_N (see Fig. 6.1b) given by

$$\Delta \mathbf{s}_1 = \mathbf{u}_{n_1} |\Delta \mathbf{s}_1| = \mathbf{u}_{n_1} \Delta s_1$$
$$\Delta \mathbf{s}_2 = \mathbf{u}_{n_2} |\Delta \mathbf{s}_2| = \mathbf{u}_{n_2} \Delta s_2$$
.
.   (6.1)
.
$$\Delta \mathbf{s}_j = \mathbf{u}_{n_j} |\Delta \mathbf{s}_j| = \mathbf{u}_{n_j} \Delta s_j$$
.
.
$$\Delta \mathbf{s}_N = \mathbf{u}_{n_N} |\Delta \mathbf{s}_N| = \mathbf{u}_{n_N} \Delta s_N$$

where $\mathbf{u}_{n_j}$ is a unit vector normal to the typical surface element, Δs_j.

If A is the entire surface of a volume, that is, if the surface is a closed surface, the $\mathbf{u}_n$'s are taken as pointing outward normal from the surface. The areas of the Δs's are all assumed to be small so that over any area Δs_j the field will be assumed constant and designated as $\mathbf{F}_j$. If we think of $|\mathbf{F}_j|$ as the number of field lines per unit area which pass through an area normal to the field at the jth surface element, then $\mathbf{F}_j \cdot \Delta s_j$ is the number of lines going through the surface Δs_j. For this reason $\mathbf{F}$ is sometimes called the flux density. If $\mathbf{F}_j \cdot \Delta s_j$ is positive, then the component of $\mathbf{F}_j$ along the unit vector $\mathbf{u}_{n_j}$ has the same sense as $\mathbf{u}_{n_j}$ (see Fig. 6.2a); if $\mathbf{F}_j \cdot \Delta s_j$ is negative, then the component of $\mathbf{F}_j$ along $\mathbf{u}_{n_j}$ has a sense which is opposite that of $\mathbf{u}_{n_j}$ (see Fig. 6.2b).

Φ, the net flux through A, is approximately given by the sum of the products $\mathbf{F}_1 \cdot \Delta s_1, \mathbf{F}_2 \cdot \Delta s_2, \ldots, \mathbf{F}_j \cdot \Delta s_j, \ldots, \mathbf{F}_N \cdot \Delta s_N$, that is,

$$\Phi \approx \sum_{j=1}^{N} \mathbf{F}_j \cdot \Delta s_j \qquad (6.2)$$

The approximation arises because we have assumed that $\mathbf{F}_j$ does not change over the finite area Δs_j when in general, of course, $\mathbf{F}_j$ will vary. In the limit as N approaches infinity in such a way that the areas of all the surface elements approach zero, we may say that $\mathbf{F}_j$ is constant over the infinitesimal areas ds_j. In that case the summation Eq. (6.2) becomes an integral, that is,

$$\Phi = \lim_{N \to \infty} \sum_{j=1}^{N} \mathbf{F}_j \cdot \Delta s_j = \iint_A \mathbf{F} \cdot ds \qquad (6.3)$$

This is the net flux crossing the surface A. If the surface is closed, it is written

$$\Phi = \oiint_A \mathbf{F} \cdot d\mathbf{s} \qquad (6.4)$$

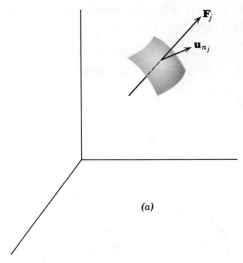

(a)

Figure 6.2   (*a*) The flux of a vector field in the same direction as $\mathbf{u}_{n_j}$.

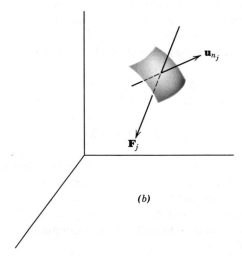

(b)

(*b*) The flux of a vector field in a direction opposite to that of $\mathbf{u}_{n_j}$.

Note that these expressions for the flux through a surface are completely independent of any coordinate system in which **F** and $d\mathbf{s}$ may be specified. To illustrate the utility of these expressions, consider the evaluation of the flux of the vector field (see Fig. 6.3)

$$\mathbf{F} = \mathbf{u}_r(r \cos^2 \phi) + \mathbf{u}_\theta(r \cos \phi \cos \theta) + \mathbf{u}_\phi(r^2 \sin^2 \theta) \tag{6.5}$$

through a sphere of radius R located at the origin.

The surface element $d\mathbf{s}$ is

$$d\mathbf{s} = \mathbf{u}_r R^2 \cos \phi \, d\phi \, d\theta \tag{6.6}$$

Over the surface of the sphere, when $r = R$, the field is given by

$$\mathbf{F} = \mathbf{u}_r(R \cos^2 \phi) + \mathbf{u}_\theta(R \cos \phi \cos \theta) + \mathbf{u}_\phi(R^2 \sin^2 \theta) \tag{6.7}$$

Then Eq. (6.4) becomes

$$\Phi = R^2 \int_{\theta=0}^{2\pi} \int_{\phi-\pi/2}^{\pi/2} (R \cos^3 \phi + R \cos^2 \phi \cos \theta + R^2 \cos \phi \sin^2 \theta) \, d\phi \, d\theta$$

$$= \frac{8\pi R^3}{3} + 2\pi R^4 \tag{6.8}$$

Equation (6.8) says that there are $8\pi R^3/3 + 2\pi R^4$ more field lines coming out of the sphere than are going in. There must then be a net source, or sources, within the sphere, that is, points from which field lines

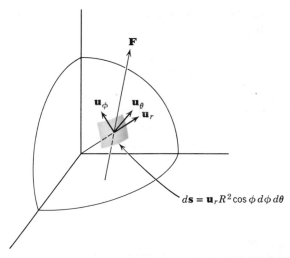

$$d\mathbf{s} = \mathbf{u}_r R^2 \cos \phi \, d\phi \, d\theta$$

Figure 6.3   An illustration for the calculation for the flux of a vector field through a sphere.

emanate which are located within the sphere. If the result of this integration had been negative, it would have indicated the presence, within the sphere, of a net sink to which field lines converge.

The name "flux" is preferred to any term like "amount," because the vector quantity, whose spatial dependence the field describes, may not correspond to any tangible quantity. For example, $\mathbf{F}$ may represent the electric field or force per unit electrical charge, in which case

$$\oiint_A \mathbf{F} \cdot d\mathbf{s} \tag{6.9}$$

does not admit of any physical interpretation except the number of electric field lines, that is, the flux of $\mathbf{F}$ through the closed surface A, going from the "inside" to the "outside."

6.3 The Divergence of a Vector Field

By examining the results of the foregoing example, we infer that in general the quantity

$$\Phi = \oiint_A \mathbf{F} \cdot d\mathbf{s} \tag{6.10}$$

depends on the size of the surface; in our example the flux depended on R (Eq. 6.8). Equation (6.10) therefore is not an intrinsic characteristic of the field. If, however, this integral is divided by the volume over which it is taken as that volume approaches zero, that is, the volume shrinks down on a point P (see Fig. 6.4):

$$\lim_{\Delta V \to 0} \frac{1}{\Delta V} \oiint_a \mathbf{F} \cdot d\mathbf{s} \tag{6.11}$$

where a is the surface area of the volume ΔV, we shall find that if the limit exists, the result is independent of the size or shape of ΔV. Here again we assume that ΔV approaches zero in such a way that its surface "a" is well behaved and that $\mathbf{F}$ is well behaved within and on "a." This quantity will depend on the spatial rate of change of $\mathbf{F}$ at P and is called the divergence of the vector field $\mathbf{F}$ at the point P and is designated div $\mathbf{F}$:

$$\operatorname{div} \mathbf{F} \equiv \lim_{\Delta V \to 0} \frac{1}{\Delta V} \oiint_a \mathbf{F} \cdot d\mathbf{s} \tag{6.12}$$

The divergence of a vector field is an intrinsic characteristic of the field. It is a scalar field and at any point is interpreted as the net flux per unit volume diverging from or leaving an infinitesimal neighborhood of that point.

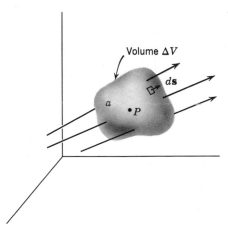

Figure 6.4   For the calculation of the flux through a closed surface.

To illustrate this fundamental field property, let us consider a specific vector field: the flow **v** of a fluid. The divergence of a vector field is related, as we have seen, to the sources or sinks and, as such, should arise quite naturally when discussing fluid flow when there is a point in space to which or from which fluid flows. Let us examine the flow of a fluid in the neighborhood of a point $P(x_0 y_0 z_0)$ (see Fig. 6.5a). Around this point P in space, let us construct a cube whose sides are Δx, Δy, and Δz. At that point the fluid velocity is $\mathbf{v} = \mathbf{u}_x v_x + \mathbf{u}_y v_y + \mathbf{u}_z v_z$ and the density is $\delta(x_0 y_0 z_0)$.

We shall now examine the rate at which m, the mass of fluid in this cube, changes with time. $\partial m / \partial t$, the rate at which the mass of fluid in the volume $\Delta x \, \Delta y \, \Delta z$ *increases*, is equal to the rate at which the mass flows in minus the rate at which mass flows out plus the net generation of fluid within $\Delta x \, \Delta y \, \Delta z$:

$$\frac{\partial m}{\partial t} = (\text{rate of mass flow in}) - (\text{rate of mass flow out}) + g \qquad (6.13)$$

where g is the net generation of fluid within $\Delta x \, \Delta y \, \Delta z$.

Referring to Fig. 6.5b, we see that in the time Δt the mass flowing into the elemental cube across the face $\Delta y \, \Delta z$ at $x_0 - \Delta x/2$ is

$$v_x\left(x_0 - \frac{\Delta x}{2}, y_0, z_0\right) \delta\left(x_0 - \frac{\Delta x}{2}, y_0, z_0\right) \Delta y \, \Delta z \, \Delta t \qquad (6.14)$$

$v_x(x_0 - \Delta x/2, y_0, z_0)$ represents the average value of v_x on this face. The mass flowing out of the face $\Delta y \, \Delta z$ at $x_0 + \Delta x/2$ during the same time interval is

$$v_x\left(x_0 + \frac{\Delta x}{2}, y_0, z_0\right) \delta\left(x_0 + \frac{\Delta x}{2}, y_0, z_0\right) \Delta y \, \Delta z \, \Delta t \qquad (6.15)$$

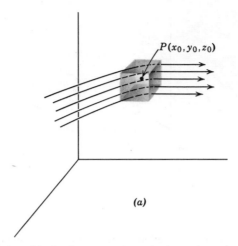

(a)

Figure 6.5 *(a)* The flux through a cube located at $P(x_0, y_0, z_0)$.

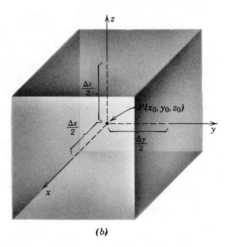

(b)

(b) Figure for the calculation of the divergence.

The reader will recall that if one wishes to express a function of $f(x, y, z)$ in terms of its value and derivatives at another point x_0, y_0, and z_0, he may do so by recourse to a Taylor expansion of $f(x, y, z)$ about the point x_0, y_0, z_0, that is,

$$f(x, y, z) = f(x_0 + \Delta x, y_0 + \Delta y, z_0 + \Delta z) = f(x_0, y_0, z_0)$$
$$+ \frac{1}{1!}\left[\frac{\partial f}{\partial x}\bigg|_{x_0 y_0 z_0} \Delta x + \frac{\partial f}{\partial y}\bigg|_{x_0 y_0 z_0} \Delta y + \frac{\partial f}{\partial z}\bigg|_{x_0 y_0 z_0} \Delta z\right]$$
$$+ \text{higher order terms} \tag{6.16}$$

If we expand Eq. (6.14) around the point $P(x_0, y_0, z_0)$ according to this Taylor series and neglect higher order terms, it becomes

$$\left[v_x(x_0, y_0, z_0) + \frac{\partial v_x}{\partial x}\left(-\frac{\Delta x}{2}\right)\right]\left[\delta(x_0, y_0, z_0) + \frac{\partial \delta}{\partial x}\left(-\frac{\Delta x}{2}\right)\right] \Delta y\, \Delta z\, \Delta t$$

$$= \left[v_x(x_0, y_0, z_0)\,\delta(x_0, y_0, z_0) - v_x \frac{\partial \delta}{\partial x}\frac{\Delta x}{2} - \delta \frac{\partial v_x}{\partial x}\frac{\Delta x}{2}\right] \Delta y\, \Delta z\, \Delta t$$

$$(6.17)$$

where $v_x(x_0, y_0, z_0)$ is the magnitude of the x-component of the velocity at $P(x_0, y_0, z_0)$ and $\delta(x_0, y_0, z_0)$ is the mass density of the air at $P(x_0, y_0, z_0)$.

By a similar expansion, Eq. (6.15), which represents the mass flow out of the cube, may be written

$$\left[v_x(x_0, y_0, z_0)\,\delta(x_0, y_0, z_0) + v_x \frac{\partial \delta}{\partial x}\frac{\Delta x}{2} + \delta \frac{\partial v_x}{\partial x}\frac{\Delta x}{2}\right] \Delta y\, \Delta z\, \Delta t \quad (6.18)$$

The net mass flow in the x-direction into the cube in the time Δt is Eq. (6.17) minus Eq. (6.18), or

$$-\left(v_x \frac{\partial \delta}{\partial x} + \delta \frac{\partial v_x}{\partial x}\right) \Delta x\, \Delta y\, \Delta z\, \Delta t = \frac{-\partial}{\partial x}(\delta v_x)\, \Delta x\, \Delta y\, \Delta z\, \Delta t \quad (6.19)$$

Similarly, the net mass flow in the y- and z-direction into the cube in the time Δt are

$$-\frac{\partial(v_y \delta)}{\partial y} \Delta x\, \Delta y\, \Delta z\, \Delta t \quad (6.20)$$

and

$$-\frac{\partial(v_z \delta)}{\partial z} \Delta x\, \Delta y\, \Delta z\, \Delta t \quad (6.21)$$

Δm by which the mass increases in the elemental cube in the time Δt is then given by,

$$\Delta m = -\left[\frac{\partial(v_x \delta)}{\partial x} + \frac{\partial(v_y \delta)}{\partial y} + \frac{\partial(v_z \delta)}{\partial z}\right] \Delta x\, \Delta y\, \Delta z\, \Delta t + g\, \Delta t \quad (6.22)$$

Dividing by Δt and letting Δt approach zero, we see that the rate at which the mass in the cube is increasing is

$$\lim_{\Delta t \to 0} \frac{\Delta m}{\Delta t} = \frac{\partial m}{\partial t} = -\left[\frac{\partial(v_x \delta)}{\partial x} + \frac{\partial(v_y \delta)}{\partial y} + \frac{\partial(v_z \delta)}{\partial z}\right] \Delta x\, \Delta y\, \Delta z + g \quad (6.23)$$

We see again that the flux depends on the volume of the body over whose surface it is evaluated. If we divide (6.23) by the volume $\Delta x\, \Delta y\, \Delta z$, we obtain

$$\frac{\partial \delta}{\partial t} = -\left[\frac{\partial(v_x\delta)}{\partial x} + \frac{\partial(v_y\delta)}{\partial y} + \frac{\partial(v_z\delta)}{\partial z}\right] + G \tag{6.24}$$

where δ is the density $\equiv m/\Delta x\, \Delta y\, \Delta z$, where $G \equiv g/\Delta x\, \Delta y\, \Delta z$ is the net source density and where the first quantity on the right-hand side of Eq. (6.24) is minus the divergence of the vector $\delta\mathbf{v}$ because of Eq. 6.12. The divergence of the mass flow $\delta\mathbf{v}$ is written

$$\text{div }(\delta\mathbf{v})$$

We may then write Eq. (6.24) as

$$\frac{\partial \delta}{\partial t} = -\text{div }(\delta\mathbf{v}) + G \tag{6.25}$$

To understand this relationship, consider an elemental volume dV inside a toy balloon which is blown up. If a pin is jabbed into the balloon, the air in it, including the air inside dV, will expand and become less dense. There is then a net flow of air across the closed surface of the elemental volume. We then say that the divergence of the air mass flow is greater than zero, that is, air is flowing out.

If we consider an incompressible liquid, of which water is a fair example, δ cannot change, in other words, δ is a constant in time and space. Then if there is no source of water Eq. (6.25) becomes

$$\text{div }\mathbf{v} = 0 \tag{6.26}$$

that is, the divergence of the velocity is zero. This means that the net flow of water through any closed surface lying entirely within the water must be zero.

The foregoing discussion can be generalized for any vector field $\mathbf{F}$. The divergence of $\mathbf{F}$, *if $\mathbf{F}$ is expressed in Cartesian coordinates*, may be written

$$\text{div }\mathbf{F} = \frac{\partial F_x}{\partial x} + \frac{\partial F_y}{\partial y} + \frac{\partial F_z}{\partial z} \tag{6.27}$$

As examples of the operations involved in determining the divergence of a vector field, consider first the two-dimensional vector field

$$\mathbf{F} = \mathbf{u}_x 3xy + \mathbf{u}_y y^2 \ln x \tag{6.28}$$

The divergence of this field is

$$\text{div }\mathbf{F} = \left(\mathbf{u}_x \frac{\partial}{\partial x} + \mathbf{u}_y \frac{\partial}{\partial y} + \mathbf{u}_z \frac{\partial}{\partial z}\right) \cdot (\mathbf{u}_x F_x + \mathbf{u}_y F_y + \mathbf{u}_z F_z)$$

$$= 3y + 2y \ln x \tag{6.29}$$

Consider also the field $\mathbf{R} = \mathbf{u}_x x + \mathbf{u}_y y + \mathbf{u}_z z$; the divergence of such a field is

$$\text{div } \mathbf{R} = \text{div } (\mathbf{u}_x x + \mathbf{u}_y y + \mathbf{u}_z z) = [1] + [1] + [1] = 3 \qquad (6.30)$$

that is, the divergence of the position vector is always 3.

Let us now reconsider the integral expression given for the divergence, Eq. (6.12). We shall now show that this equation and Eq. (6.27) are equivalent expressions for the divergence. The divergence may be written

$$\text{div } \mathbf{F} = \lim_{\Delta V \to 0} \frac{1}{\Delta V} \oiint_a \mathbf{u}_n \cdot \mathbf{F} \, ds$$

$$= \lim_{\Delta V \to 0} \frac{1}{\Delta V} \oiint_a F_x [\mathbf{u}_x \cdot \mathbf{u}_n] \, ds + \lim_{\Delta V \to 0} \frac{1}{\Delta V} \oiint_a F_y [\mathbf{u}_y \cdot \mathbf{u}_n] \, ds$$

$$+ \lim_{\Delta V \to 0} \frac{1}{\Delta V} \oiint_a F_z [\mathbf{u}_z \cdot \mathbf{u}_n] \, ds \qquad (6.31)$$

where F_x, F_y, and F_z are the magnitudes of the x-, y-, and z-components of $\mathbf{F}$, respectively.

Each member of Eq. (6.31) is similar in form to the magnitude of Eq. (5.41) so that each member of Eq. (6.31) becomes

$$\lim_{\Delta V \to 0} \frac{1}{\Delta V} \oiint_a F_x [\mathbf{u}_x \cdot \mathbf{u}_n] \, ds = \frac{\partial F_x}{\partial x} \qquad (6.32)$$

$$\lim_{\Delta V \to 0} \frac{1}{\Delta V} \oiint_a F_y [\mathbf{u}_y \cdot \mathbf{u}_n] \, ds = \frac{\partial F_y}{\partial y} \qquad (6.33)$$

$$\lim_{\Delta V \to 0} \frac{1}{\Delta V} \oiint_a F_z [\mathbf{u}_z \cdot \mathbf{u}_n] \, ds = \frac{\partial F_z}{\partial z} \qquad (6.34)$$

so that

$$\text{div } \mathbf{F} = \lim_{\Delta V \to 0} \frac{1}{\Delta V} \oiint_a \mathbf{u}_n \cdot \mathbf{F} \, ds = \frac{\partial F_x}{\partial x} + \frac{\partial F_y}{\partial y} + \frac{\partial F_z}{\partial z} \qquad (6.35)$$

We see therefore that Eq. (6.12) is equivalent to Eq. (6.27) as a means of expressing the divergence of a vector field. Equation (6.25) can be approximated by

$$\text{div } \mathbf{F} = \frac{1}{dV} \oiint_a \mathbf{u}_n \cdot \mathbf{F} \, |ds| \qquad (6.36)$$

where the approximation may be as close as we desire because dV can be made as small as the limiting process requires.

Equations (6.35) and (6.36) can help us picture the meaning of the divergence in the following physical terms. $\mathbf{F} \cdot d\mathbf{s}$, where $d\mathbf{s}$ is an element of a closed area, represents the flux across $d\mathbf{s}$ passing out of the closed area.

The integration of $\mathbf{F} \cdot d\mathbf{s}$ over the entire closed area is the net flux out of the closed area. If the small volume surrounding P contains a source or sink, then field lines will diverge from or converge to P, and there will be a net flux of field lines out of or into the small volume surrounding P; the divergence of the vector field $\mathbf{F}$ will then be different from zero at that point. If, for example, the small volume around P contains hydrogen and oxygen which combine chemically, there would be a net flow of water of water vapor from that point, and we would say that there is a source of water at P. From Eq. 6.25 we see that whenever $\partial\delta/\partial t = 0$ then div $\delta\mathbf{v} = G$. Since the surface integral in Eq. (6.35) is the net flux out of ΔV, it is associated with the source of the field contained within ΔV. For that reason the divergence of a field for steady-state situations may be thought of as a source (or sink) density. It turns out that such sources are associated with irrotational fields only. Relating the divergence of a vector field to the sources (and sinks) of a vector field is a fundamental consideration to which we shall return in Chapters 11 and 12.

PROBLEMS

1. If $|\mathbf{R}|$ is the magnitude of the position vector $\mathbf{R}$, show that

$$\text{div } |\mathbf{R}|^{n+1} \mathbf{u}_R = (n + 3) |\mathbf{R}|^n$$

2. Given the vector field

$$\mathbf{F} = \mathbf{u}_x x^3 yz - \mathbf{u}_y yz^2 + \mathbf{u}_z \frac{x^3}{z} \ln y$$

what is the value of div $\mathbf{F}$ at the point $(6, 1, -1)$?

3. Show that

$$\text{div } [\text{grad } g\,(x, y, z)] = \frac{\partial^2 g}{\partial x^2} + \frac{\partial^2 g}{\partial y^2} + \frac{\partial^2 g}{\partial z^2}$$

4. Under what conditions does

$$\text{div } \left[\frac{\mathbf{F} \times \mathbf{R}}{|\mathbf{R}|} \right] = 0?$$

5. Show that $g = 1/|\mathbf{R}|$ satisfies

$$\text{div grad } g = 0$$

except at $\mathbf{R} = 0$.

6. If $\mathbf{v}$ is the linear velocity of a point on a rigid body, show that

$$\text{div } \mathbf{v} = 0.$$

7. If

$$\text{div } \mathbf{E} = \rho_v$$

where $\rho_v = 6x^2y + 3z$, give all the possible expressions for $\mathbf{E}$.

7

The Curl of a Vector Field

7.1 Introduction

In addition to the divergence of a vector field, there is another very important property of a vector field: its "curl," which also describes the spatial rate of change of a vector field. We shall first discuss the curl of a vector field in physical terms and delay the more mathematical treatment of this field property until the latter portion of this chapter. The curl of a vector field is related to the circulation of that field, and therefore before treating the curl let us first discuss the circulation of a field. We shall see in this chapter and in Chapters 11 and 12 that for certain vector fields the curl at any point, like the divergence, may be considered as a measure of a vector "source" or "sink" strength at that point.

7.2 The Circulation of a Vector Field

The scalar product line integral over a closed path Γ, discussed previously, is a scalar which is given a special name, the circulation, C of the vector field $\mathbf{F}$ around the closed curve Γ, that is, (see Fig. 7.1)

$$C = \oint_{\Gamma} \mathbf{F} \cdot d\mathbf{l} \tag{7.1}$$

The circulation is a scalar quantity which in certain instances has an obvious interpretation. For example, if $\mathbf{F}$ is a force field, the circulation of $\mathbf{F}$ represents the work done in moving along a prescribed closed path in the region of space where $\mathbf{F}$ exists. In most cases, however, the circulation of $\mathbf{F}$ can be thought of as a result of the processes described in connection with Eq. (3.72),

$$\oint_{\Gamma} \mathbf{F} \cdot d\mathbf{l} = \lim_{N \to \infty} \sum_{j=1}^{N} \mathbf{F}_j \cdot \Delta \mathbf{l}_j \tag{7.2}$$

Another aspect of the circulation integral may be seen by again considering

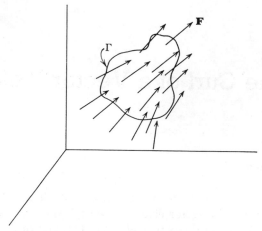

Figure 7.1   An illustration of the circulation of a vector field around a curve Γ.

F as a force field. Then $\langle F \rangle_{\tan_\Gamma}$, the average value of the magnitude of the component of the force acting along Γ is the total work done in moving around Γ divided by the path length, the length of the closed path Γ,

$$\langle F \rangle_{\tan_\Gamma} = \lim_{N \to \infty} \frac{\sum_{j=1}^{N} \mathbf{F}_j \cdot \Delta \mathbf{l}}{\sum_{j=1}^{N} |\Delta \mathbf{l}|} = \frac{\oint_\Gamma \mathbf{F} \cdot d\mathbf{l}}{\oint_\Gamma |d\mathbf{l}|} = \frac{1}{L} \oint_\Gamma \mathbf{F} \cdot d\mathbf{l} \qquad (7.3)$$

where $\langle F \rangle_{\tan_\Gamma}$ is the average value of the magnitude of the tangential component of the force field around the path Γ whose length is $\oint_\Gamma |d\mathbf{l}| = L$. In this we see that the circulation integral of a field **F** around a closed curve Γ is just the average value of the magnitude of tangential component of **F** along Γ multiplied by L, the length of Γ,

$$\langle F \rangle_{\tan_\Gamma} L = \oint_\Gamma \mathbf{F} \cdot d\mathbf{l} \qquad (7.4)$$

Let us consider the circulation of a vector field **F** when a field line which is a closed curve is also the path of integration (see Fig. 7.2), then if the direction of integration is in the field direction, $\mathbf{F} \cdot d\mathbf{l}$ is always positive and the circulation is always greater than zero. Many vector fields whose field lines do not form closed curves also have circulations which are greater than zero. An illustration of this can be seen by considering the straight line field shown in Fig. 7.3. The circulation of such a field along a square path in the direction indicated is not zero as may be seen from the

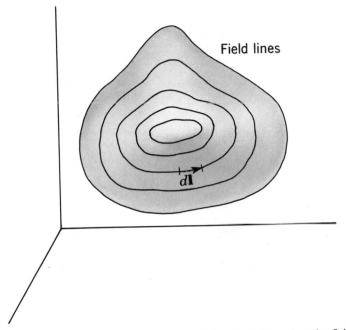

Figure 7.2 An illustration for the calculation of the circulation when the field lines and the path of integration are coincident.

following discussion. The closed line integral may be divided into line integrals over equal path length from points 1 to 2, 2 to 3, 3 to 4, and 4 back to 1,

$$\oint_\Gamma \mathbf{F} \cdot d\mathbf{l} = \int_1^2 \mathbf{F} \cdot d\mathbf{l} + \int_2^3 \mathbf{F} \cdot d\mathbf{l} + \int_3^4 \mathbf{F} \cdot d\mathbf{l} + \int_4^1 \mathbf{F} \cdot d\mathbf{l} \qquad (7.5)$$

where $d\mathbf{l}$, along the path from 3 to 4 has a sense which is

opposite to that of $d\mathbf{l}$ along the path from 1 to 2, and
$d\mathbf{l}$, along the path from 4 to 1, has the opposite sense of
$d\mathbf{l}$ along the path from 2 to 3.

If $\mathbf{F}$ is perpendicular to paths 2 to 3 and 4 to 1 (see Fig. 7.3), then the integrals

$$\int_2^3 \mathbf{F} \cdot d\mathbf{l} \qquad \text{and} \qquad \int_4^1 \mathbf{F} \cdot d\mathbf{l} \qquad (7.6)$$

are zero. If, as is shown in Fig. 7.3, the field is more intense along path 1 to 2 than along 3 to 4, the circulation will be greater than zero.

$$\int_1^2 \mathbf{F}_{12} \cdot d\mathbf{l} + \int_3^4 \mathbf{F}_{34} \cdot d\mathbf{l} = \int_1^2 |\mathbf{F}_{12}| \, |d\mathbf{l}| - \int_3^4 |\mathbf{F}_{34}| \, |d\mathbf{l}| > 0 \qquad (7.7)$$

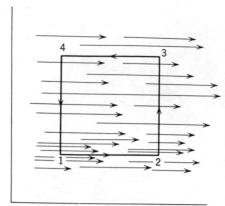

Figure 7.3   An example of the situation when the circulation is not zero.

Clearly, then, the circulation can be greater than zero even though the field lines are straight.

As an example of the evaluation of the circulation of a field, consider the circulation of the two-dimensional field $\mathbf{G}$ given by

$$\mathbf{G} = \mathbf{u}_\rho \rho \cos \theta + \mathbf{u}_\theta \frac{\sin^2 \theta}{\rho^2} \tag{7.8}$$

along a path which is a circle of radius R whose center is located at the origin (see Fig. 7.4). On such a path the field is

$$\mathbf{G}_{\text{circle}} = \mathbf{u}_\rho R \cos \theta + \mathbf{u}_\theta \frac{\sin^2 \theta}{R^2} \tag{7.9}$$

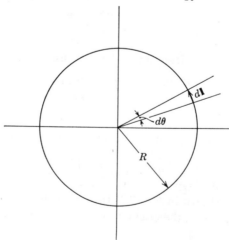

Figure 7.4   For the calculation of the circulation when the path of integration is a circle.

Then since $d\mathbf{l}$, an element of the circumference of the circle, is given by $\mathbf{u}_\theta R\, d\theta$, then

$$\mathbf{G} \cdot d\mathbf{l} = \frac{\sin^2 \theta}{R}\, d\theta \tag{7.10}$$

so that the circulation is

$$\oint_\Gamma \mathbf{G} \cdot d\mathbf{l} = \int_0^{2\pi} \frac{\sin^2 \theta}{R}\, d\theta = \frac{\pi}{R} \tag{7.11}$$

Equation (7.11) implies that the average value of the magnitude of the tangential component of $\mathbf{G}$ along the circle is $1/2R^2$, that is, $\pi/R \div 2\pi R$.

It can be correctly inferred from this example that the value of the circulation of a vector field along a path depends on the length, shape, size of the surface enclosed, the orientation of the space curve Γ in the field and the nature of the field.

7.3   The Curl of a Vector Field

Let us now apply the foregoing concept of field circulation to an arbitrary but small curve enclosing an element of surface $d\mathbf{s}$ on which a point P resides. Here, as before, the area enclosed by the curve is so small that it may be considered a plane and hence can be represented as a vector $d\mathbf{s} = \mathbf{u}_n\, |d\mathbf{s}|$ where $\mathbf{u}_n$, a normal to the surface element, serves to orient the plane of the curve γ, which is the periphery of $d\mathbf{s}$ (see Fig. 7.5).

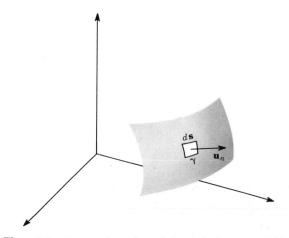

Figure 7.5   For the discussion of the curl of a vector field.

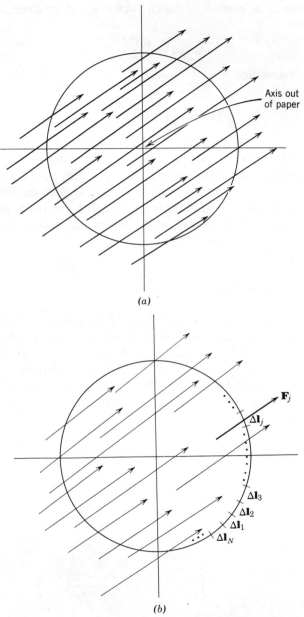

(a)

(b)

Figure 7.6   (a) For the discussion of a physical interpretation of the curl. (b) For the discussion of a physical interpretation of the curl. (c) When the flow is symmetric around a symmetric body the curl is zero. (d) An asymmetric flow can give rise to a rotation.

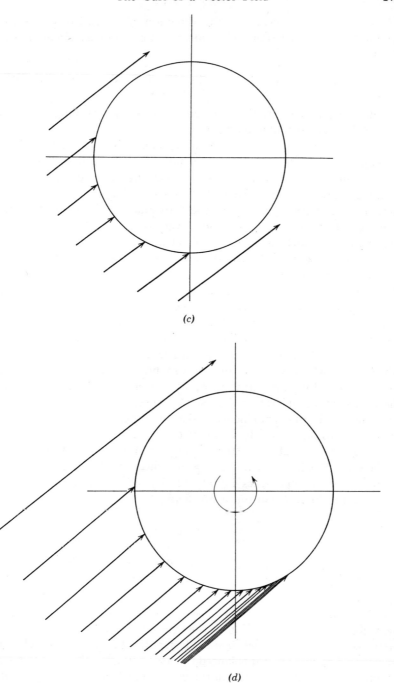

(c)

(d)

We define the component in the $\mathbf{u}_n$ direction of the curl of $\mathbf{F}$ at P to be the limit as $|\Delta\mathbf{s}| \to 0$ (so that γ shrinks down on P) of the circulation of $\mathbf{F}$ divided by $|\Delta\mathbf{s}|$.

$$\text{curl } \mathbf{F} \cdot \mathbf{u}_n = \lim_{\Delta s \to 0} \frac{1}{|\Delta\mathbf{s}|} \oint_\gamma \mathbf{F} \cdot d\mathbf{l} \qquad (7.12)$$

We assume here that γ is well-behaved as $\Delta s \to 0$, for example, γ does not approach a curve of infinite length.

To illustrate how the curl of a vector field manifests itself, let us consider a two-dimensional flow pattern of a fluid. We have seen that the net flow of fluid out of a small volume is a measure of the divergence of the fluid mass flow. If, instead, we now wish to examine the ability of the fluid to exert a net torque on a symmetric body placed in it, that is, the ability to cause a body to spin, let us place a very small bicycle wheel in a two-dimensional stream (see Fig. 7.6a). To idealize this situation let us assume that the bicycle wheel is also two-dimensional and composed of a rim which lies in the plane of the fluid and an axle which is normal to that plane. If the wheel, whose initial angular velocity is zero, is to start spinning about the axle, the fluid must exert a net torque on the wheel. Since the action of the torque to spin the wheel results from forces acting through the same center of rotation, the center of the wheel, and at the same distance from the center of rotation, the wheel radius, the question as to whether the wheel will start to spin can be resolved by examining the forces acting along the periphery of the wheel. We must therefore sum the forces acting at every point on the wheel periphery which tend to spin the wheel—the components of the forces acting on the wheel which are tangent to the wheel. If we divide the wheel into N small elements of length $\Delta\mathbf{l}_1, \Delta\mathbf{l}_2, \ldots \Delta\mathbf{l}_j, \ldots, \Delta\mathbf{l}_N$ (see Fig. 7.6b), then $\mathbf{F}_j \cdot \Delta\mathbf{l}_j$ is a measure of the force $\mathbf{F}_j$ which is acting along the wheel at $\Delta\mathbf{l}_j$. The sum of these quantities as N approaches infinity so that all the $\Delta\mathbf{l}$'s approach zero is called the *circulation* of the vector field,

$$\lim_{N \to \infty} \sum_{j=1}^{N} \mathbf{F}_j \cdot \Delta\mathbf{l}_j \equiv \oint_\Gamma \mathbf{F}_j \cdot d\mathbf{l}_j \qquad (7.13)$$

where the line integral is taken around the periphery of the wheel. This integral is then seen to be a measure of the tangential forces acting to spin the wheel.

If the fluid flow as shown in Fig. 7.6c is symmetrically distributed about the wheel in the direction of flow, the wheel will not start to spin because the forces acting on the left-hand side tending to spin the wheel in the clockwise direction are just balanced by those acting on the right-hand side attempting to rotate the wheel in the counterclockwise direction. Such a field is said to have no curl. If, on the other hand, the flow is not symmetric at this point, it will exert more force on one side than on the other (see Fig. 7.6*d*) and the wheel will start to turn about its axle. Such a field has a curl at this point. Note particularly that the curl of a field manifests itself by turning the wheel about its axle, along which can be represented the angular velocity vector normal to the fluid flow.

To determine what mathematical manipulations we must perform to measure the curl of a field and to obtain a more quantitative concept of the meaning of the curl of a vector field, we must evaluate the closed line integral we called the field circulation, Eq. (7.13). Let $P(x_0 y_0)$ be a point in a vector field at which we wish to ascertain the value of the field's curl. For simplicity, assume that, Γ, the path of integration around P, is a small square (see Fig. 7.7) whose sides are parallel to the coordinate axes. The sides of the square are vectors $\Delta \mathbf{x}$, $\Delta \mathbf{y}$, $-\Delta \mathbf{x}$, and $-\Delta \mathbf{y}$. If the path is followed according to the counterclockwise direction indicated by the arrows in Fig. 7.7, the circulation of a vector field $\mathbf{F}(x, y)$ at the point $P(x_0 y_0)$ is

$$\oint_{\Gamma} \mathbf{F} \cdot d\mathbf{l} = \int_{1}^{2} \mathbf{F} \cdot d\mathbf{l} + \int_{2}^{3} \mathbf{F} \cdot d\mathbf{l} + \int_{3}^{4} \mathbf{F} \cdot d\mathbf{l} + \int_{4}^{1} \mathbf{F} \cdot d\mathbf{l} \qquad (7.14)$$

We shall assume that the distance from 1 to 2 is so short that over this distance the vector field is constant and that this constant value is the value of $\mathbf{F}$ at the midpoint between 1 and 2. Similar assumptions will be made

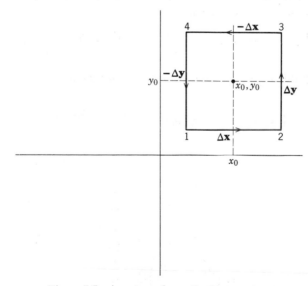

Figure 7.7   A rectangular path of integration.

concerning the value of $\mathbf{F}$ on the path 2 to 3, etc.; then Eq. (7.14) becomes

$$\oint_\Gamma \mathbf{F} \cdot d\mathbf{l} = \mathbf{F}\left(x_0,\ y_0 - \frac{\Delta y}{2}\right) \cdot \int_1^2 d\mathbf{l} + \mathbf{F}\left(x_0 + \frac{\Delta x}{2},\ y_0\right) \cdot \int_2^3 d\mathbf{l}$$

$$+ \mathbf{F}\left(x_0,\ y_0 + \frac{\Delta y}{2}\right) \cdot \int_3^4 d\mathbf{l} + \mathbf{F}\left(x_0 - \frac{\Delta x}{2},\ y_0\right) \cdot \int_4^1 d\mathbf{l} \quad (7.15)$$

However, the integral $\int_1^2 d\mathbf{l}$ is the vector $\Delta\mathbf{x}$ representing the displacement from 1 to 2. Similarly,

$$\Delta\mathbf{y} = \int_2^3 d\mathbf{l}, \qquad -\Delta\mathbf{x} = \int_3^4 d\mathbf{l} \qquad \text{and} \qquad -\Delta\mathbf{y} = \int_4^1 d\mathbf{l} \quad (7.16)$$

so that Eq. (7.15) becomes

$$\oint_\Gamma \mathbf{F} \cdot d\mathbf{l} = F_x\left(x_0,\ y_0 - \frac{\Delta y}{2}\right) \Delta x + F_y\left(x_0 + \frac{\Delta x}{2},\ y_0\right) \Delta y$$

$$- F_x\left(x_0,\ y_0 + \frac{\Delta y}{2}\right) \Delta x - F_y\left(x_0 - \frac{\Delta x}{2},\ y_0\right) \Delta y \quad (7.17)$$

If Δx and Δy are small, in other words, if the point (x, y) lies very close to (x_0, y_0), we can expand F_x and F_y in a Taylor series about the point (x_0, y_0). Then, by analogy with the procedure used in conjunction with Eq. (6.16) we neglect higher order terms so that any differentiable function of two variables may be written

$$f(x, y) = f(x_0, y_0) + \frac{\partial f}{\partial x}\bigg|_{(x_0, y_0)} \Delta x + \frac{\partial f}{\partial y}\bigg|_{(x_0, y_0)} \Delta y \quad (7.18)$$

Applying this type of expansion to the components of $\mathbf{F}$, we may write (7.17) as

$$\oint_\Gamma \mathbf{F} \cdot d\mathbf{l} = \left[F_x(x_0, y_0) - \frac{\partial F_x}{\partial y}\bigg|_{(x_0, y_0)} \frac{\Delta y}{2}\right] \Delta x$$

$$+ \left[F_y(x_0, y_0) + \frac{\partial F_y}{\partial x}\bigg|_{(x_0, y_0)} \frac{\Delta x}{2}\right] \Delta y$$

$$- \left[F_x(x_0, y_0) + \frac{\partial F_x}{\partial y}\bigg|_{(x_0, y_0)} \frac{\Delta y}{2}\right] \Delta x$$

$$- \left[F_y(x_0, y_0) - \frac{\partial F_y}{\partial x}\bigg|_{(x_0, y_0)} \frac{\Delta x}{2}\right] \Delta y$$

$$= \left(\frac{\partial F_y}{\partial x} - \frac{\partial F_x}{\partial y}\right) \Delta x\, \Delta y \quad (7.19)$$

In the limit, as the path Γ shrinks down on the point P, Eq. (7.19) becomes

$$\oint_\Gamma \mathbf{F} \cdot d\mathbf{l} = \left(\frac{\partial F_y}{\partial x} - \frac{\partial F_x}{\partial y}\right) dx\, dy = \left(\frac{\partial F_y}{\partial x} - \frac{\partial F_x}{\partial y}\right) |d\mathbf{s}_z| \qquad (7.20)$$

where $|d\mathbf{s}_z| = dx\, dy$ is the magnitude of the small area enclosed by Γ on the plane $z = 0$. Equation (7.20) can be written

$$\oint_\Gamma \mathbf{F} \cdot d\mathbf{l} = \left[\mathbf{u}_z\left(\frac{\partial F_y}{\partial x} - \frac{\partial F_x}{\partial y}\right)\right] \cdot d\mathbf{s}_z \qquad (7.21)$$

or

$$\frac{1}{|d\mathbf{s}_z|} \oint_\Gamma \mathbf{F} \cdot d\mathbf{l} = \left[\mathbf{u}_z\left(\frac{\partial F_y}{\partial x} - \frac{\partial F_x}{\partial y}\right)\right] \cdot \mathbf{u}_z$$

$$= |(\text{curl } \mathbf{F})_z| \qquad (7.22)$$

Equation (7.22) is thus the magnitude of the z-component of the curl of $\mathbf{F}$. In the above discussion, $\mathbf{u}_z$ is, of course, the unit vector $\mathbf{u}_n$ in Eq. (7.12).

Then the curl of a vector field is a point property of the field that is itself a vector field whose component at a point in a particular direction is the circulation of the field around a curve which is the periphery of an infinitesimally small area lying in a plane normal to that direction.

If $\mathbf{F}$ is a force field, the magnitude and the direction of the curl of $\mathbf{F}$ at a point P are a measure of the torque on or the angular acceleration of an infinitesimally small ball placed at P. The axis of rotation of the ball is the direction and sense of the curl (using the right-hand rule).

In three dimensions the curl of a vector field expressed in Cartesian coordinates is

$$\text{curl } \mathbf{F} = \mathbf{u}_x\left(\frac{\partial F_z}{\partial y} - \frac{\partial F_y}{\partial z}\right) + \mathbf{u}_y\left(\frac{\partial F_x}{\partial z} - \frac{\partial F_z}{\partial x}\right) + \mathbf{u}_z\left(\frac{\partial F_y}{\partial x} - \frac{\partial F_x}{\partial y}\right) \qquad (7.23)$$

or in matrix notation

$$\text{curl } \mathbf{F} = \begin{vmatrix} \mathbf{u}_x & \mathbf{u}_y & \mathbf{u}_z \\ \dfrac{\partial}{\partial x} & \dfrac{\partial}{\partial y} & \dfrac{\partial}{\partial z} \\ F_x & F_y & F_z \end{vmatrix} \qquad (7.24)$$

Another physical interpretation of this important field property may be obtained by considering the vortex motion of a fluid. To describe the vortex mathematically, let us assume that every point of the field is moving with a constant angular velocity $\boldsymbol{\omega}$ about an axis through some origin (see Fig. 7.8). The angular velocity may be written

$$\boldsymbol{\omega} = \mathbf{u}_x\omega_x + \mathbf{u}_y\omega_y + \mathbf{u}_z\omega_z \qquad (7.25)$$

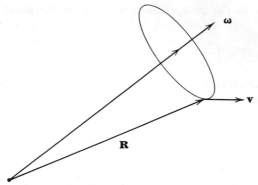

Figure 7.8   For the discussion of the relation between the curl and angular velocity of a fluid.

Utilizing the results of Section 2.3, p. 38, we may describe the linear velocity $\mathbf{v}$ at any point P in the fluid as

$$\mathbf{v} = \boldsymbol{\omega} \times \mathbf{R} \qquad [\text{Eq. (2.36)}] \qquad (7.26)$$

where $\mathbf{R} = \mathbf{u}_x x + \mathbf{u}_y y + \mathbf{u}_z z$ is the vector locating the point P. We shall see in Chapter 8 [Eq. (8.22)] that the curl of the vector product of two vectors, $\mathbf{C}$ a constant and $\mathbf{F}$ a vector, is given by

$$\text{curl } \mathbf{C} \times \mathbf{F} = \mathbf{C} \text{ div } \mathbf{F} - (\mathbf{C} \cdot \text{grad})\mathbf{F} \qquad (7.27)$$

Since $\boldsymbol{\omega}$ is a constant, the curl of the linear velocity is

$$\text{curl } \mathbf{v} = \text{curl}\,(\boldsymbol{\omega} \times \mathbf{R})$$
$$= \boldsymbol{\omega}(\text{div } \mathbf{R}) - (\boldsymbol{\omega} \cdot \text{grad})\mathbf{R} \qquad (7.28)$$

In Section 6.3 we showed that div $\mathbf{R} = 3$ [Eq. (6.30)] and the last term in Eq. (7.28) can be written

$$[\boldsymbol{\omega} \cdot \text{grad}]\mathbf{R} = \left(\omega_x \frac{\partial}{\partial x} + \omega_y \frac{\partial}{\partial y} + \omega_z \frac{\partial}{\partial z} \right)(\mathbf{u}_x x + \mathbf{u}_y y + \mathbf{u}_z z)$$
$$= \mathbf{u}_x \omega_x + \mathbf{u}_y \omega_y + \mathbf{u}_z \omega_z = \boldsymbol{\omega}$$

so that Eq. (7.28) is

$$\text{curl } \mathbf{v} = 2\boldsymbol{\omega} \qquad (7.29)$$

We see therefore that the curl of a vector field which represents the vortex motion of a fluid is twice the angular velocity of the fluid.

There is an integral expression for the curl of a vector field which also gives an insight into the physical meaning of the curl:

$$\text{curl } \mathbf{F} = \lim_{\Delta V \to 0} \frac{1}{\Delta V} \oiint_a \mathbf{u}_n \times \mathbf{F}\, ds \qquad (7.30)$$

where ΔV is a small volume whose surface is a; an element of a is $d\mathbf{s} = \mathbf{u}_n |d\mathbf{s}| = \mathbf{u}_n \, ds$ (see Fig. 7.9). Here we assume that the surface whose area is a is well-behaved as ΔV approaches zero.

To show that the relationship for the curl given by Eq. (7.30) is valid, let us resolve it into its component form:

$$\text{curl } \mathbf{F} = \mathbf{u}_x \lim_{\Delta V \to 0} \frac{1}{\Delta V} \oiint_a \mathbf{u}_x \cdot (\mathbf{u}_n \times \mathbf{F}) \, ds$$

$$+ \mathbf{u}_y \lim_{\Delta V \to 0} \frac{1}{\Delta V} \oiint_a \mathbf{u}_y \cdot (\mathbf{u}_n \times \mathbf{F}) \, ds$$

$$+ \mathbf{u}_z \lim_{\Delta V \to 0} \frac{1}{\Delta V} \oiint_a \mathbf{u}_z \cdot (\mathbf{u}_n \cdot \mathbf{F}) \, ds \qquad (7.31)$$

Since $\mathbf{u}_x \cdot \mathbf{u}_n \times \mathbf{F} = \mathbf{u}_n \cdot \mathbf{F} \times \mathbf{u}_x$, Eq. (7.31) becomes

$$\text{curl } \mathbf{F} = \mathbf{u}_x \lim_{\Delta V \to 0} \frac{1}{\Delta V} \oiint_a \mathbf{u}_n \cdot (\mathbf{F} \times \mathbf{u}_x) \, ds$$

$$+ \mathbf{u}_y \lim_{\Delta V \to 0} \frac{1}{\Delta V} \oiint_a \mathbf{u}_n \cdot (\mathbf{F} \times \mathbf{u}_y) \, ds$$

$$+ \mathbf{u}_z \lim_{\Delta V \to 0} \frac{1}{\Delta V} \oiint_a \mathbf{u}_n \cdot (\mathbf{F} \times \mathbf{u}_z) \, ds \qquad (7.32)$$

Comparing the magnitudes of the components of Eq. (7.32) with the corresponding terms of Eq. (6.31) where the vector field $\mathbf{F}$ in Eq. (6.31)

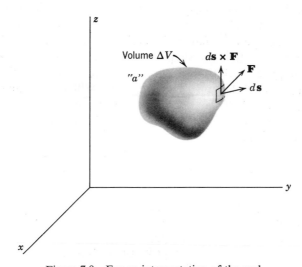

Figure 7.9   For an interpretation of the curl.

corresponds to the vector fields $\mathbf{F} \times \mathbf{u}_x$, $\mathbf{F} \times \mathbf{u}_y$, or $\mathbf{F} \times \mathbf{u}_z$ in Eq. (7.32), we may write Eq. (7.32) as

$$\mathbf{u}_x \operatorname{div} (\mathbf{F} \times \mathbf{u}_x) + \mathbf{u}_y \operatorname{div} (\mathbf{F} \times \mathbf{u}_y) + \mathbf{u}_z \operatorname{div} (\mathbf{F} \times \mathbf{u}_z) \qquad (7.33)$$

However,

$$\mathbf{u}_x \operatorname{div} (\mathbf{F} \times \mathbf{u}_x) = \mathbf{u}_x \operatorname{div} (\mathbf{u}_y F_z - \mathbf{u}_z F_y) = \mathbf{u}_x \left(\frac{\partial F_z}{\partial y} - \frac{\partial F_y}{\partial z} \right) \qquad (7.34a)$$

$$\mathbf{u}_y \operatorname{div} (\mathbf{F} \times \mathbf{u}_y) = \mathbf{u}_y \operatorname{div} (\mathbf{u}_z F_x - \mathbf{u}_x F_z) = \mathbf{u}_y \left(\frac{\partial F_x}{\partial z} - \frac{\partial F_z}{\partial x} \right) \qquad (7.34b)$$

and

$$\mathbf{u}_z \operatorname{div} (\mathbf{F} \times \mathbf{u}_z) = \mathbf{u}_z \operatorname{div} (\mathbf{u}_x F_y - \mathbf{u}_y F_x) = \mathbf{u}_z \left(\frac{\partial F_y}{\partial x} - \frac{\partial F_x}{\partial y} \right) \qquad (7.34c)$$

so that Eq. (7.30) is equivalent to Eq. (7.23) or (7.24), that is,

$$\operatorname{curl} \mathbf{F} = \lim_{\Delta V \to 0} \frac{1}{\Delta V} \oiint_a \mathbf{u}_n \times \mathbf{F} \, ds$$

$$= \mathbf{u}_x \left(\frac{\partial F_z}{\partial y} - \frac{\partial F_y}{\partial z} \right) + \mathbf{u}_y \left(\frac{\partial F_x}{\partial z} - \frac{\partial F_z}{\partial x} \right) + \mathbf{u}_z \left(\frac{\partial F_y}{\partial x} - \frac{\partial F_x}{\partial y} \right) \qquad (7.35)$$

Equation (7.35) may be approximated by

$$\operatorname{curl} \mathbf{F} = \frac{1}{dV} \oiint_a \mathbf{u}_n \times \mathbf{F} \, |ds| \qquad (7.36)$$

where the difference between Eqs. (7.35) and (7.36) can be made as small as possible by choosing dV as small as the limiting process requires.

We shall conclude this chapter by deriving Eq. (7.12) from Eq. (7.36). To do so, we recall that the shape of the element of volume dV in Eq. (7.36) is completely arbitrary. We choose dV to be a right cylinder. An area element of the top of this cylinder will be designated $ds_T = \mathbf{u}_{n_T} |ds_T|$ (see Fig. 7.10) and of the bottom $ds_B = \mathbf{u}_{n_B} |ds_B|$, where $ds_B = -ds_T$. $ds_S = \mathbf{u}_{n_S} |ds_S|$ is an element of the cylinder side; the altitude of the cylinder is ϵ.

If $ds = \mathbf{u}_n |ds|$ in Eq. (7.12) is an element of the top, the scalar product of Eq. (7.36) with $\mathbf{u}_n$ is (since $\mathbf{u}_{n_T} \times \mathbf{F}$ is normal to $\mathbf{u}_{n_T}$)

$$\mathbf{u}_n \cdot \operatorname{curl} \mathbf{F} = \frac{1}{dV} \iint_{\text{sides}} \mathbf{u}_n \cdot (\mathbf{u}_{n_S} \times \mathbf{F}) \, |ds_S|$$

$$= \frac{1}{dV} \iint_{\text{sides}} \mathbf{F} \cdot (\mathbf{u}_n \times \mathbf{u}_{n_S}) \, |ds_S| \qquad (7.37)$$

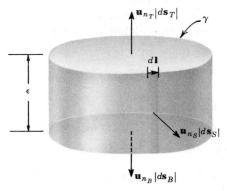

Figure 7.10   Figure for the discussion of an interpretation of the curl.

Since $|ds_S| = \epsilon |dl|$ (see Fig. 7.10), where dl is an element of the curve γ, which is the periphery of the top of the cylinder, and since $\mathbf{u}_{n_T} \times \mathbf{u}_{n_S} = \mathbf{u}_l$, where $\mathbf{u}_l$ is a unit vector in the dl direction (see Fig. 7.10), we may write Eq. (7.37) as

$$\mathbf{u}_n \cdot \operatorname{curl} \mathbf{F} = \frac{1}{dV} \iint_{\text{sides}} \mathbf{F} \cdot \mathbf{u}_l \, |ds_S| = \frac{\epsilon}{dV} \oint_{\gamma} \mathbf{F} \cdot \mathbf{u}_l \, |dl| \qquad (7.38)$$

However, the volume of a right cylinder is the area of the base multiplied by the altitude so that $|ds_T| = |ds_B| = \dfrac{dV}{\epsilon} = |ds|$; thus Eq. (7.38) becomes

$$\mathbf{u}_n \cdot \operatorname{curl} \mathbf{F} = \frac{1}{|ds|} \oint_{\gamma} \mathbf{F} \cdot d\mathbf{l} \qquad (7.39)$$

In Chapter 6 it was demonstrated that the divergence of a vector field at a point is a measure of the net *normal* component of the field passing out through the surface of an infinitesimal volume surrounding that point. We argued further that if the divergence were nonzero at some point, a source (or sink) must be located there. It seemed reasonable then to associate the divergence of a field with the sources (or sinks) of that field.

We have shown in this chapter that the curl of a vector field at a point is a measure of the net *tangential* component of the field along the surface of an infinitesimal volume surrounding that point. By analogy with our discussion of the divergence, we conclude that if the curl of a field is nonzero at a point, "something" must be there which gives rise to the field. Thus we are led to the idea that the curl of a field, like the divergence, represents a field source (or sink) density.

Sources associated with the divergence of a field are fundamentally different from sources associated with the curl. However, these two classes of sources give rise to all the fields we shall consider. This important subject will be treated in more detail in Chapters 11 and 12.

PROBLEMS

1. Find the curl of the vector field

$$\mathbf{F} = \mathbf{u}_x[y^2 + 2z] + \mathbf{u}_y[xy + 6z] + \mathbf{u}_z[z^2 + 2xz + y]$$

2. $\mathbf{F}$ is a vector field, and g and h are any scalar fields; then if $g\mathbf{F} = \nabla h$, show that $\mathbf{F} \cdot \text{curl } \mathbf{F} = 0$.

3. If $\mathbf{F}_x = \cos y$ and $\mathbf{F}_y = 0$, sketch the field lines for $\mathbf{F}$ and determine the divergence and curl of $\mathbf{F}$.

4. If $\mathbf{R}_1$ and $\mathbf{R}_2$ are position vectors locating a point $P(x, y, z)$ from two different fixed locations, determine the value of

$$\text{curl } [\mathbf{R}_1 \times \mathbf{R}_2].$$

5. If $\mathbf{A}$ is any vector and $\mathbf{R}$ is the position vector, show that

$$(\mathbf{A} \times \text{curl}) \times \mathbf{R} = -2\mathbf{A}$$

6. If
$$\text{curl } \mathbf{F} = \mathbf{K}_S$$
and
$$\mathbf{K}_S = \mathbf{u}_z 6z$$

give all the possible expressions for $\mathbf{F}$.

8

Differential Field Operators

8.1 Introduction

In the preceding three chapters we have discussed the more important differential field properties: the gradient, divergence, and curl. Although in certain instances it was necessary for illustrative purposes to introduce a particular coordinate system, it was emphasized that such field properties are fundamental to the field and completely independent of the coordinate system in which the field is expressed. These differential field properties are extremely important in science and engineering, and the mathematical operations necessary to ascertain their value must be performed with considerable frequency. Consequently, a shorthand notation has been developed to denote the mathematical manipulations which must be carried out on the analytic expression representing the field to obtain the desired field property. It follows that since the operations necessary to determine a differential field property depend on the coordinate system in which the field is represented, the symbolic form of the differential field operators depends on the coordinate system employed.

In this chapter we shall introduce differential field operators and discuss their form and properties in Cartesian coordinates. We shall defer generalizing the results of this chapter for any orthogonal coordinate systems until Chapter 10, where they can be treated more succinctly by means of the material presented in Chapter 9.

8.2 The Operator ∇ When the Fields Involved Are Expressed in Cartesian Coordinates

The expressions for the gradient of a scalar field as well as the divergence and curl of a vector field can be written succinctly by employing the symbol ∇, called "del" or "nabla," which, when employed with fields

189

expressed in Cartesian coordinates, is defined by

$$\nabla \equiv \mathbf{u}_x \frac{\partial}{\partial x} + \mathbf{u}_y \frac{\partial}{\partial y} + \mathbf{u}_z \frac{\partial}{\partial z} \tag{8.1}$$

By employing this symbol, the gradient of a scalar field $h(x, y, z)$ is written (see Eq. 5.17)

$$\begin{aligned}
\text{grad } h &\equiv \nabla h \\
&= \left\{ \mathbf{u}_x \frac{\partial}{\partial x} + \mathbf{u}_y \frac{\partial}{\partial y} + \mathbf{u}_z \frac{\partial}{\partial z} \right\} h \\
&= \mathbf{u}_x \frac{\partial h}{\partial x} + \mathbf{u}_y \frac{\partial h}{\partial y} + \mathbf{u}_z \frac{\partial h}{\partial z}
\end{aligned} \tag{8.2}$$

We see that the symbol ∇, defined in Eq. (8.1), when operating on an expression describing a scalar field in Cartesian coordinates, transforms that expression into a vector field which is the gradient of the scalar field.

To emphasize the fact that the form of the differential field operator ∇ depends on the coordinate system involved, we state here that from Eq. (8.1) we *cannot* conclude that the same form for ∇ holds in cylindrical or spherical coordinates, that is,

$$\nabla_{\text{cyl}} \neq \mathbf{u}_\rho \frac{\partial}{\partial \rho} + \mathbf{u}_\theta \frac{\partial}{\partial \theta} + \mathbf{u}_z \frac{\partial}{\partial z}$$

and

$$\nabla_{\text{sph}} \neq \mathbf{u}_r \frac{\partial}{\partial r} + \mathbf{u}_\theta \frac{\partial}{\partial \theta} + \mathbf{u}_\phi \frac{\partial}{\partial \phi}$$

Later we shall see what form ∇ takes in each of these two coordinate systems.

By utilizing the symbol ∇, the divergence of a vector field $\mathbf{F}(x, y, z) = \mathbf{u}_x F_x(x, y, z) + \mathbf{u}_y F_y(x, y, z) + \mathbf{u}_z F_z(x, y, z)$ may be written

$$\begin{aligned}
\text{div } \mathbf{F} &\equiv \nabla \cdot \mathbf{F} \\
&= \left(\mathbf{u}_x \frac{\partial}{\partial x} + \mathbf{u}_y \frac{\partial}{\partial y} + \mathbf{u}_z \frac{\partial}{\partial z} \right) \cdot (\mathbf{u}_x F_x + \mathbf{u}_y F_y + \mathbf{u}_z F_z) \\
&= \frac{\partial F_x}{\partial x} + \frac{\partial F_y}{\partial y} + \frac{\partial F_z}{\partial z}
\end{aligned} \tag{8.3}$$

We see that when considering a vector field written in terms of its Cartesian components, the symbol $\nabla \cdot$ transforms the expression for the vector field into an expression representing a scalar field that is the divergence of the given vector field.

Similarly, the curl of a vector field

$$\mathbf{F}(x, y, z) = \mathbf{u}_x F_x(x, y, z) + \mathbf{u}_y F_y(x, y, z) + \mathbf{u}_z F_z(x, y, z)$$

becomes

$$\text{curl } \mathbf{F} \equiv \nabla \times \mathbf{F}$$

$$= \left(\mathbf{u}_x \frac{\partial}{\partial x} + \mathbf{u}_y \frac{\partial}{\partial y} + \mathbf{u}_z \frac{\partial}{\partial z}\right) \times (\mathbf{u}_x F_x + \mathbf{u}_y F_y + \mathbf{u}_z F_z)$$

$$= \mathbf{u}_x\left(\frac{\partial F_z}{\partial y} - \frac{\partial F_y}{\partial z}\right) + \mathbf{u}_y\left(\frac{\partial F_x}{\partial z} - \frac{\partial F_z}{\partial x}\right) + \mathbf{u}_z\left(\frac{\partial F_y}{\partial x} - \frac{\partial F_x}{\partial y}\right) \quad (8.4)$$

Equation (8.4) shows that the symbol $\nabla\times$ can be considered an operator which transforms the expression representing a vector field into one representing a vector field which is the curl of the given field.

In addition to the three field properties discussed, there are two additional field characteristics that may be determined by operations which can be succinctly written using the symbol ∇: the directional derivative and the Laplacian.

The spatial rate of change of a scalar field $g(x, y, z)$ in a particular direction $d\mathbf{l}$ is given by [see Eq. (5.22)]

$$\frac{dg}{|d\mathbf{l}|} = (\mathbf{u}_l \cdot \nabla g)$$

$$= \frac{\partial g}{\partial x} \mathbf{u}_l \cdot \mathbf{u}_x + \frac{\partial g}{\partial y} \mathbf{u}_l \cdot \mathbf{u}_y + \frac{\partial g}{\partial z} \mathbf{u}_l \cdot \mathbf{u}_z$$

$$= \frac{\partial g}{\partial x} \cos [d\mathbf{l}, d\mathbf{x}] + \frac{\partial g}{\partial y} \cos [d\mathbf{l}, d\mathbf{y}] + \frac{\partial g}{\partial z} \cos [d\mathbf{l}, d\mathbf{z}] \quad (8.5)$$

where $\mathbf{u}_l$ is a unit vector in the $d\mathbf{l}$ direction,

$$\mathbf{u}_l \equiv \frac{d\mathbf{l}}{|d\mathbf{l}|}$$

and $\cos [d\mathbf{l}, d\mathbf{x}]$, $\cos [d\mathbf{l}, d\mathbf{y}]$, and $\cos [d\mathbf{l}, d\mathbf{z}]$ are the direction cosines of the displacement $d\mathbf{l}$.

We see then that the operator $(\mathbf{u}_l \cdot \nabla)$, when operating on a scalar field, yields the spatial rate of change of that field in the $d\mathbf{l}$-direction.

The same operator $(\mathbf{u}_l \cdot \nabla)$ may be used to calculate the spatial rate of change of a vector field in the $d\mathbf{l}$-direction

$$\frac{d\mathbf{F}}{|d\mathbf{l}|} = (\mathbf{u}_l \cdot \nabla)\mathbf{F}$$

$$= [\mathbf{u}_l \cdot \mathbf{u}_x] \frac{\partial \mathbf{F}}{\partial x} + [\mathbf{u}_l \cdot \mathbf{u}_y] \frac{\partial \mathbf{F}}{\partial y} + [\mathbf{u}_l \cdot \mathbf{u}_z] \frac{\partial \mathbf{F}}{\partial z} \quad (8.6)$$

The Laplacian operator ∇^2 appears frequently in the study of fields. When applied to a scalar field h, it takes the form

$$\nabla^2 h = \nabla \cdot \nabla h$$

$$= \left(\mathbf{u}_x \frac{\partial}{\partial x} + \mathbf{u}_y \frac{\partial}{\partial y} + \mathbf{u}_z \frac{\partial}{\partial z} \right) \cdot \left(\mathbf{u}_x \frac{\partial}{\partial x} + \mathbf{u}_y \frac{\partial}{\partial y} + \mathbf{u}_z \frac{\partial}{\partial z} \right) h$$

$$= \frac{\partial^2 h}{\partial x^2} + \frac{\partial^2 h}{\partial y^2} + \frac{\partial^2 h}{\partial z^2} \tag{8.7}$$

As is apparent from Eq. (8.7), this operator appears when we must determine the divergence of a vector field which is the gradient of a scalar field,

$$\text{div grad } h = \nabla \cdot \nabla h = \nabla^2 h \tag{8.8}$$

For the present we shall consider the Laplacian of a vector field $\mathbf{F}$ to be

$$\nabla^2 \mathbf{F} = \frac{\partial^2 \mathbf{F}}{\partial x^2} + \frac{\partial^2 \mathbf{F}}{\partial y^2} + \frac{\partial^2 \mathbf{F}}{\partial z^2} \tag{8.9}$$

that is, we shall consider only the Cartesian form of the Laplacian when dealing with vector fields.

The value of the Laplacian of a field at a particular point is a measure of the degree to which the value of the field at that point differs from the average value of the field in the neighborhood of the point.

To derive this result for a scalar field, let us assume that g_{av}, the average value of the scalar field $g(x, y, z)$ in the neighborhood of the point x_0, y_0, z_0, is

$$g_{av} \equiv \lim_{R \to 0} \frac{1}{\frac{4}{3}\pi R^3} \iiint\limits_{\substack{\text{sphere of} \\ \text{radius } R}} g(x, y, z) \, dV \tag{8.10}$$

where R is the radius of a small sphere surrounding the point x_0, y_0, z_0.

If we assume that $g(x, y, z)$ and its first derivatives are continuous and the point x_0, y_0, z_0 is taken to be the origin, we may write $g(x, y, z)$ in a Maclaurin series:

$$g(x, y, z) = g(0, 0, 0) + \frac{\partial g}{\partial x} x + \frac{\partial g}{\partial y} y + \frac{\partial g}{\partial z} z$$

$$+ \frac{1}{2!} \left(\frac{\partial^2 g}{\partial x^2} x^2 + \frac{\partial^2 g}{\partial x \, \partial y} xy + \frac{\partial^2 g}{\partial y^2} y^2 + \frac{\partial^2 g}{\partial y \, \partial z} yz \right.$$

$$\left. + \frac{\partial^2 g}{\partial z^2} z^2 + \frac{\partial^2 g}{\partial z \, \partial x} zx \right)$$

$$+ \frac{1}{3!} \text{(higher order terms in } x, y, \text{ and } z) \tag{8.11}$$

Substituting Eq. (8.11) into (8.10) yields

$$g_{av}(x, y, z) = \lim_{R \to 0} \frac{1}{\frac{4}{3}\pi R^3} \int_{-R}^{R} \int_{-(R^2-z^2)^{1/2}}^{(R^2-z^2)^{1/2}} \int_{-(R^2-z^2-y^2)^{1/2}}^{(R^2-z^2-y^2)^{1/2}}$$

$$\times \left[g(0, 0, 0) + \frac{\partial g}{\partial x} x + \frac{\partial g}{\partial y} y + \frac{\partial g}{\partial z} z \right.$$

$$+ \frac{1}{2!}\left(\frac{\partial^2 g}{\partial x^2} x^2 + \frac{\partial^2 g}{\partial x \, \partial y} xy + \frac{\partial^2 g}{\partial y^2} y^2 + \frac{\partial^2 g}{\partial y \, \partial z} yz + \frac{\partial^2 g}{\partial z^2} z^2 + \frac{\partial^2 g}{\partial z \, \partial x} zx \right)$$

$$+ \left. \frac{1}{3!} \text{(higher order terms in } x, y, \text{ and } z) \right] dx \, dy \, dz \qquad (8.12)$$

Since the integration over the spherical volume is symmetric about the origin, the integrations of the terms containing odd powers of the space variables vanish. Observing that

$$\int_{-R}^{R} \int_{-(R^2-z^2)^{1/2}}^{(R^2-z^2)^{1/2}} \int_{-(R^2-z^2-y^2)^{1/2}}^{(R^2-z^2-y^2)^{1/2}} x^2 \, dx \, dy \, dz = \tfrac{4}{15}\pi R^3 \qquad (8.13)$$

with similar results for integrations over y^2 and z^2, we may write Eq. (8.12) as

$$g_{av}(x, y, z) = \lim_{R \to 0} \frac{1}{\frac{4}{3}\pi R^3}\left[\frac{4}{3}\pi R^3 g(0, 0, 0) + \frac{1}{2!}\left(\frac{\partial^2 g}{\partial x^2} + \frac{\partial^2 g}{\partial y^2} + \frac{\partial^2 g}{\partial z^2}\right)\frac{4}{15}\pi R^3 \right.$$

$$+ \text{(higher order terms in } R)$$

$$= \left. g(0, 0, 0) + \frac{1}{10}\left(\frac{\partial^2 g}{\partial x^2} + \frac{\partial^2 g}{\partial y^2} + \frac{\partial^2 g}{\partial z^2}\right)\right] \qquad (8.14)$$

or

$$g(0, 0, 0) - g_{av} = -\tfrac{1}{10}\nabla^2 g \qquad (8.15)$$

Equation (8.15) represents the fact that $\nabla^2 g$ at a point indicates the degree to which g differs from g_{av} in the neighborhood of that point.

This result can be extended to vector fields providing the vector components are twice differentiable. For vector fields, the Laplacian indicates the difference in either the direction or magnitude of a field at a point from the average value of its direction and magnitude in the neighborhood of the point.

We see from Eq. (8.15) that if $\nabla^2 g$ at a point is negative, g at that point is greater than the average value of g in the neighborhood of that point. In other words, a negative value of $\nabla^2 g$ at a point indicates a tendency for g to get larger or to "concentrate" at that point. This fact led Maxwell to propose that $-\nabla^2 g$ be termed the concentration of g.

If g at a point is different from the average value of g in the neighborhood of that point, something must be located there which causes g to change.

The "something" at that point which causes g to increase or decrease may be considered as a source or sink for the field g. For example, the presence of a constant heat source of Q units of heat per unit volume per unit time causes a "concentration" of temperature, that is,

$$\nabla^2 T = -aQ \qquad \text{(steady state)} \tag{8.16}$$

where a is a constant; similarly, the existence of a stationary positive charge density ρ_v at a point in space causes a concentration of the electrostatic potential Φ,

$$\nabla^2 \Phi = -\frac{\rho_v}{\epsilon} \tag{8.17}$$

where ϵ is a constant.

We shall return to further considerations involving the Laplacian in Chapters 11 and 12 where we discuss the concept of potential.

8.3 Differential Operators and the Position Vector R

The value of many scalar fields encountered in science and engineering vary as R^v, where $R = (x^2 + y^2 + z^2)^{1/2}$ is the magnitude of the position vector $\mathbf{R} = \mathbf{u}_x x + \mathbf{u}_y y + \mathbf{u}_z z$ locating a field point $P(x, y, z)$ from the origin and v is any real number (see Fig. 8.1). Let us then illustrate the use of the operator ∇ by calculating the gradient and Laplacian of R^v.

$$\begin{aligned}
\nabla R^v &= \mathbf{u}_x v R^{v-1}\frac{\partial R}{\partial x} + \mathbf{u}_y v R^{v-1}\frac{\partial R}{\partial y} + \mathbf{u}_z v R^{v-1}\frac{\partial R}{\partial z} \\
&= v R^{v-2}\{\mathbf{u}_x x + \mathbf{u}_y y + \mathbf{u}_z z\} \\
&= v R^{v-2}\mathbf{R} = v R^{v-1}\mathbf{u}_R
\end{aligned} \tag{8.18}$$

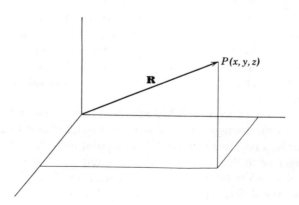

Figure 8.1 The position vector **R**.

where $\mathbf{u}_R \equiv \mathbf{R}/R$ is a unit vector in the **R**-direction. If $\nu = 1$, the gradient is just a unit vector in the **R**-direction; it has the direction and sense of the vector from the origin to $P(x, y, z)$.

In discussing Eq. (8.18), we have assumed that the point $P(x, y, z)$ is located relative to the origin. We may, for convenience, wish to locate $P(x, y, z)$ not from the origin but from another point $P'(x', y', z')$ (see Fig. 8.2). To do so, we consider the position vector $\mathbf{R}'$ as locating the point $P'(x', y', z')$ and the position vector $\mathbf{R}$ as locating $P(x, y, z)$ from the origin. The position vector locating $P(x, y, z)$ from $P'(x', y', z')$ is then $\mathbf{R} - \mathbf{R}'$ so that Eq. (8.18) is modified to be

$$\nabla |\mathbf{R} - \mathbf{R}'|^\nu = \nu |\mathbf{R} - \mathbf{R}'|^{\nu-1} \mathbf{u}_{\mathbf{R}-\mathbf{R}'} \tag{8.19}$$

where $|\mathbf{R} - \mathbf{R}'|$ is the distance from $P(x, y, z)$ to $P'(x', y', z')$; and $\mathbf{u}_{\mathbf{R}-\mathbf{R}'}$ is a unit vector having the sense and direction of $\mathbf{R} - \mathbf{R}'$.

The Laplacian of $|\mathbf{R} - \mathbf{R}'|^\nu$ is determined as follows:

$$
\begin{aligned}
\nabla^2 |\mathbf{R} - \mathbf{R}'|^\nu &= \nabla \cdot \nabla |\mathbf{R} - \mathbf{R}'|^\nu = \nabla \cdot (\nu \mathbf{u}_{\mathbf{R}-\mathbf{R}'} |\mathbf{R} - \mathbf{R}'|^{\nu-1}) \\
&= \nabla \cdot [\nu(\mathbf{R} - \mathbf{R}') |\mathbf{R} - \mathbf{R}'|^{\nu-2}] \\
&= \nu \left\{ \frac{\partial}{\partial x} [(x - x') |\mathbf{R} - \mathbf{R}'|^{\nu-2}] + \frac{\partial}{\partial y} [(y - y') |\mathbf{R} - \mathbf{R}'|^{\nu-2}] \right. \\
&\quad \left. + \frac{\partial}{\partial z} [(z - z') |\mathbf{R} - \mathbf{R}'|^{\nu-2}] \right\} \\
&= \nu [|\mathbf{R} - \mathbf{R}'|^{\nu-2} + (\nu - 2)(x - x')^2 |\mathbf{R} - \mathbf{R}'|^{\nu-4} \\
&\quad + |\mathbf{R} - \mathbf{R}'|^{\nu-2} + (\nu - 2)(y - y')^2 |\mathbf{R} - \mathbf{R}'|^{\nu-4} \\
&\quad + |\mathbf{R} - \mathbf{R}'|^{\nu-2} + (\nu - 2)(z - z')^2 |\mathbf{R} - \mathbf{R}'|^{\nu-4}] \\
&= \nu [3 |\mathbf{R} - \mathbf{R}'|^{\nu-2} + (\nu - 2) |\mathbf{R} - \mathbf{R}'|^{\nu-2}] \\
&= \nu(\nu + 1) |\mathbf{R} - \mathbf{R}'|^{\nu-2} \tag{8.20}
\end{aligned}
$$

as long as $|\mathbf{R} - \mathbf{R}'|^\nu$ remains finite. Two special cases are of particular interest

1. $\nu = -1$.
2. $\nu = 2$.

In Case 1, the Laplacian is zero, that is, the gradient of $|\mathbf{R} - \mathbf{R}'|^{-1}$ has vanishing divergence. The Laplacian of $|\mathbf{R} - \mathbf{R}'|^2$ (Case 2) is a constant.

Of course, Eq. (8.20) is valid only if $|\mathbf{R} - \mathbf{R}'|^\nu$ is finite. Physically this means that the field points P and P' cannot coincide if $\nu < 0$.

In the following formulas, c is a constant scalar, and **C** a constant vector, whereas $\mathbf{R} - \mathbf{R}'$ is the position vector of a field point P as located

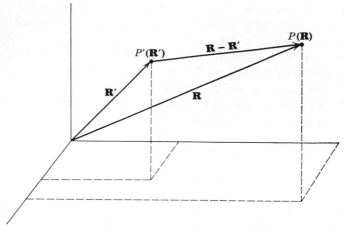

Figure 8.2   Locating $P(\mathbf{R})$ from $P'(\mathbf{R}')$.

from another fixed point P' and $\mathbf{u}_{\mathbf{R}-\mathbf{R}'}$ is a unit vector along $\mathbf{R} - \mathbf{R}'$.

$$\text{grad } [c\,|\mathbf{R} - \mathbf{R}'|] = c\,\nabla\,|\mathbf{R} - \mathbf{R}'| = c\mathbf{u}_{\mathbf{R}-\mathbf{R}'} \qquad (8.21a)$$

$$\mathbf{C} \cdot \text{grad }|\mathbf{R} - \mathbf{R}'| = \mathbf{C} \cdot \nabla\,|\mathbf{R} - \mathbf{R}'| = \mathbf{C} \cdot \mathbf{u}_{\mathbf{R}-\mathbf{R}'} \qquad (8.21b)$$

$$\text{div } [c(\mathbf{R} - \mathbf{R}')] = \nabla \cdot c(\mathbf{R} - \mathbf{R}') = 3c \qquad (8.21c)$$

$$\text{curl } [c(\mathbf{R} - \mathbf{R}')] = \nabla \times c(\mathbf{R} - \mathbf{R}') = 0 \qquad (8.21d)$$

$$\text{grad } [\mathbf{C} \cdot (\mathbf{R} - \mathbf{R}')] = \nabla \mathbf{C} \cdot (\mathbf{R} - \mathbf{R}') = \mathbf{C} \qquad (8.21e)$$

$$\text{curl } [\mathbf{C} \times (\mathbf{R} - \mathbf{R}')] = 2\mathbf{C} \qquad (8.21f)$$

$$\text{div } \left[\frac{c\mathbf{u}_{\mathbf{R}-\mathbf{R}'}}{|\mathbf{R} - \mathbf{R}'|^2} \right] = 0 \qquad \mathbf{R} \neq \mathbf{R}' \qquad (8.21g)$$

Formulas (8.21a and b) follow because c and $\mathbf{C}$ are not dependent on x, y, or z, whereas formulas (8.21c, d, e, f, and g may be established by resolving $(\mathbf{R} - \mathbf{R}')$ and $\mathbf{C}$ into their components in the x-, y-, and z-directions and operating on the components according to Eqs. (8.2), (8.3), or (8.4).

8.4   Field Operators and the Sums and Products of Field Quantities

Each of the following formulas can be established by considering the field quantities in Cartesian coordinates and performing the indicated operations in accordance with the definition of ∇ in Cartesian coordinates.

Of particular interest are Eqs. (8.22q and r). Equation (8.22q) says that the divergence of a vector field which is the curl of any given vector field is zero for all regions of space where the respective fields are defined and their first spatial derivatives exist. Similarly, Eq. (8.22r) states that the curl of a vector field which is the result of the gradient of any given scalar field is zero for all regions of space where the respective fields are defined and their spatial derivatives exist. We shall return to a more thorough study of these two equations and their significance in Chapter 11.

$$\text{grad } (ch) = c \text{ grad } h \tag{8.22a}$$

$$\text{grad } (h + g) = \text{grad } h + \text{grad } g \tag{8.22b}$$

$$\text{grad } (hg) = g \text{ grad } h + h \text{ grad } g \tag{8.22c}$$

$$\text{grad } (\mathbf{F} \cdot \mathbf{G}) = (\mathbf{F} \cdot \nabla)\mathbf{G} + (\mathbf{G} \cdot \nabla)\mathbf{F} + \mathbf{F} \times (\nabla \times \mathbf{G}) + \mathbf{G} \times (\nabla \times \mathbf{F}) \tag{8.22d}$$

$$\text{div } (c\mathbf{F}) = c \text{ div } \mathbf{F} \tag{8.22e}$$

$$\text{div } (\mathbf{F} + \mathbf{G}) = \nabla \cdot (\mathbf{F} + \mathbf{G}) = \nabla \cdot \mathbf{F} + \nabla \cdot \mathbf{G} \tag{8.22f}$$

$$\text{div } (h\mathbf{F}) = \mathbf{F} \cdot \nabla h + h\nabla \cdot \mathbf{F} \tag{8.22g}$$

$$\text{div } (\mathbf{F} \times \mathbf{G}) = -\mathbf{F} \cdot \nabla \times \mathbf{G} + \mathbf{G} \cdot \nabla \times \mathbf{F} \tag{8.22h}$$

$$\text{curl } (c\mathbf{F}) = c \text{ curl } \mathbf{F} \tag{8.22i}$$

$$\text{curl } (\mathbf{F} + \mathbf{G}) = \text{curl } \mathbf{F} + \text{curl } \mathbf{G} \tag{8.22j}$$

$$\text{curl } (h\mathbf{F}) \cdot = h \text{ curl } \mathbf{F} + \nabla h \times \mathbf{F} \tag{8.22k}$$

$$\text{curl } (\mathbf{F} \times \mathbf{G}) = \mathbf{F}(\nabla \cdot \mathbf{G}) + (\mathbf{G} \cdot \nabla)\mathbf{F} - \mathbf{G}(\nabla \cdot \mathbf{F}) - (\mathbf{F} \cdot \nabla)\mathbf{G} \tag{8.22l}$$

$$\text{div grad } h = \nabla \cdot \nabla h = \nabla^2 h \tag{8.22m}$$

$$\text{div grad } (ch) = c\nabla^2 h \tag{8.22n}$$

$$\text{div grad } (gh) = 2\nabla h \cdot \nabla g + g\nabla^2 h + h\nabla^2 g \tag{8.22p}$$

$$\text{div curl } \mathbf{F} = \nabla \cdot \nabla \times \mathbf{F} = 0 \tag{8.22q}$$

$$\text{curl grad } h = \nabla \times \nabla h = 0 \tag{8.22r}$$

$$\text{curl curl } \mathbf{F} = \nabla \times (\nabla \times \mathbf{F}) = \nabla(\nabla \cdot \mathbf{F}) - \nabla^2\mathbf{F} \tag{8.22s}$$

As an example of the approach which can be used to establish Eqs. (8.22a–s), we shall treat (8.22q).

$$\text{div curl } \mathbf{F} = \nabla \cdot \nabla \times \mathbf{F}$$

$$= \nabla \cdot \left[\mathbf{u}_x\left(\frac{\partial F_z}{\partial y} - \frac{\partial F_y}{\partial z}\right) + \mathbf{u}_y\left(\frac{\partial F_x}{\partial z} - \frac{\partial F_z}{\partial x}\right) + \mathbf{u}_z\left(\frac{\partial F_y}{\partial x} - \frac{\partial F_x}{\partial y}\right) \right]$$

$$= \frac{\partial}{\partial x}\left(\frac{\partial F_z}{\partial y} - \frac{\partial F_y}{\partial z}\right) + \frac{\partial}{\partial y}\left(\frac{\partial F_x}{\partial z} - \frac{\partial F_z}{\partial x}\right) + \frac{\partial}{\partial z}\left(\frac{\partial F_y}{\partial x} - \frac{\partial F_x}{\partial y}\right)$$

$$= \frac{\partial^2 F_z}{\partial x \, \partial y} - \frac{\partial^2 F_y}{\partial x \, \partial z} + \frac{\partial^2 F_x}{\partial y \, \partial z} - \frac{\partial^2 F_z}{\partial y \, \partial x} + \frac{\partial^2 F_y}{\partial z \, \partial x} - \frac{\partial^2 F_x}{\partial z \, \partial y}$$

Since the order of differentiation is immaterial, it follows that $\nabla \cdot \nabla \times \mathbf{F} = 0$.

8.5 Conclusion

The form of the operator ∇ is such that we may be tempted to consider it as a vector and, indeed, in many situations it is helpful to regard it thus. However, we must exercise caution and not interpret ∇ blindly as a vector without considering the manner in which it is used. For example, although

$$\mathbf{F} \cdot (h\mathbf{G}) = h\mathbf{F} \cdot \mathbf{G} \qquad (8.23)$$

where $\mathbf{F}$ and $\mathbf{G}$ are vector fields and h is a scalar field, we cannot replace $\mathbf{F}$ by ∇, that is,

$$\nabla \cdot (h\mathbf{G}) \neq h\nabla \cdot \mathbf{G}$$

but $\qquad \nabla \cdot (h\mathbf{G}) = h\nabla \cdot \mathbf{G} + \mathbf{G} \cdot \nabla h \qquad$ (see 8.22g)

Similarly, although

$$\mathbf{F} \times h\mathbf{G} = h\mathbf{F} \times \mathbf{G} \qquad (8.24)$$

∇ cannot be inserted for $\mathbf{F}$,

$$\nabla \times (h\mathbf{G}) \neq h\nabla \times \mathbf{G}$$

but rather

$$\nabla \times (h\mathbf{G}) = h\nabla \times \mathbf{G} + (\nabla h) \times \mathbf{G} \qquad \text{(see 8.22k).}$$

PROBLEMS

1. Verify Eq. (8.21a) through (8.21g).
2. Verify Eq. (8.22a) through (8.22s).
3. Give a geometrical interpretation of $\nabla |\mathbf{R}| = \mathbf{u}_R$.
4. Show that $(\mathbf{A} \times \nabla) \cdot \mathbf{R} = 0$, where $\mathbf{A}$ is any vector.
5. If a scalar field is $h(\mathbf{R})$, show that $[\nabla h(\mathbf{R})] \times \mathbf{R} = 0$. Interpret the physical significance of this result.
6. Show that $d\mathbf{R} \times \nabla h(\mathbf{R})$ yields the equations necessary to determine the field lines of $\nabla h(\mathbf{R})$.
7. Prove that a necessary condition for a scalar field to have an extremum at a point P is

$$\nabla_P h(\mathbf{R}) = 0$$

9

The Integral Properties of Fields—Stokes's, Gauss's, and Green's Theorems

9.1 Introduction

There are many instances in science and engineering when the application of the concept of fields to physical problems leads to line, surface, and volume integrals which involve integrands containing field operators. In these situations it is of great value to be able to go from one type of such integral to another, for example, from a surface to a line integral. The importance of integral transformations is twofold: by reducing the number of dimensions, they may assist in evaluating certain integrals and, more significantly, many of these transformations can be used to present or describe a physical situation more clearly.

In this chapter we shall discuss surface-to-line integral transformations, Stokes's theorem, volume-to-surface integral transformations, Gauss's theorem, and Green's theorem.

9.2 Surface-to-Line Integral Transformations—Stokes's Theorem

We shall now state and discuss the following three surface-to-line integral transformations:

$$\iint_A \mathbf{u}_n \times \nabla h \, |ds| = \oint_\Gamma h \, d\mathbf{l} \tag{9.1}$$

$$\iint_A \mathbf{u}_n \cdot (\nabla \times \mathbf{F}) \, |ds| = \oint_\Gamma \mathbf{F} \cdot d\mathbf{l} \tag{9.2}$$

$$\iint_A (\mathbf{u}_n \times \nabla) \times \mathbf{F} \, |ds| = \oint_\Gamma d\mathbf{l} \times \mathbf{F} \tag{9.3}$$

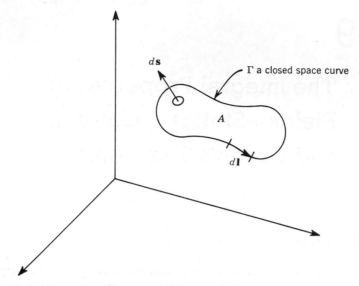

Figure 9.1   A closed space curve for the discussion of Stokes's theorem.

The surface A is a regular two-sided surface; in other words, we are excluding from our discussion surfaces like a Mobius strip. The symbol Γ may represent a curve or a finite number of curves forming a closed boundary of A. In these equations A is an open surface which exists in a region of space where a scalar field h or a vector field $\mathbf{F}$ exists. These fields, together with their first derivatives, are assumed to be continuous at all points of A and Γ. The symbol $d\mathbf{s}$, a surface element of A and $d\mathbf{l}$, is an element of length of the curve Γ (see Fig. 9.1). We shall assume that Γ is well behaved as $\Delta\mathbf{s}$ approaches zero.

We shall use the previously stated convention regarding the relative direction of $\mathbf{u}_n$ and $d\mathbf{l}$, in other words, if $\mathbf{u}_n$ is in the direction and sense of an advancing right-hand screw, then the direction and sense of $d\mathbf{l}$ along Γ are those of the threads as the screw advances.

Let the area A be divided into N very small regular areas $\Delta\mathbf{s}_1, \Delta\mathbf{s}_2, \ldots$ $\Delta\mathbf{s}_j, \ldots \Delta\mathbf{s}_N$ (see Fig. 9.2). We shall assume that these areas are so small that they are approximately planar and may therefore be represented by a vector; in addition, the $\Delta\mathbf{s}$'s are sufficiently small that, to a first approximation, the scalar field h may be assumed to be constant over the surface of each of the $\Delta\mathbf{s}$'s. The value of the scalar field at $\Delta\mathbf{s}_1$ is designated h_1, the value at $\Delta\mathbf{s}_2$ is h_2, etc. If the periphery of $\Delta\mathbf{s}_j$ is a curve γ_j, then the integration of h around γ_j, taken in accordance with our direction

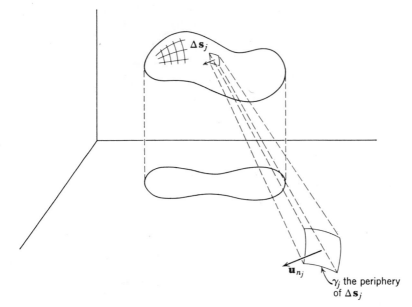

Figure 9.2   The division of the area enclosed by a closed space curve into elemental areas.

convention, is

$$\oint_{\gamma_j} h_j \, d\mathbf{l}$$

where $d\mathbf{l}$ is an element of length of the curve γ_j.

The sum of similar integrals all taken in the same direction around the periphery of all the $\Delta\mathbf{s}$'s is equivalent to the line integral of h around Γ in the same direction,

$$\sum_{j=1}^{N} \oint_{\gamma_j} h_j \, d\mathbf{l} = \oint_{\Gamma} h \, d\mathbf{l} \qquad (9.4)$$

This is true because, except for those portions of the peripheries γ_1, $\gamma_2, \ldots, \gamma_j, \ldots, \gamma_N$ which form Γ, the periphery of A, the integrations will be in the opposite directions from those of its adjacent areas and thereby will cancel each other. For example, in Fig. 9.3 the line integral of h around the interior area $\Delta\mathbf{s}_{17}$ will be canceled out by portions of the line integrals around surrounding areas $\Delta\mathbf{s}_{14}$, $\Delta\mathbf{s}_{16}$, $\Delta\mathbf{s}_{18}$, and $\Delta\mathbf{s}_{20}$, whereas the line integral of h around the area $\Delta\mathbf{s}_{35}$ is not completely nullified by similar integrals around neighboring areas $\Delta\mathbf{s}_{31}$, $\Delta\mathbf{s}_{32}$, and $\Delta\mathbf{s}_{34}$ because a portion of the periphery of $\Delta\mathbf{s}_{35}$ is coincident with Γ the periphery of A.

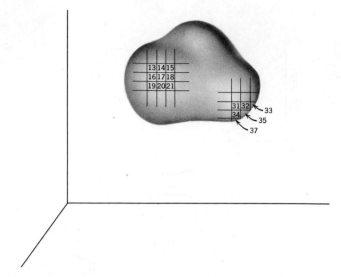

Figure 9.3   The illustration of internal and peripheral elemental areas.

The approximation represented by Eq. (9.4) becomes more exact as N approaches infinity in such a way that the magnitudes of all the small areas $\Delta \mathbf{s}_1, \Delta \mathbf{s}_2, \ldots, \Delta \mathbf{s}_j, \ldots, \Delta \mathbf{s}_N$ approach zero; we may then write

$$\lim_{N \to \infty} \sum_{j=1}^{N} \oint_{\gamma_j} h_j \, d\mathbf{l} = \oint_{\Gamma} h \, d\mathbf{l} \tag{9.5}$$

In view of Eq. (5.56),

$$\mathbf{u}_n \times \operatorname{grad} h = \frac{1}{|\Delta \mathbf{s}|} \oint_{\gamma} h \, d\mathbf{l} \tag{5.56}$$

for a small area $\Delta \mathbf{s}$. The approximation becomes more exact as $|\Delta \mathbf{s}|$ approaches zero. We may then write for a typical element of area $\Delta \mathbf{s}_j$ in this discussion,

$$\mathbf{u}_{n_j} \times \operatorname{grad} h_j \, |\Delta \mathbf{s}_j| = \oint_{\gamma_j} h_j \, d\mathbf{l} \tag{9.6}$$

where $\Delta \mathbf{s}_j = \mathbf{u}_{n_j} |\Delta \mathbf{s}_j|$.

Substituting (9.6) into (9.5), we obtain

$$\lim_{\substack{|\Delta \mathbf{s}_j| \to 0 \\ N \to \infty}} \sum_{j=1}^{N} \mathbf{u}_{n_j} \times \operatorname{grad} h \, |\Delta \mathbf{s}_j| = \oint_{\Gamma} h \, d\mathbf{l} \tag{9.7}$$

However, the left-hand side of (9.7) is the surface integral

$$\iint_A \mathbf{u}_n \times \operatorname{grad} h \, |ds|$$

so that Eq. (9.1) is established.

Another surface-to-line integral transformation we wish to discuss [Eq. (9.2)] is of considerable importance in applied mathematics and is known as the Stokes's theorem:

$$\iint_A \mathbf{u}_n \cdot \operatorname{curl} \mathbf{F} \, |ds| = \oint_\Gamma \mathbf{F} \cdot d\mathbf{l} \qquad (9.2)$$

This equation states that the integral of the normal component of the curl of a vector field over an area A is equal to the integral of the tangential component of the field along the curve Γ which is the periphery of A.

Before considering a rigorous demonstration of Stokes's theorem for three-dimensional fields, let us discuss some elementary ideas concerning the simplest type of surface integration, namely, integration involving a plane surface. Let us begin by evaluating the integral

$$\iint_A \frac{\partial F_x}{\partial y} \, |ds| \qquad (9.8a)$$

where A is the area of the surface on the plane $z = 0$ shown in Fig. 9.4a and where F_x is the magnitude of the x-component of a vector field $\mathbf{F}$. We shall assume that A can be subdivided into a number of areas a_1, $a_2, \ldots a_j, \ldots a_N$ which have the form shown in Fig. 9.4b. The surface a_j is bounded on the right and left by the straight lines, $x = x_1$ and $x = x_2$ and on the top and bottom by the regular curves $\gamma_{T_j}(x, y)$ and $\gamma_{B_j}(x, y)$. We see that $d\mathbf{s} = \mathbf{u}_z \, dx \, dy$ so that Eq. (9.8a) becomes

$$\sum_{j=1}^N \iint_{a_j} \frac{\partial F_x}{\partial y} \, dx \, dy \qquad (9.8b)$$

Considering the typical surface a_j, we then perform the integration with respect to y between the curves $\gamma_{T_j}(x, y)$ and $\gamma_{B_j}(x, y)$ which yields

$$\iint_{a_j} \frac{\partial F_x}{\partial y} \, dx \, dy = \int_{x_1}^{x_2} [F_{x_{\gamma_{T_j}}}(x, y) - F_{x_{\gamma_{B_j}}}(x, y)] \, dx \qquad (9.9)$$

where $F_{x_{\gamma_{jT}}}(x, y)$ is the magnitude of the x-component of $\mathbf{F}$ as we move along γ_{T_j}, and $F_{x_{\gamma_{B_j}}}$ is the same quantity along γ_{B_j}.

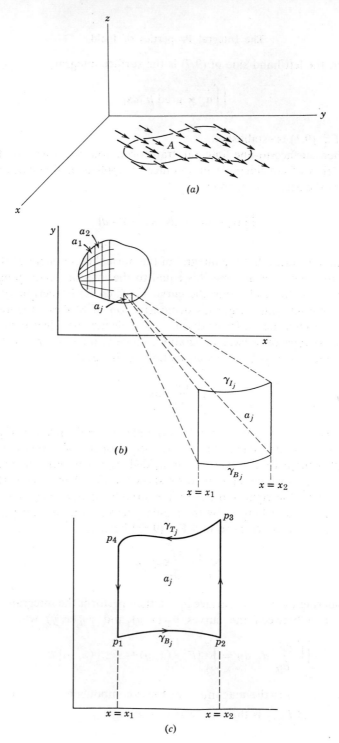

(a)

(b)

(c)

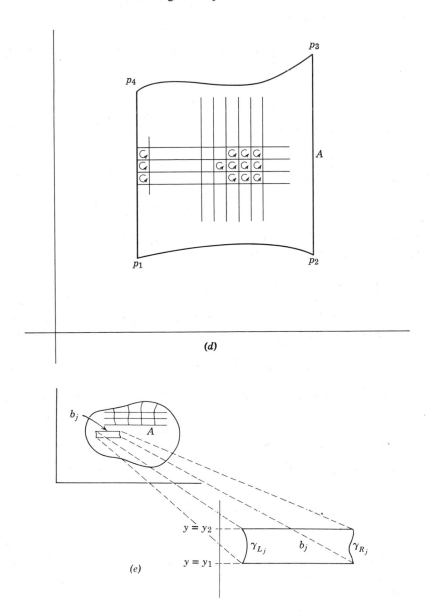

Figure 9.4 (a) A plane surface A in a two-dimensional field. (b) Illustrating the periphery of an external elemental area. (c) For evaluating the surface integral in Eq. (9.9). (d) Illustrating that line integrals around interior areas cancel. (e) Dividing an area A into elemental areas.

By referring to Fig. 9.4c, we see that

$$\int_{x_1}^{x_2} F_{x_{\gamma_{T_j}}} dx = \int_{p_4}^{p_3} F_x dx \tag{9.10}$$

and

$$\int_{x_1}^{x_2} F_{x_{\gamma_B}} dx = \int_{p_1}^{p_2} F_x dx \tag{9.11}$$

so that Eq. (9.9) becomes

$$\iint_{a_j} \frac{\partial F_x}{\partial y} dx\, dy = \left(\int_{p_4}^{p_3} F_x dx - \int_{p_1}^{p_2} F_x dx \right)$$

$$= - \left(\int_{p_3}^{p_4} F_x dx + \int_{p_1}^{p_2} F_x dx \right) \tag{9.12}$$

However, by referring to Figure 9.4c again, we see that for the indicated path γ_j, which is the periphery of a_j

$$\oint_{\gamma_j} F_x dx = \int_{p_1}^{p_2} F_x dx + \int_{p_2}^{p_3} F_x dx + \int_{p_3}^{p_4} F_x dx + \int_{p_4}^{p_1} F_x dx \tag{9.13}$$

But along the paths from p_2 to p_3 and from p_4 to p_1 x does not change, so that the integrals over these paths are zero. Then Eq. (9.13) is

$$\oint_{\gamma_j} F_x dx = \int_{p_1}^{p_2} F_x dx + \int_{p_3}^{p_4} F_x dx \tag{9.14}$$

but this is just the negative of the left-hand side of Eq. (9.12) so that

$$\iint_{a_j} \frac{\partial F_x}{\partial y} dx\, dy = - \oint_{\gamma_j} F_x dx \tag{9.15}$$

By utilizing Eq. (9.8b) we may determine that the integral over A is

$$\iint_{A} \frac{\partial F_x}{\partial y} dx\, dy = - \sum_{j=1}^{N} \oint_{\gamma_j} F_x dx \tag{9.16}$$

In Fig. 9.4d we see that, except for those portions of the γ's which lie on Γ, the periphery of A, the line integrations over adjacent areas cancel because the integrations will have opposite senses. Then Eq. (9.16) becomes

$$\iint_{A} \frac{\partial F_x}{\partial y} dx\, dy = - \oint_{\Gamma} F_x dx \tag{9.17}$$

Instead of dividing A as shown in Fig. 9.4b and c, we subdivide A into small areas having the form shown in Fig. 9.4e. Here the area b_j of a typical surface is bounded by the straight lines $y = y_1$ and $y = y_2$ and by the curves γ_{R_j} on the right and γ_{L_j} on the left. We may then write

$$\iint_A \frac{\partial F_y}{\partial x}\, dy\, dx = \sum_{j=1}^{N} \iint_{b_j} \frac{\partial F_y}{\partial x}\, dy\, dx$$

$$= \sum_{j=1}^{N} \int_{y_1}^{y_2} (F_{y\gamma_{R_j}} - F_{y\gamma_{L_j}})\, dy$$

$$= \sum_{j=1}^{N} \oint_{\gamma_j} F_y\, dy = \oint_{\Gamma} F_y\, dy \qquad (9.18)$$

where γ_j is, in this expression, the periphery of the area b_j. Subtracting Eq. (9.17) from Eq. (9.18), we see that

$$\iint_A \left(\frac{\partial F_y}{\partial x} - \frac{\partial F_x}{\partial y} \right) dx\, dy = \oint_{\Gamma} (F_x\, dx + F_y\, dy)$$

$$= \oint_{\Gamma} \mathbf{F} \cdot d\mathbf{l} \qquad (9.19)$$

Equation (9.19) may be rewritten as

$$\iint_A \mathbf{u}_z \cdot \operatorname{curl} \mathbf{F}\, dx\, dy = \oint_{\Gamma} \mathbf{F} \cdot d\mathbf{l} \qquad (9.20)$$

for a two-dimensional field, $\mathbf{F}(x, y)$.

The reader should compare the foregoing discussion with that preceding Eq. (7.21). Note that if the integration in Eq. (9.20) is performed over an area $d\mathbf{s}_z$, the result is Eq. (7.21). Equation (9.20) is essentially a statement of Stokes's theorem for a two-dimensional field.

To demonstrate this theorem for a three-dimensional field, consider again an open surface in a region of space where a three-dimensional field $\mathbf{F}$ and its first derivatives are continuous. As before, A is assumed to be composed of N very small area $\Delta\mathbf{s}_1, \Delta\mathbf{s}_2, \dots, \Delta\mathbf{s}_j, \dots, \Delta\mathbf{s}_N$ whose peripheries are $\gamma_1, \gamma_2, \dots \gamma_j, \dots, \gamma_N$, respectively. Let each small area be sufficiently small that the value of the field on each area may be assumed to be approximately constant (see Fig. 9.5). The line integral around Γ of the vector field, the circulation of $\mathbf{F}$ around Γ taken in the direction dictated by the outward direction of the area A, is equivalent to the sum of the line integrals in the same direction taken around $\gamma_1, \gamma_2, \dots \gamma_j, \dots, \gamma_N$, that is,

$$\oint_{\Gamma} \mathbf{F} \cdot d\mathbf{l} = \sum_{j=1}^{N} \oint_{\gamma_j} \mathbf{F}_j \cdot d\mathbf{l} \qquad (9.21)$$

This is true because, as we argued previously, the line integrals over peripheries interior to Γ are zero because for two contiguous areas the

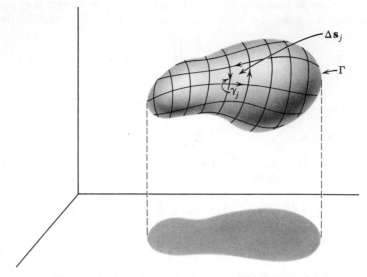

Figure 9.5   A typical surface element and its periphery.

integrals are taken in opposite directions over the same path and only
those portions of the γ_j's which are coincident with Γ contribute to the
sum.

Equation (9.21) represents an approximation which becomes more valid
as N approaches infinity so that the magnitude of all the Δs's approach
zero, thus we may write

$$\oint_\Gamma \mathbf{F} \cdot d\mathbf{l} = \lim_{N \to \infty} \sum_{j=1}^{N} \oint_{\gamma_j} \mathbf{F}_j \cdot d\mathbf{l} \qquad (9.22)$$

Approximating Eq. (7.39) for a very small area Δs, we may write

$$\frac{1}{|\Delta s|} \oint_\gamma \mathbf{F} \cdot d\mathbf{l} \simeq \mathbf{u}_n \cdot \text{curl } \mathbf{F} \qquad (7.41)$$

Applying the above to Δs_j of this discussion, we may write

$$\oint_{\gamma_j} \mathbf{F}_j \cdot d\mathbf{l} = \mathbf{u}_{n_j} \cdot \text{curl } \mathbf{F}_j \, |\Delta s_j| \qquad (9.23)$$

Substituting (9.23) into (9.22) yields

$$\oint_\Gamma \mathbf{F} \cdot d\mathbf{l} = \lim_{\substack{N \to \infty \\ |\Delta s_j| \to 0}} \sum_{j=1}^{N} \mathbf{u}_{n_j} \cdot \text{curl } \mathbf{F}_j \, |\Delta s_j| \qquad (9.24)$$

The right-hand side of Eq. (9.24) is just the surface integral

$$\iint_A \mathbf{u}_n \cdot \operatorname{curl} \mathbf{F} \, |ds|$$

so that (9.2) is demonstrated.

Equation (9.2) is called Stokes's theorem. Utilizing Stokes's theorem we are able to express a line integral around a closed path as a surface integral over the area enclosed by the path. The converse of this theorem is also valid: If two vector fields $\mathbf{F}$ and $\mathbf{G}$ are so related to each other that the surface integral of the normal component of $\mathbf{F}$ over a surface is equal to the line integral of $\mathbf{G}$ around the contour bounding the surface, then $\mathbf{F} = \operatorname{curl} \mathbf{G}$.

To understand Stokes's theorem, let us consider a group of contiguous rectangles which exist in a region of space where a vector field is defined (see Fig. 9.6). The arrows within the rectangles correspond to the direction of the circulation of the field around the periphery of a rectangle. In Section 7.3, we saw that this circulation integral defines around a small closed path γ, the component of the curl which is normal to the plane of γ. Consider the rectangle marked ①; that part of the circulation in rectangle ① along the side that it has in common with the rectangle ② is

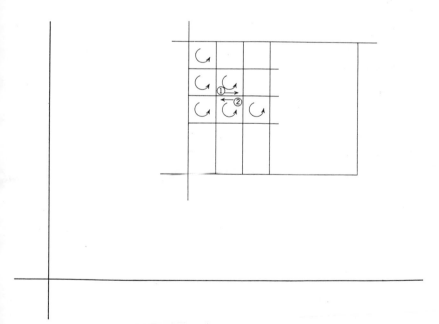

Figure 9.6   An illustration for the discussion of Stokes's theorem.

canceled because the paths of integration are taken in opposite senses. Therefore the sum of the product of the curl of the vector field and the area of the rectangle ① and the product of the curl of the vector field and the area of rectangle ② can be found by determining the circulation around the perimeter of the rectangle composed of rectangles ① and ② without considering the contribution of the common side. Larger figures may be formed by adding other small rectangles to the one composed of ① and ②; but no matter how large such a figure becomes or what its shape is, the summation of the products of the curl of the vector field within an area element $d\mathbf{s}$ is given by the circulation of that vector field about the periphery of the surface.

It is instructive to establish Stokes's theorem in yet another manner. To do so, we let the vector field be resolved into its Cartesian components

$$\mathbf{F} = \mathbf{u}_x F_x + \mathbf{u}_y F_y + \mathbf{u}_z F_z$$

Assume that a regular surface A exists in a region of space where $\mathbf{F}$ is defined. This means that the projections of A on the coordinate planes are the interior of regular closed curves on these planes. Each of the three coordinate variables describing a point on A is a function of the other two coordinate variables. We shall assume that this functional relationship, together with its spatial derivatives, is continuous. Then we may write

$$\iint_A \mathbf{u}_n \cdot \text{curl } \mathbf{F} \, |ds| = \iint_A \mathbf{u}_n \cdot [\text{curl } (\mathbf{u}_x F_x + \mathbf{u}_y F_y + \mathbf{u}_z F_z)] \, |ds| \qquad (9.25)$$

Let us consider the first term of Eq. (9.25),

$$\iint_A \mathbf{u}_n \cdot \text{curl } (\mathbf{u}_x F_x) \, |ds| = \iint_A \mathbf{u}_n \cdot \left(\mathbf{u}_y \frac{\partial F_x}{\partial z} - \mathbf{u}_z \frac{\partial F_x}{\partial y} \right) |ds| \qquad (9.25a)$$

Since $\mathbf{R} = \mathbf{u}_x x + \mathbf{u}_y y + \mathbf{u}_z z$, the position vector for any point on A, may be considered as a function of x and y only, we may write

$$\frac{\partial \mathbf{R}}{\partial y} = \mathbf{u}_y + \mathbf{u}_z \frac{\partial z}{\partial y} \qquad (9.26)$$

The expression $\partial \mathbf{R}/\partial y$ defines a vector which is always tangent to the curve formed by the intersection of A with the plane $x = 0$ and is therefore normal to $d\mathbf{s}$. Then

$$\mathbf{u}_n \cdot \left(\mathbf{u}_y + \mathbf{u}_z \frac{\partial z}{\partial y} \right) = \mathbf{u}_n \cdot \frac{\partial \mathbf{R}}{\partial y} = 0$$

or

$$\mathbf{u}_n \cdot \mathbf{u}_y = -(\mathbf{u}_n \cdot \mathbf{u}_z) \frac{\partial z}{\partial y} \qquad (9.27)$$

Similarly, on A, where $z = z(x, y)$, F_x, the magnitude of the x-component of $\mathbf{F}$, may be considered as a function of x and y,

$$F_x[x, y, z(x, y)] = F_x(x, y) \qquad (9.28)$$

so that

$$\left(\frac{\partial F_x}{\partial y}\right)_D = \left(\frac{\partial F_x}{\partial y}\right)_I + \frac{\partial F_x}{\partial z}\frac{\partial z}{\partial y} \qquad (9.29)$$

where $(\partial F_x/\partial y)_I$ means the partial derivative of $F_x = F_x(x, y, z)$ where x, y, and z are considered to be independent variables, and $(\partial F_x/\partial y)_D$ means the partial derivative of $F_x(x, y, z) = F_x[x, y, z(x, y)]$, where x and y are the independent variables and z is a dependent variable. Then we may write, for the integrand of the integral on the right-hand side of Eq. (9.25a),

$$\left[\mathbf{u}_n \cdot \mathbf{u}_y\left(\frac{\partial F_x}{\partial z}\right) - \mathbf{u}_n \cdot \mathbf{u}_z\left(\frac{\partial F_x}{\partial y}\right)_I\right] = \left[-\mathbf{u}_n \cdot \mathbf{u}_z\left(\frac{\partial F_x}{\partial z}\right)\frac{\partial z}{\partial y} - \mathbf{u}_n \cdot \mathbf{u}_z\left(\frac{\partial F_x}{\partial y}\right)_I\right]$$

$$= -\mathbf{u}_n \cdot \mathbf{u}_z\left[\frac{\partial F_x}{\partial z}\frac{\partial z}{\partial y} + \left(\frac{\partial F_x}{\partial y}\right)_I\right]$$

$$\text{(see Eq. 9.27)}$$

$$= -\mathbf{u}_n \cdot \mathbf{u}_z\left(\frac{\partial F_x}{\partial y}\right)_D \qquad \text{(see Eq. 9.29)}$$

$$(9.30)$$

so that Eq. (9.25a) becomes

$$\iint\limits_A \mathbf{u}_n \cdot \text{curl } \mathbf{u}_x F_x \, |ds| = -\iint\limits_A \left(\frac{\partial F_x}{\partial y}\right)_D dx\, dy \qquad (9.31)$$

By analogy with Eq. (9.15), the right-hand side of Eq. (9.31) is

$$\oint_{\Gamma_z} F_x \, dx \qquad (9.32)$$

where the integral is taken around the curve Γ_z which forms the periphery of the projection of Γ on the plane $z = 0$. Now F_x at any point x, y of Γ_z has the same value as F_x at any point x, y, z on the curve Γ; in addition, a change in x when passing from one point on Γ to another is the same as when passing between the projection of those two points on the curve Γ_z. We may then write

$$\oint_{\Gamma_z} F_x \, dx = \oint_{\Gamma} F_x \, dx \qquad (9.33)$$

and so Eq. (9.31) becomes

$$\iint_A \mathbf{u}_n \cdot \text{curl}\,(\mathbf{u}_x F_x)\,|ds| = \oint_\Gamma F_x\,dx \qquad (9.34a)$$

Similarly, the other terms of Eq. (9.25) become

$$\iint_A \mathbf{u}_n \cdot \text{curl}\,(\mathbf{u}_y F_y)\,|ds| = \oint_\Gamma F_y\,dy \qquad (9.34b)$$

and

$$\iint_A \mathbf{u}_n \cdot \text{curl}\,(\mathbf{u}_z F_z)\,|ds| = \oint_\Gamma F_z\,dz \qquad (9.34c)$$

Summing Eqs. (9.34a, b, c), we obtain Stokes's theorem

$$\iint_A \mathbf{u}_n \cdot \text{curl}\,\mathbf{F}\,|ds| = \oint_\Gamma \mathbf{F} \cdot d\mathbf{l} \qquad (9.2)$$

This demonstration of Stokes's theorem has been for a surface A which is regular. Any ordinary surface can be divided into areas which are regular for which Stokes's theorem is valid. It follows that if Stokes's theorem is valid for all the parts of which a surface is composed, it is true for the entire surface.

To establish Eq. (9.3) we apply Stokes's theorem to the vector $\mathbf{F} \times \mathbf{C}$; that is, we replace $\mathbf{F}$ in Eq. (9.2) by $\mathbf{F} \times \mathbf{C}$, where $\mathbf{C}$ is a constant but arbitrary vector field. Equation (9.2) then becomes

$$\oint_\Gamma (\mathbf{F} \times \mathbf{C}) \cdot d\mathbf{l} = \iint_A \mathbf{u}_n \cdot [\nabla \times (\mathbf{F} \times \mathbf{C})]\,|ds| \qquad (9.35)$$

By a cyclic permutation of the integrand of the line integral [see Eq. (2.44)] and by applying Eq. (8.22l) to the integrand of the surface integral, Eq. (9.35) becomes

$$\oint_\Gamma \mathbf{C} \cdot (d\mathbf{l} \times \mathbf{F}) = \iint_A \mathbf{u}_n \cdot [(\mathbf{C} \cdot \nabla)\mathbf{F} - \mathbf{C}(\nabla \cdot \mathbf{F})]\,|ds| \qquad (9.36)$$

However, the integrand of the surface integral is

$$\mathbf{C} \cdot [(\mathbf{u}_n \times \nabla) \times \mathbf{F}]$$

so that Eq. (9.36) is written

$$\oint_\Gamma \mathbf{C} \cdot (d\mathbf{l} \times \mathbf{F}) = \iint_A \mathbf{C} \cdot [(\mathbf{u}_n \times \nabla) \times \mathbf{F}] \, |d\mathbf{s}| \tag{9.37}$$

or

$$\mathbf{C} \cdot \oint_\Gamma d\mathbf{l} \times \mathbf{F} = \mathbf{C} \cdot \iint_A (\mathbf{u}_n \times \nabla) \times \mathbf{F} \, |d\mathbf{s}|$$

However, for this to be true for all $\mathbf{C}$, the relationship stated in Eq. (9.3) must be valid:

$$\oint_\Gamma d\mathbf{l} \times \mathbf{F} = \iint_A (\mathbf{u}_n \times \nabla) \times \mathbf{F} \, |d\mathbf{s}| \tag{9.3}$$

9.3 Volume-to-Surface Integral Transformations—Gauss's Theorem

We shall now discuss the following three volume-to-surface integral transformations:

$$\iiint_V \operatorname{grad} h \, dV = \oiint_A \mathbf{u}_n h \, |d\mathbf{s}| \tag{9.38}$$

$$\iiint_V \operatorname{div} \mathbf{F} \, dV = \oiint_A \mathbf{u}_n \cdot \mathbf{F} \, |d\mathbf{s}| \tag{9.39}$$

$$\iiint_V \operatorname{curl} \mathbf{F} \, dV = \oiint_A \mathbf{u}_n \times \mathbf{F} \, |d\mathbf{s}| \tag{9.40}$$

where V and A are a volume and its surface, located in a region of space where the fields h or $\mathbf{F}$ are differentiable; dV is a volume element of V and $d\mathbf{s}$ is a surface element of the external surface A.

Imagine that the volume V is divided into N very small volumes ΔV_1, $\Delta V_2, \ldots, \Delta V_j, \ldots, \Delta V_N$ [see Fig. 9.7a]. The surface of the jth volume element will be designated a_j, and an element of this surface by $d\mathbf{s}_j = \mathbf{u}_{n_j} |d\mathbf{s}_j|$, where $\mathbf{u}_{n_j}$ is a unit vector associated with $d\mathbf{s}_j$ (see Fig. 9.7b). If we now calculate the surface integral of $h_j \, d\mathbf{s}_j$ over the surface a_j,

$$\oiint_{a_j} h_j \mathbf{u}_{n_j} |d\mathbf{s}_j|$$

and sum these integrals for all the N surfaces of the N small volumes, we obtain

$$\sum_{j=1}^N \oiint_{a_j} h_j \mathbf{u}_{n_j} |d\mathbf{s}_j|$$

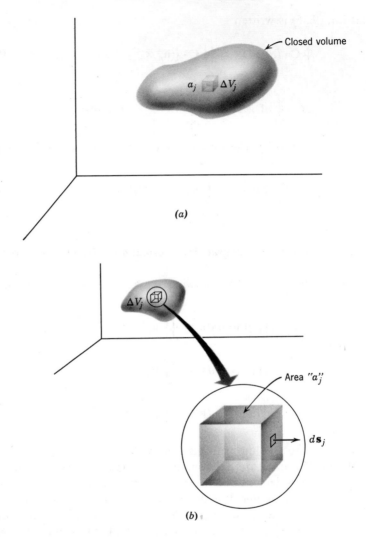

Figure 9.7   (a) A typical volume element ΔV_j having surface of area a_j.   (b) A typical surface element of a typical volume element.

Now, except for the surfaces which form the external surface A, these surface integrals will cancel because $\mathbf{u}_n$ is in one direction for the surface of one of the internal volumes, but in the opposite direction for the surface of the adjoining volumes. The sum of the contributions from the excepted surfaces, that is, those surface integrals over external surfaces, is equivalent to the surface integrals of h over the external surface A:

$$\oiint_A \mathbf{u}_n h \, |ds| = \sum_{j=1}^{N} \oiint_{a_j} \mathbf{u}_{n_j} h_j \, |ds_j| \qquad (9.41)$$

Equation (9.41) represents an approximation which becomes more exact as N approaches infinity so that all the ΔV's approach zero. We assume that Δs_j is well behaved as ΔV_j approaches zero. It is then correct to write

$$\oiint_A \mathbf{u}_n h \, |ds| = \lim_{\substack{N \to \infty \\ \Delta V_j \to 0}} \sum_{j=1}^{N} \oiint_{a_j} \mathbf{u}_{n_j} h_j \, |ds_j| \qquad (9.42)$$

Recalling from Section 5.3 that

$$\operatorname{grad} h \simeq \frac{1}{\Delta V} \oiint_a \mathbf{u}_n h \, |ds| \qquad \text{[see Eq. (5.40)]} \qquad (9.43)$$

for a small volume ΔV where the approximation becomes more exact as ΔV approaches zero, we may then write for the typical small volume ΔV_j, in this discussion.

$$(\operatorname{grad} h_j) \Delta V_j \simeq \oiint_{a_j} \mathbf{u}_{n_j} h_j \, |ds_j| \qquad (9.44)$$

Substituting (9.44) into (9.42), we obtain

$$\oiint_A \mathbf{u}_n h \, |ds| = \lim_{\substack{N \to \infty \\ \Delta V_j \to 0}} \sum_{j=1}^{N} (\operatorname{grad} h_j) \Delta V_j \qquad (9.45)$$

But the right-hand side of Eq. (9.45) is just the volume integral

$$\iiint_V \operatorname{grad} h \, dV$$

The validity of Eq. (9.38) is then apparent.

The other two volume-to-surface integral transformations can be established in an analogous manner.

Since

$$\operatorname{div} \mathbf{F}_j \simeq \frac{1}{\Delta V_j} \oiint_{a_j} \mathbf{u}_{n_j} \cdot \mathbf{F}_j \, |ds_j| \qquad \text{[see Eq. (6.36)]} \qquad (9.46)$$

we may write

$$\oiint_A \mathbf{u}_n \cdot \mathbf{F} \, |ds| = \sum_{j=1}^{N} \oiint_{a_j} \mathbf{u}_{n_j} \cdot \mathbf{F}_j \, |ds_j| = \sum_{j=1}^{N} \operatorname{div} \mathbf{F}_j \, \Delta V_j \qquad (9.47)$$

In the limit, as N approaches infinity so that ΔV_j approaches zero, the right-hand side of Eq. (9.47) becomes a volume integral. Equation (9.47) then may be written

$$\oiint_A \mathbf{u}_n \cdot \mathbf{F} \, |ds| = \iiint_V \operatorname{div} \mathbf{F} \, dV \tag{9.39}$$

and Eq. (9.39) is established. Relation (9.39) is called either the divergence theorem of Gauss's integral theorem.

Similarly, since

$$\operatorname{curl} \mathbf{F}_j \simeq \frac{1}{\Delta V_j} \iint_{a_j} \mathbf{u}_{n_j} \times \mathbf{F}_j \, |ds_j| \qquad \text{[see Eq. (7.36)]} \tag{9.48}$$

for a small volume ΔV_j, we may write

$$\oiint_A \mathbf{u}_n \times \mathbf{F} \, |ds| = \sum_{j=1}^{N} \oiint_{a_j} \mathbf{u}_{n_j} \times \mathbf{F}_j \, |ds_j| = \sum_{j=1}^{N} \operatorname{curl} \mathbf{F}_j \, \Delta V_j \tag{9.49}$$

In the limit as N approaches infinity so that ΔV_j approaches zero, the right-hand side of Eq. (9.49) becomes the integral

$$\iiint_V \operatorname{curl} \mathbf{F} \, dV$$

Thus (9.40) is valid.

9.4   Gauss's Law

In the preceding discussion concerning the integral properties of fields, we have assumed that the integrals involved are proper, which requires, among other things, that the integrands remain bounded over the entire range of integration. For Gauss's divergence theorem we have assumed that $\mathbf{F}$ remains finite within V and on A. As an example of when this is not true, let us consider the field

$$\mathbf{F} = \frac{\mathbf{u}_{R-R'}}{|\mathbf{R} - \mathbf{R}'|^2} \tag{9.50}$$

For $\mathbf{R} = \mathbf{R}'$, the field takes on the value infinity, and we may expect difficulties in evaluating integrals which result from such field singularities. The point $\mathbf{R} = \mathbf{R}'$ is called a field singularity.

In the following discussion we shall limit our treatment to a single illustration of the importance of field singularities and, in so doing, derive Gauss's law. We shall return to a discussion of improper integrals and field singularities in Chapter 11.

Let us consider Gauss's divergence theorem, Eq. (9.39).

$$\iiint_V \nabla \cdot \mathbf{F(R)}\, dV(\mathbf{R}) = \oiint_A \mathbf{F(R)} \cdot d\mathbf{s(R)} \qquad (9.51)$$

where ∇ denotes operations on the unprimed coordinates.

For this example we shall take as $\mathbf{F}$ a vector field whose value at $P(\mathbf{R})$ (see Fig. 9.8a) depends on its position from another point $P'(\mathbf{R}')$ in the following manner:

$$\mathbf{F} = \frac{\mathbf{u_{R-R'}}}{|\mathbf{R} - \mathbf{R'}|^2} \qquad (9.52)$$

where $|\mathbf{R} - \mathbf{R'}|$ is the distance from $P(\mathbf{R})$ to $P'(\mathbf{R}')$ and $\mathbf{u_{R-R'}}$ is a unit vector along $\mathbf{R} - \mathbf{R'}$, the vector from P' to P. Here the point P is constrained to be inside of or on the surface A, whereas the point P' can assume any position, including a point outside of, within, or on A. For such a field Eq. (9.51) becomes

$$\oiint_A \frac{\mathbf{u_n} \cdot \mathbf{u_{R-R'}}\, |d\mathbf{s(R)}|}{|\mathbf{R} - \mathbf{R'}|^2} = 0 \qquad \text{(for } P' \text{ outside } A) \qquad (9.53)$$

because div $\mathbf{F} = 0$ for this field as long as $\mathbf{F}$ remains finite. This means that $\mathbf{R} - \mathbf{R'}$ cannot be zero, that is, for Eq. (9.53) to be correct P' cannot assume a position within or on the surface A. If P' does occupy a position within V, we may resolve the difficulty by surrounding $P'(\mathbf{R})$ with a small sphere of radius ϵ (see Figure 9.8b) and consider only the volume between the surface of V and the surface of the sphere of radius ϵ as $\epsilon \to 0$. Within the volume which excludes this sphere $|\mathbf{R} - \mathbf{R'}|^{-2}$ remains finite and Eq. (9.51) is zero since div $\mathbf{F} = 0$ within $V - V_\epsilon$, that is,

$$\iiint_{V-V_\epsilon} \nabla \cdot \left[\frac{\mathbf{u_{R-R'}}}{|\mathbf{R} - \mathbf{R'}|^2} \right] dV(\mathbf{R}) = \oiint_{A+A_\epsilon} \frac{\mathbf{u_n} \cdot \mathbf{u_{R-R'}}}{|\mathbf{R} - \mathbf{R'}|^2} |d\mathbf{s(R)}| = 0$$

$$= \iint_A \frac{\mathbf{u_n} \cdot \mathbf{u_{R-R'}}}{|\mathbf{R} - \mathbf{R'}|^2} |d\mathbf{s(R)}| + \iint_{A_\epsilon} \frac{\mathbf{u_n} \cdot \mathbf{u_{R-R'}}\, |d\mathbf{s(R)}|}{|\mathbf{R} - \mathbf{R'}|^2} \qquad (9.54)$$

where V_ϵ and A_ϵ are the volume, $\frac{4}{3}\pi\epsilon^3$, and surface, $4\pi\epsilon^2$, of the sphere surrounding the point $P'(\mathbf{R}')$. Since $\mathbf{R}$ locates any point within or on A, we designate the elements of volume and surface as $dV(\mathbf{R})$ and $d\mathbf{s(R)}$, respectively (see Fig. 9.8c).

From Eq. (9.54) we may write

$$\iint_A \frac{\mathbf{u}_{R-R'} \cdot d\mathbf{s}(\mathbf{R})}{|\mathbf{R} - \mathbf{R}'|^2} = -\iint_{A\epsilon} \frac{\mathbf{u}_{R-R'} \cdot \mathbf{u}_n \, |d\mathbf{s}(\mathbf{R})|}{|\mathbf{R} - \mathbf{R}'|^2} \qquad (9.55)$$

Since $\mathbf{u}_{R-R'}$ and $\mathbf{u}_n$ have the opposite sense at A_z [$\mathbf{u}_n$ points toward $P'(\mathbf{R}')$] and since

$$|d\mathbf{s}| = \epsilon^2 \cos \phi \, d\theta \, d\phi$$
$$= |\mathbf{R} - \mathbf{R}'|^2 \cos \phi \, d\theta \, d\phi \qquad (9.56)$$

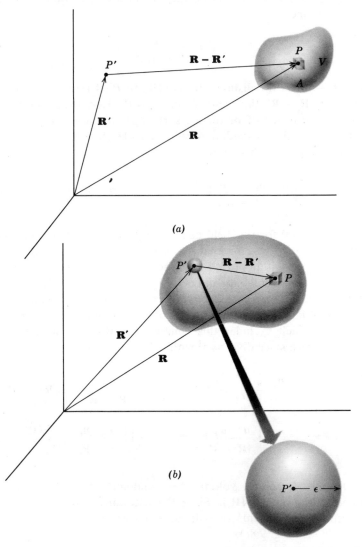

Figure 9.8   (*a*) The field at $P(\mathbf{R})$ depends on its distance from $P'(\mathbf{R}')$. (*b*) The discontinuity at $P(\mathbf{R})$ when $R' = R$. (*c*) Surrounding the singular point with a small sphere.

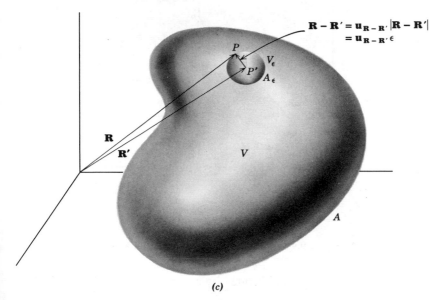

(c)

Eq. (9.55) becomes

$$\oiint_A \frac{\mathbf{u}_{R-R'} \cdot d\mathbf{s}(\mathbf{R})}{|\mathbf{R} - \mathbf{R}'|^2} = \int_{\theta=0}^{2\pi} d\theta \int_{\phi=-\pi/2}^{\pi/2} \cos\phi \, d\phi$$

$$= 4\pi \qquad \text{(for } P' \text{ inside } A) \qquad (9.57)$$

as $\epsilon = |\mathbf{R} - \mathbf{R}'|$ approaches zero.

Equations (9.53) and (9.57) constitute a very important theorem called Gauss's law

$$\oiint_A \frac{\mathbf{u}_n \cdot \mathbf{u}_{R-R'}}{|\mathbf{R} - \mathbf{R}'|^2} |d\mathbf{s}(\mathbf{R})| = 0 \qquad (P' \text{ outside } A)$$

$$= 4\pi \qquad (P' \text{ inside } A) \qquad (9.58)$$

This theorem may also be established by considering further the definition of an elemental solid angle in Eq. (3.88),

$$d\Omega = \frac{\mathbf{u}_n \cdot \mathbf{u}_R}{R^2} |d\mathbf{s}| = -\nabla\left(\frac{1}{R}\right) \cdot d\mathbf{s}$$

where the vector $\mathbf{R}$ locates $d\mathbf{s}$ from the point at which $d\mathbf{s}$ is subtended. By analogy with this definition $d\mathbf{s}$, the solid angle subtended by a surface $d\mathbf{s}(\mathbf{R})$ (located by $\mathbf{R}$) at a point P' (located by $\mathbf{R}'$) (see Fig. 9.9), is given by

$$d\Omega = \frac{\mathbf{u}_{R-R} \cdot d\mathbf{s}(\mathbf{R})}{|\mathbf{R} - \mathbf{R}'|^2} \qquad (9.59a)$$

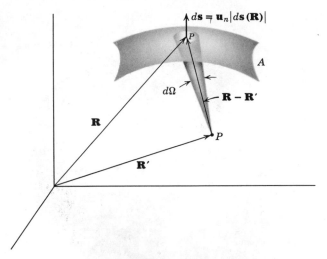

Figure 9.9   For the discussion of the solid angle.

so that Ω, the solid angle subtended by a surface A at P', is

$$\Omega = \oiint_A d\Omega = \oiint_A \frac{\mathbf{u}_{R-R'} \cdot d\mathbf{s}(\mathbf{R})}{|\mathbf{R} - \mathbf{R}'|^2} \qquad (9.59b)$$

The left-hand side of Eq. (9.58) is the solid angle subtended at P' by a surface A. If we use Eq. (9.59b) to calculate the total solid angle subtended by the sphere, we note that $\mathbf{u}_{R-R'}$ and $d\mathbf{s}(\mathbf{R})$ have the same sense; thus $\mathbf{u}_{R-R'} \cdot d\mathbf{s}(\mathbf{R}) = \mathbf{u}_{R-R'} \cdot \mathbf{u}_n \, |d\mathbf{s}(\mathbf{R})| = |d\mathbf{s}(\mathbf{R})| = |\mathbf{R} - \mathbf{R}'|^2 \cos \phi \, d\theta \, d\phi$ and Eq. (9.59b) becomes

$$\Omega = \int_{\theta=0}^{2\pi} d\theta \int_{\phi=-\pi/2}^{\pi/2} \cos \phi \, d\phi = 4\pi \qquad (P' \text{ inside } A) \qquad (9.60)$$

for a sphere. But the solid angle subtended by a surface surrounding a point is always 4π.

Gauss's law may also be established by considering a cone whose vertex is at P' where $d\Omega$ is the solid angle associated with the apex of the cone. If the point P' located by $\mathbf{R}'$ lies outside A, this cone will intersect A an even number of times regardless of the orientation of the cone (see Figure 9.10a). The surface elements $d\mathbf{s}_1, d\mathbf{s}_2 \cdots d\mathbf{s}_N$ cut out by this cone all subtend at P', solid angles whose magnitudes are the same but which are alternately negative and positive. Since there are an even number of such areas, the sum of the solid angles they intercept is zero for the elemental cone, but this would be true for any cone with a vertex at P' as long as P'

is outside of A. We can then say that the solid angle subtended by a surface A from P' when P' is not within A is zero

$$\oiint_A \frac{\mathbf{u}_{\mathbf{R}-\mathbf{R}'} \cdot d\mathbf{s}(\mathbf{R})}{|\mathbf{R} - \mathbf{R}'|^2} = 0 \qquad (P' \text{ outside } A) \qquad (9.61)$$

If the area A encloses P' (see Fig. 9.10b), any cone whose vertex is at P' will intersect A an odd number of times regardless of the position of P'

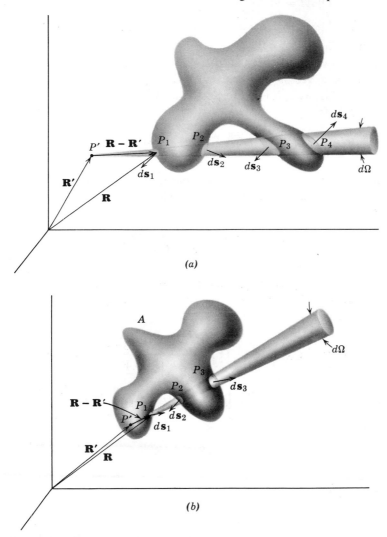

(a)

(b)

Figure 9.10 (a) Solid angle subtended at a point external to a closed surface. (b) Solid angle subtended by a point internal to a closed surface.

within A. The first and the last of such elementary solid angles subtended by these surface elements $d\mathbf{s}_1$, $d\mathbf{s}_2$, etc., will be positive because $\mathbf{u}_{\mathbf{R}-\mathbf{R}'}$ and $\mathbf{u}_n$ will be in the same sense. The total solid angle subtended at a point interior to A is the sum of the solid angles of all cones whose vertices are at P', that is, 4π. Then

$$\oint\!\!\!\!\!\oint_A d\Omega = \iint \frac{\mathbf{u}_{\mathbf{R}-\mathbf{R}'} \cdot d\mathbf{s}(\mathbf{R})}{|\mathbf{R} - \mathbf{R}'|^2} = 4\pi \qquad (P \text{ inside } A) \qquad (9.62)$$

which is similar to Eq. (9.58).

Gauss's law is useful because it provides an easy way to calculate the value of a vector field in sufficiently symmetric situations. As an example of this, we consider the electric field surrounding a point charge q located at $P'(\mathbf{R}')$

$$\mathbf{E}(\mathbf{R}) = \frac{q\mathbf{u}_{\mathbf{R}-\mathbf{R}'}}{4\pi\epsilon_0 |\mathbf{R} - \mathbf{R}'|^2} \qquad (\text{MKS units}) \qquad (9.63)$$

where ϵ_0 is the permittivity of free space; or, if there is a continuous distribution of charge, then the electric field is

$$\mathbf{E}(\mathbf{R}) = \iiint_V \frac{\rho_v(\mathbf{R}')\mathbf{u}_{\mathbf{R}-\mathbf{R}'}}{4\pi\epsilon_0 |\mathbf{R} - \mathbf{R}'|^2} \, dV(\mathbf{R}') \qquad (9.64)$$

where $\rho_v(\mathbf{R}')$ is the charge density at $P'(\mathbf{R}')$ and V is the volume of the charged body. If we calculate the flux through A, the surface of this body, we obtain

$$\oint\!\!\!\!\!\oint_A \mathbf{E}(\mathbf{R}) \cdot d\mathbf{s}(\mathbf{R}) = \oint\!\!\!\!\!\oint_A \left[\iiint_V \frac{\rho_v(\mathbf{R}')\mathbf{u}_{\mathbf{R}-\mathbf{R}'} \, dV(\mathbf{R}')}{4\pi\epsilon_0 |\mathbf{R} - \mathbf{R}'|^2}\right] \cdot d\mathbf{s}(\mathbf{R})$$

$$= \frac{1}{4\pi\epsilon_0} \iiint_V \rho_v(\mathbf{R}') \, dV(\mathbf{R}') \oint\!\!\!\!\!\oint_A \frac{\mathbf{u}_{\mathbf{R}-\mathbf{R}'} \cdot d\mathbf{s}(\mathbf{R})}{|\mathbf{R} - \mathbf{R}'|^2}$$

$$= \frac{1}{\epsilon_0} \iiint_V \rho_v(\mathbf{R}') \, dV(\mathbf{R}')$$

$$= \frac{\text{total charge within } V}{\epsilon_0} \qquad (9.65)$$

We may use this result to calculate the field surrounding a long wire on which resides a charge of ρ_l per unit length. To do this we surround the wire with a long cylinder of radius $|\mathbf{R}|$ and apply Eq. (9.65). Since $\mathbf{E}$ and $d\mathbf{s}$ are in the same direction, Eq. (9.65) becomes

$$\oiint_A \mathbf{E}(\mathbf{R}) \cdot d\mathbf{s}(\mathbf{R}) = E(\mathbf{R}) \oiint_A |d\mathbf{s}(\mathbf{R})|$$

$$= E(\mathbf{R}) 2\pi |\mathbf{R}| l$$

$$= \frac{\rho_l l}{\epsilon_0}$$

where l is the length of the wire. Then we may solve for the magnitude of the field

$$|E(\mathbf{R})| = \frac{\rho_l}{2\pi\epsilon_0 |\mathbf{R}|}$$

That is, the electrostatic field falls off inversely as the distance from a line of charge.

9.5　Green's Theorem

Two relationships, usually referred to as Green's theorems of the first and second (or symmetric) form, are extremely important in the study of fields. They may be stated as

$$\iiint_V h\nabla^2 g \, dV + \iiint_V \nabla h \cdot \nabla g \, dV = \oiint_A h\mathbf{u}_n \cdot \nabla g \, |d\mathbf{s}| \tag{9.67}$$

and

$$\iiint_V (g\nabla^2 h - h\nabla^2 g) \, dV = \oiint_A (g\nabla h - h\nabla g) \cdot d\mathbf{s} \tag{9.68}$$

where, within V, g, and h, are continuous and twice differentiable scalar fields.

To derive these relationships, we shall apply the divergence theorem to a vector field $\mathbf{F}$ which, together with its first spatial derivatives is, continuous within a volume V, that is,

$$\iiint_V \text{div } \mathbf{F} \, dV = \oiint_A \mathbf{u}_n \cdot \mathbf{F} \, |d\mathbf{s}| \tag{9.69}$$

Let $\mathbf{F} = h\mathbf{G}$, where h is a scalar field and $\mathbf{G}$ a vector field, then

$$\text{div } \mathbf{F} = \text{div } (h\mathbf{G}) = h \text{ div } \mathbf{G} + \text{grad } h \cdot \mathbf{G} \tag{9.70}$$

If the field $\mathbf{G}$ is the gradient of a scalar field g, that is, if $\mathbf{G} = \operatorname{grad} g$, then $\operatorname{div} \mathbf{G} = \nabla^2 g$ and Eq. (9.69) becomes

$$\iiint_V h\nabla^2 g \, dV + \iiint_V \nabla g \cdot \nabla h \, dV = \oiint_A h\mathbf{u}_n \cdot \nabla g \, |ds| \qquad (9.71)$$

Equation (9.71) was derived essentially by letting $\mathbf{F} = h \operatorname{grad} g$. If instead we let $\mathbf{F} = g \operatorname{grad} h$, we obtain

$$\iiint_V g\nabla^2 h \, dV + \iiint_V \nabla h \cdot \nabla g \, dV = \oiint_A g\mathbf{u}_n \cdot \nabla h \, |ds| \qquad (9.72)$$

Subtracting Eq. (9.71) from (9.72) yields

$$\iiint_V \{g\nabla^2 h - h\nabla^2 g\} \, dV = \oiint_A \mathbf{u}_n \cdot \{g\nabla h - h\nabla g\} \, |ds| \qquad (9.73)$$

Equation (9.71) is sometimes called Green's theorem and Eq. (9.73) the symmetric form of Green's theorem.

To illustrate the utility of Green's theorem, we shall now show that if the divergence and curl of a vector field $\mathbf{F}$ are specified in V, some volume of space, the field is uniquely determined if the normal component of $\mathbf{F}$ over A, the surface bounding V, is given. To prove this theorem let us imagine that there is a vector field $\mathbf{F}'$ which has the same divergence and curl in V as $\mathbf{F}$ and the same normal component over A as $\mathbf{F}$ but which, for some reason, may be different from $\mathbf{F}$. Letting this difference $\mathbf{F}' - \mathbf{F} \equiv \mathbf{G}$, we may write

$$\operatorname{div} \mathbf{G} = \operatorname{div}(\mathbf{F}' - \mathbf{F}) = \operatorname{div} \mathbf{F}' - \operatorname{div} \mathbf{F} = 0 \qquad (9.74)$$

$$\operatorname{curl} \mathbf{G} = \operatorname{curl}(\mathbf{F}' - \mathbf{F}) = \operatorname{curl} \mathbf{F}' - \operatorname{curl} \mathbf{F} = 0 \qquad (9.75)$$

and

$$\mathbf{u}_n \cdot \mathbf{G} = \mathbf{u}_n \cdot \mathbf{F}' - \mathbf{u}_n \cdot \mathbf{F} = 0 \qquad (9.76)$$

Since $\operatorname{curl} \mathbf{G} = 0$, we see from Eq. (8.22r) that $\mathbf{G}$ must be a vector field which is the gradient of some scalar field g,

$$\mathbf{G} = \operatorname{grad} g \qquad (9.77)$$

Since $\operatorname{div} \mathbf{G} = 0$, we may write $\nabla^2 g = 0$ within the volume V. Furthermore, since $\mathbf{u}_n \cdot \mathbf{G} = 0$, the component of the gradient of g normal to A vanishes,

$$\mathbf{u}_n \cdot \nabla g = 0 \qquad (9.78)$$

on the surface A. Green's theorem, Eq. (9.71), then yields

$$\iiint_V (\nabla g)^2 \, dV = 0 \qquad (9.79)$$

if we take $h = g$. It follows then that since $\nabla^2 g$ cannot be negative, it must be zero,

$$\nabla g = 0 = G = F' - F \qquad (9.80)$$

for every point in V or on A. We conclude therefore that

$$F' = F \qquad (9.81)$$

and that F is uniquely determined.

We have shown that if, within a volume, the divergence and curl of a field are stipulated together with the value of the normal component of the field on the surface of that volume, the field is uniquely determined. We restate this fact to emphasize the importance of the divergence and curl to the very existence of a field. If, in all space, the divergence and curl are zero, then there can be no field. In other words, the divergence and curl, as we have stated previously, may be considered to be the sources (or sinks) of vector fields.

Scalar fields which satisfy the Laplace equation, $\nabla^2 g = 0$, are called harmonic. We shall return to a discussion of these fields in Chapter 11 when we discuss field potentials.

PROBLEMS

1. If the scalar fields f, g, and their derivatives are defined on an open surface A bounded by a closed curve Γ, show that

$$\oint_\Gamma g \operatorname{grad} f \cdot d\mathbf{l} = -\oint_\Gamma f \operatorname{grad} g \cdot d\mathbf{l}$$

2. What is the geometrical interpretation of the integral

$$\oint_\Gamma \mathbf{R} \times d\mathbf{R}$$

where Γ is a plane closed curve?

3. Show that the integral

$$\oint_\Gamma \mathbf{R} \cdot d\mathbf{R}$$

vanishes.

4. By applying Stokes's theorem, obtain Green's theorem for a plane

$$\oint_\Gamma \left\{ F_x \, dx + F_y \, dy \right\} = \iint_A \left(\frac{\partial F_y}{\partial x} - \frac{\partial F_x}{\partial y} \right) dx \, dy$$

5. In deriving Eq. (9.3) we used the fact that

$$[(\mathbf{C} \cdot \nabla)\mathbf{F} - (\mathbf{C}\nabla) \cdot \mathbf{F}] = \mathbf{C} \cdot (\mathbf{u}_n \times \nabla) \times \mathbf{F}$$

Prove that this relationship is valid.

6. Show that

$$(\mathbf{u}_n \times \nabla) \times \mathbf{R} = -2\mathbf{u}_n$$

7. Express

$$\iint_A |d\mathbf{s}|$$

as a line integral around the periphery of A.

8. Show that

$$\frac{1}{3} \oiint_A \mathbf{R} \cdot d\mathbf{s} = V$$

where A is the surface of the volume V.

9. Find the value of

$$\oiint_A \mathbf{F} \cdot d\mathbf{s}$$

when

$$\mathbf{F} = \mathbf{u}_x x^2 + \mathbf{u}_y(y + b) - \mathbf{u}_z z$$

over the surface of a cube bounded by the planes $x = 0$, $y = 0$, $z = 0$, and $x = 1$, $y = 1$, and $z = 1$.

10. Although the gas inside a balloon exerts a force on the balloon walls, the balloon does not move rectilinearly or rotate. Show that a force per unit area of constant magnitude acting normal to the balloon walls results in a zero net force and moment about an origin.

10

Field Operators in Orthogonal Curvilinear Coordinate Systems

10.1 Introduction

Up to this point we have discussed field operators which can be used when the field is expressed in Cartesian coordinates. In such a coordinate system an incremental change in one of the coordinate variables is directly proportional to the magnitude of a spatial displacement. For example, an increment in x, say dx, is tantamount to moving from a point x_1 to a new point $x_1 + dx$ (Fig. 10.1a). Some other coordinate variables in coordinate systems we have examined do not exhibit this fundamental property, for example, in polar coordinates an increment in the coordinate variable θ, $d\theta$ alone is not related to the magnitude of a displacement. However, if we multiply $d\theta$ by ρ, the result is a quantity which is the magnitude of a displacement in space (see Fig. 10.1b). In this chapter we shall generalize on this particular result, namely, that to represent the magnitude of a real displacement in space, it may be necessary to multiply a coordinate variable increment by factors which may depend on all the coordinate variables.

In discussing the gradient, divergence, and curl properties, we have been concerned with the spatial rate of change of a scalar or vector field. This has always involved the idea of an incremental length, for example, line elements, surface elements, and volume elements. It is fundamental, then, to our discussion to be able to describe the magnitude of an infinitesimal spatial displacement in terms of incremental changes in the coordinate variables. We have already done this in Chapter 4 for Cartesian, cylindrical, and spherical coordinate systems. Here we shall first generalize the relationships among the magnitudes of infinitesimal displacements and incremental changes in the variables of orthogonal systems so that we may then treat the field properties in such systems. Having done this we will be in a position to discuss the form of the field operators in orthogonal curvilinear coordinate systems.

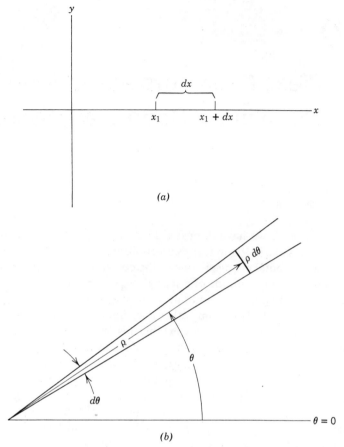

Figure 10.1 (*a*) An example of when a coordinate change is equivalent to the magnitude of a displacement. (*b*) An example of when a coordinate change is not equivalent to a displacement.

10.2 The Relationships between Infinitesimal Spatial Displacements and Infinitesimal Coordinate Variable Changes in Orthogonal Curvilinear Coordinate Systems

A Cartesian coordinate system consists of a gridwork of orthogonal straight lines, for two-dimensional systems, or planes (for three-dimensional systems), each representing a constant value of one of the coordinate variables. As we have seen in Chapter 4, the concept of a coordinate system can be generalized so that any coordinate system may be thought of as a gridwork of curves or surfaces. There we dicussed only orthogonal coordinate systems where the curves or surfaces representing constant values of the coordinates intersect each other at right angles, and we shall continue to discuss such systems.

Let us assume three orthogonal coordinates w_1, w_2, and w_3; thus three sets of coordinate surfaces, $w_1 = $ a constant, $w_2 = $ a constant, and $w_3 = $ a constant, intersect at right angles (see Fig. 10.2). A line element $d\mathbf{l}_1$ on the curve formed by the intersection of the surfaces $w_2 = $ a constant and $w_3 = $ a constant, on which only w_1 varies by an amount dw_1, may be represented by

$$d\mathbf{l}_1 = \mathbf{u}_1 e_1(w_1, w_2, w_3)\, dw_1 \qquad (10.1)$$

where $\mathbf{u}_1 = $ a unit vector with the sense and direction of $d\mathbf{l}_1$,

$e_1 = $ a transformation parameter which may be a function of w_1, w_2, and w_3; e_1 is necessary to relate a change in the coordinate w_1 to a real displacement in the direction of increasing w_1. For example, in the displacement $\rho\, d\theta$ associated with a change in θ, the transformation parameter is ρ.

Similarly, along the curves formed by the intersection of the other surfaces, we find that

$$d\mathbf{l}_2 = \mathbf{u}_2 e_2(w_1, w_2, w_3)\, dw_2 \qquad (10.2)$$

$$d\mathbf{l}_3 = \mathbf{u}_3 e_3(w_1, w_2, w_3)\, dw_3 \qquad (10.3)$$

The magnitude of the square of the distance moved $d\mathbf{l}$ when w_1, w_2, and

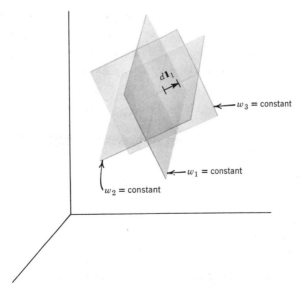

Figure 10.2 $d\mathbf{l}_1$ is normal to surface of constant w_1.

w_3 are changed by dw_1, dw_2, and dw_3, respectively, is given by

$$(dl)^2 = d\mathbf{l} \cdot d\mathbf{l} = (dl_1)^2 + (dl_2)^2 + (dl_3)^2$$
$$= e_1^2(dw_1)^2 + e_2^2(dw_2)^2 + e_3^2(dw_3)^2 \qquad (10.4)$$

The three surfaces ds_1, ds_2, and ds_3 obtained when:

1. w_1 is constant and w_2 and w_3 vary by dw_2 and dw_3 respectively
2. w_2 is constant and w_3 and w_1 vary by dw_3 and dw_1 respectively
3. w_3 is constant and w_1 and w_2 vary by dw_1 and dw_2 respectively

are

$$d\mathbf{s}_1 = e_2 e_3 \, dw_2 \, dw_3 \mathbf{u}_1 \qquad (10.5)$$
$$d\mathbf{s}_2 = e_3 e_1 \, dw_3 \, dw_1 \mathbf{u}_2 \qquad (10.6)$$

and

$$d\mathbf{s}_3 = e_1 e_2 \, dw_1 \, dw_2 \mathbf{u}_3 \qquad (10.7)$$

where $\mathbf{u}_1$, $\mathbf{u}_2$, and $\mathbf{u}_3$ are normal to the surfaces $e_2 e_3 \, dw_2 \, dw_3$, $e_3 e_1 \, dw_3 \, dw_1$, and $e_1 e_2 \, dw_1 \, dw_2$, respectively.

The volume element bounded by these area elements is

$$dV = e_1 e_2 e_3 \, dw_1 \, dw_2 \, dw_3 \qquad (10.8)$$

EXAMPLES

A. Cylindrical Coordinates

$$x = \rho \cos \theta \qquad \rho \text{ corresponds to } w_1 \quad (4.24) \qquad (10.9a)$$
$$y = \rho \sin \theta \qquad \theta \text{ corresponds to } w_2 \quad (4.25) \qquad (10.9b)$$
$$z = z \qquad z \text{ corresponds to } w_3 \quad (4.26) \qquad (10.9c)$$
$$d\mathbf{l}_1 = d\mathbf{l}_\rho = d\rho \mathbf{u}_\rho, \qquad e_1 = 1 \qquad (10.10a)$$
$$d\mathbf{l}_2 = d\mathbf{l}_\theta = \rho \, d\theta \mathbf{u}_\theta, \qquad e_2 = \rho \qquad (10.10b)$$
$$d\mathbf{l}_3 = d\mathbf{l}_z = dz \mathbf{u}_z, \qquad e_3 = 1 \qquad (10.10c)$$

so that

$$d\mathbf{s}_1 = d\mathbf{s}_\rho = \rho \, d\theta \, dz \mathbf{u}_\rho \quad (4.20) \qquad (10.11a)$$
$$d\mathbf{s}_2 = d\mathbf{s}_\theta = d\rho \, dz \mathbf{u}_\theta \quad (4.21) \qquad (10.11b)$$
$$d\mathbf{s}_3 = d\mathbf{s}_z = \rho \, d\rho \, d\theta \mathbf{u}_z \quad (4.22) \qquad (10.11c)$$

and

$$dV = \rho \, d\rho \, d\theta \, dz \quad (4.23) \qquad (10.12)$$

B. Spherical Coordinates

$$x = r \cos \phi \cos \theta \qquad r \text{ corresponds to } w_1 \quad (4.38)$$
$$y = r \cos \phi \sin \theta \qquad \theta \text{ corresponds to } w_2 \quad (4.39)$$
$$z = r \sin \phi \qquad \phi \text{ corresponds to } w_3 \quad (4.40)$$

then

$$dl_1 = dl_r = dr\mathbf{u}_r, \qquad\qquad e_1 = 1 \qquad\qquad (10.13a)$$

$$dl_2 = dl_\theta = r\cos\phi\, d\theta\mathbf{u}_\theta, \qquad e_2 = r\cos\phi \qquad (10.13b)$$

$$dl_3 = dl_\phi = r\, d\phi\mathbf{u}_\phi, \qquad\qquad e_3 = r \qquad\qquad (10.13c)$$

Therefore Eqs. (10.5), (10.6), and (10.7) yield

$$d\mathbf{s}_r = r^2\cos\phi\, d\theta\, d\phi\mathbf{u}_r \qquad (4.34) \qquad\qquad (10.14a)$$

$$d\mathbf{s}_\theta = r\, dr\, d\phi\mathbf{u}_\theta \qquad (4.35) \qquad\qquad (10.14b)$$

$$d\mathbf{s}_\phi = r\cos\phi\, dr\, d\theta\mathbf{u}_\phi \qquad (4.36) \qquad\qquad (10.14c)$$

and

$$dV = r^2\cos\phi\, dr\, d\theta\, d\phi \qquad (4.37) \qquad\qquad (10.15)$$

We must always bear in mind that the dl's always represent the magnitude of real physical displacements, whereas the dw's represent infinitesimal changes in the coordinate variables.

10.3 Gradient, Divergence, and Curl Operators for Fields Expressed in Orthogonal Curvilinear Coordinate Systems

Having described a displacement in an orthogonal curvilinear coordinate system, we are now in a position to discuss field operators in these systems.

THE GRADIENT

Since we saw in Chapter 5 that the directional derivative in any direction is just the scalar product of the gradient and a unit vector in that direction, we may write

$$\text{grad } h = \mathbf{u}_1\{\text{grad } h \cdot \mathbf{u}_1\} + \mathbf{u}_2\{\text{grad } h \cdot \mathbf{u}_2\} + \mathbf{u}_3\{\text{grad } h \cdot \mathbf{u}_3\}$$

$$= \mathbf{u}_1\frac{\partial h}{\partial l_1} + \mathbf{u}_2\frac{\partial h}{\partial l_2} + \mathbf{u}_3\frac{\partial h}{\partial l_3}$$

By substituting for ∂l_1, ∂l_2, and ∂l_3 utilizing Eqs. (10.1), (10.2), and (10.3), we see that

$$\frac{\partial h}{\partial l_1} = \frac{1}{e_1}\frac{\partial h}{\partial w_1}, \qquad \frac{\partial h}{\partial l_2} = \frac{1}{e_2}\frac{\partial h}{\partial w_2}, \qquad \frac{\partial h}{\partial l_3} = \frac{1}{e_3}\frac{\partial h}{\partial w_3} \qquad (10.16)$$

Therefore at any point P, the value of the gradient of a scalar field h expressed in curvilinear coordinates w_1, w_2, and w_3 is

$$\text{grad } h = \mathbf{u}_1\left(\frac{1}{e_1}\frac{\partial h}{\partial w_1}\right) + \mathbf{u}_2\left(\frac{1}{e_2}\frac{\partial h}{\partial w_2}\right) + \mathbf{u}_3\left(\frac{1}{e_3}\frac{\partial h}{\partial w_3}\right) \qquad (10.17)$$

where $\mathbf{u}_j$ is a unit vector normal to the surface $w_j = $ a constant which passes through P and collinear with the intersection of the planes through P which are associated with constant values of the other coordinate variables.

For cylindrical coordinates, Eq. (10.17) becomes [utilizing Eqs. (10.10a, b, and c)]

$$\text{grad } h(\rho, \theta, z) = \mathbf{u}_\rho \frac{\partial h}{\partial \rho} + \mathbf{u}_\theta \frac{1}{\rho} \frac{\partial h}{\partial \theta} + \mathbf{u}_z \frac{\partial h}{\partial z} \qquad (10.18)$$

For spherical coordinates, Eq. (10.17) becomes [utilizing Eqs. (10.13a, b, and c)],

$$\text{grad } h(r, \theta, \phi) = \mathbf{u}_r \frac{\partial h}{\partial r} + \mathbf{u}_\theta \frac{1}{r \cos \phi} \frac{\partial h}{\partial \theta} + \mathbf{u}_\phi \frac{1}{r} \frac{\partial h}{\partial \phi} \qquad (10.19)$$

THE DIVERGENCE

We begin by applying the divergence theorem (Eq. 9.39)

$$\iiint_V \text{div } \mathbf{F} \, dV = \oiint_A \mathbf{u}_n \cdot \mathbf{F} \, |ds| \qquad (10.20)$$

to a small volume element $dV = dl_1 \, dl_2 \, dl_3$ bounded by surfaces which represent constant values of w_1, $w_1 + dw_1$, etc. (see Fig. 10.3). If we have

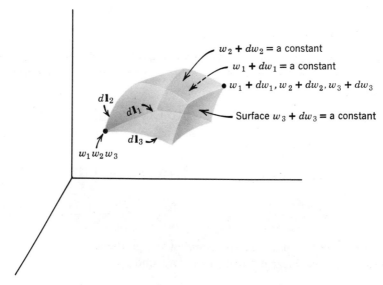

Figure 10.3 Illustration for the discussion of the divergence in orthogonal coordinate systems.

a vector field $\mathbf{F} = \mathbf{u}_1 F_1 + \mathbf{u}_2 F_2 + \mathbf{u}_3 F_3$, the flux into this elemental volume through the face at w_1, whose area is $d\mathbf{s}_1 = \mathbf{u}_1 \, dl_2 \, dl_3$, is

$$(\mathbf{F} \cdot d\mathbf{s}_1)_{w_1} = (F_1 \, dl_2 \, dl_3)_{w_1}$$

and the flux out through the face at $w_1 + dw_1$ is

$$(\mathbf{F} \cdot d\mathbf{s}_1)_{w_1 + dw} = F_1 \, dl_2 \, dl_3 \Big|_{w_1 + dw}$$

so that the net flux through these two faces is

$$(F_1 \, dl_2 \, dl_3)_{w_1 + dw} - (F_1 \, dl_2 \, dl_3)_{w_1}$$

Expanding $(F_1 \, dl_2 \, dl_3)_{w_1 + dw}$ by a Taylor expansion about w_1 and neglecting higher order terms, we obtain

$$\frac{\partial}{\partial w_1} (F_1 \, dl_2 \, dl_3) \, dw_1 = \frac{\partial}{\partial w_1} (F_1 e_2 e_3 \, dw_2 \, dw_3) \, dw_1$$

$$= \frac{\partial}{\partial w_1} (F_1 e_2 e_3) \, dw_1 \, dw_2 \, dw_3$$

$$= \frac{1}{e_1 e_2 e_3} \frac{\partial}{\partial w_1} (F_1 e_2 e_3) \, dl_1 \, dl_2 \, dl_3$$

$$= \frac{1}{e_1 e_2 e_3} \frac{\partial}{\partial w_1} (F_1 e_2 e_3) \, dV$$

Proceeding similarly with the other pairs of faces of the volume dV and setting the net outward flux equal to div $\mathbf{F} \, dV$ we obtain from (10.20),

$$\text{div } \mathbf{F} = \frac{1}{e_1 e_2 e_3} \left[\frac{\partial}{\partial w_1} (F_1 e_2 e_3) + \frac{\partial}{\partial w_2} (F_2 e_3 e_1) + \frac{\partial}{\partial w_3} (F_3 e_1 e_2) \right] \quad (10.21)$$

Thus in cylindrical coordinates we can then write [utilizing Eq. (10.10a, b, and c)]

$$\text{div } \mathbf{F} = \frac{1}{\rho} \frac{\partial}{\partial \rho} (\rho F_\rho) + \frac{1}{\rho} \frac{\partial F_\theta}{\partial \theta} + \frac{\partial F_z}{\partial z} \quad (10.22)$$

and in spherical coordinates

$$\text{div } \mathbf{F} = \frac{1}{r^2 \cos \phi} \left[\frac{\partial}{\partial r} (F_r r^2 \cos \phi) + \frac{\partial}{\partial \theta} (F_\theta r) + \frac{\partial}{\partial \phi} (F_\phi r \cos \phi) \right]$$

$$= \frac{1}{r^2} \frac{\partial}{\partial r} (r^2 F_r) + \frac{1}{r \cos \phi} \frac{\partial}{\partial \theta} (F_\theta) + \frac{1}{r \cos \phi} \frac{\partial}{\partial \phi} (F_\phi \cos \phi) \quad (10.23)$$

THE CURL

For two dimensions we may apply Stokes's theorem

$$\iint_A \text{curl } \mathbf{F} \cdot d\mathbf{s} = \oint_\Gamma \mathbf{F} \cdot d\mathbf{l} \tag{10.24}$$

to an approximately rectangular area bounded by the surfaces $w_1 = \text{a}$ constant, $w_1 + dw_1 = \text{a}$ constant, $w_2 = \text{a}$ constant, and $w_2 + dw_2 = \text{a}$ constant. The integrand of the line integral around Γ is then

$$
\begin{aligned}
\mathbf{F} \cdot d\mathbf{l} &= F_1 \, dl_1 \Big|_{w_1, w_2} + F_2 \, dl_2 \Big|_{w_1 + dw_1, w_2} - F_1 \, dl_1 \Big|_{w_1, w_2 + dw_2} - F_2 \, dl_2 \Big|_{w_1, w_2} \\
&= F_1 \, dl_1 \Big|_{w_1, w_2} + F_2 \, dl_2 \Big|_{w_1, w_2} + \frac{\partial}{\partial w_1} (F_2 \, dl_2) \Big|_{w_1, w_2} dw_1 \\
&\quad - F_1 \, dl_1 \Big|_{w_1, w_2} - \frac{\partial}{\partial w_2} (F_1 \, dl_1) \Big|_{w_1, w_2} dw_2 - F_2 \, dl_2 \Big|_{w_1, w_2} \\
&= \frac{1}{e_1 e_2} \left[\frac{\partial}{\partial w_1} (F_2 e_2) - \frac{\partial}{\partial w_2} (F_1 e_1) \right] dl_1 \, dl_2 \tag{10.25}
\end{aligned}
$$

The coefficient of $dl_1 \, dl_2$ must be the component of curl $\mathbf{F}$ in the $\mathbf{u}_3$ direction,

$$\text{curl}_3 \, \mathbf{F} = \frac{1}{e_1 e_2} \left[\frac{\partial}{\partial w_1} (F_2 e_2) - \frac{\partial}{\partial w_2} (F_1 e_1) \right] \tag{10.26}$$

Similar expressions can be derived for $\text{curl}_2 \, \mathbf{F}$ and $\text{curl}_1 \, \mathbf{F}$. The curl $\mathbf{F}$ can then be written

$$
\begin{aligned}
\text{curl } \mathbf{F} &= \frac{\mathbf{u}_1}{e_2 e_3} \left[\frac{\partial}{\partial w_2} (F_3 e_3) - \frac{\partial}{\partial w_3} (F_2 e_2) \right] \\
&\quad + \frac{\mathbf{u}_2}{e_3 e_1} \left[\frac{\partial}{\partial w_3} (F_1 e_1) - \frac{\partial}{\partial w_1} (F_3 e_3) \right] \\
&\quad + \frac{\mathbf{u}_3}{e_1 e_2} \left[\frac{\partial}{\partial w_1} (F_2 e_2) - \frac{\partial}{\partial w_2} (F_1 e_1) \right] \tag{10.27}
\end{aligned}
$$

In cylindrical coordinates we then have

$$
\begin{aligned}
\text{curl } \mathbf{F} &= \frac{\mathbf{u}_\rho}{\rho} \left[\frac{\partial}{\partial \theta} (F_z) - \frac{\partial}{\partial z} (F_\theta \rho) \right] + \mathbf{u}_\theta \left[\frac{\partial}{\partial z} (F_\rho) - \frac{\partial}{\partial \rho} (F_z) \right] \\
&\quad + \frac{\mathbf{u}_z}{\rho} \left[\frac{\partial}{\partial \rho} (F_\theta \rho) - \frac{\partial}{\partial \theta} (F_\rho) \right] \tag{10.28}
\end{aligned}
$$

and in spherical coordinates

$$
\begin{aligned}
\operatorname{curl} \mathbf{F} = {} & \frac{\mathbf{u}_r}{r \cos \phi}\left[\frac{\partial}{\partial \theta}(F_\phi) - \frac{\partial}{\partial \phi}(F_\theta \cos \phi)\right] \\
& + \frac{\mathbf{u}_\theta}{r}\left[\frac{\partial}{\partial \phi}(F_r) - \frac{\partial}{\partial r}(F_\phi r)\right] \\
& + \frac{\mathbf{u}_\phi}{r \cos \phi}\left[\frac{\partial}{\partial r}(F_\theta r \cos \phi) - \frac{\partial}{\partial \theta}(F_r)\right]
\end{aligned} \tag{10.29}
$$

THE LAPLACIAN

The Laplacian of a scalar field is the divergence of the gradient of that field. Thus the Laplacian of $h(w_1, w_2, w_3)$ expressed in the orthogonal curvilinear coordinates is

$$
\begin{aligned}
& \nabla^2 h(w_1, w_2, w_3) \\
& = \frac{1}{e_1 e_2 e_3}\left[\frac{\partial}{\partial w_1}\left(\frac{e_2 e_3}{e_1}\frac{\partial h}{\partial w_1}\right) + \frac{\partial}{\partial w_2}\left(\frac{e_3 e_1}{e_2}\frac{\partial h}{\partial w_2}\right) + \frac{\partial}{\partial w_3}\left(\frac{e_1 e_2}{e_3}\frac{\partial h}{\partial w_3}\right)\right]
\end{aligned} \tag{10.30}
$$

In cylindrical coordinates this becomes

$$
\nabla^2 h(\rho, \theta, z) = \frac{1}{\rho}\frac{\partial}{\partial \rho}\left(\rho\frac{\partial h}{\partial \rho}\right) + \frac{1}{\rho^2}\frac{\partial^2 h}{\partial \theta^2} + \frac{\partial^2 h}{\partial z^2} \tag{10.31}
$$

If h is expressed in spherical coordinates, its Laplacian is

$$
\nabla^2 h(r, \theta, \phi) = \frac{1}{r^2}\frac{\partial}{\partial r}\left(r^2\frac{\partial h}{\partial r}\right) + \frac{1}{r^2 \cos^2 \phi}\frac{\partial^2 h}{\partial \theta^2} + \frac{1}{r^2 \cos \phi}\frac{\partial}{\partial \phi}\left(\cos \phi\frac{\partial h}{\partial \phi}\right) \tag{10.32}
$$

In Chapter 8 we defined the Laplacian of a vector field $\mathbf{F}$ as the Laplacian, expressed in rectangular coordinates, operating on each rectangular coordinate component of $\mathbf{F}$. The generalization of this definition for orthogonal curvilinear coordinate systems follows from Eq. (8.22s):

$$
\nabla \cdot \nabla \mathbf{F} = \nabla^2 \mathbf{F} = \nabla(\nabla \cdot \mathbf{F}) - \nabla \times \nabla \times \mathbf{F}
$$

We shall not perform the calculation here, but if we were to proceed with the operations given on the right-hand side of this equation in accordance with the generalized curvilinear coordinate operators discussed previously, we would find that the difference between $\nabla(\nabla \cdot \mathbf{F})$ and $\nabla \times \nabla \times \mathbf{F}$ is not the result which follows from the application of the Laplacian to the orthogonal curvilinear components of $\mathbf{F}$.

10.4   Further Considerations

The relationships discussed in the foregoing sections can also be treated in a different manner. When writing Eq. (5.24), we saw that

$$\nabla g = \nabla w_1 \frac{\partial g}{\partial w_1} + \nabla w_2 \frac{\partial g}{\partial w_2} + \nabla w_3 \frac{\partial g}{\partial w_3} \qquad (10.33)$$

where the field on which this operates is an explicit function of the scalar variables w_1, w_2, and w_3, each of which is a function of x, y, and z. If w_1, w_2, and w_3 form an orthogonal coordinate system, then, according to Eqs. (10.1), (10.2), and (10.3),

$$d\mathbf{l}_1 = \mathbf{u}_1 e_1 \, dw_1 \qquad (10.34a)$$

$$d\mathbf{l}_2 = \mathbf{u}_2 e_2 \, dw_2 \qquad (10.34b)$$

$$d\mathbf{l}_3 = \mathbf{u}_3 e_3 \, dw_3 \qquad (10.34c)$$

where $d\mathbf{l}_1$ is the displacement associated with a change dw_1 in the coordinate variable w_1. Then

$$\nabla w_1 \cdot d\mathbf{l}_1 = \nabla w_1 \cdot \mathbf{u}_1 e_1 \, dw_1 = dw_1 \qquad (10.35)$$

or

$$\nabla w_1 \cdot \mathbf{u}_1 e_1 = 1 \qquad (10.36)$$

which implies that

$$\nabla w_1 = \frac{\mathbf{u}_1}{e_1} \qquad (10.37a)$$

Similarly,

$$\nabla w_2 = \frac{\mathbf{u}_2}{e_2} \qquad (10.37b)$$

and

$$\nabla w_3 = \frac{\mathbf{u}_3}{e_3} \qquad (10.37c)$$

so that Eq. (10.33) may be written

$$\nabla g = \frac{\mathbf{u}_1}{e_1} \frac{\partial g}{\partial w_1} + \frac{\mathbf{u}_2}{e_2} \frac{\partial g}{\partial w_2} + \frac{\mathbf{u}_3}{e_3} \frac{\partial g}{\partial w_3} \qquad (10.38)$$

which is identical to Eq. (10.17).
  If the operator

$$\nabla = \frac{\mathbf{u}_1}{e_1} \frac{\partial}{\partial w_1} + \frac{\mathbf{u}_2}{e_2} \frac{\partial}{\partial w_2} + \frac{\mathbf{u}_3}{e_3} \frac{\partial}{\partial w_3} \qquad (10.39)$$

is to operate on a vector, it is convenient to represent the vector

$$\mathbf{F} = \mathbf{u}_1 F_1 + \mathbf{u}_2 F_2 + \mathbf{u}_3 F_3 \qquad (10.40)$$

as

$$\mathbf{F} = e_2 e_3 \nabla w_2 \times \nabla w_3 F_1 + e_3 e_1 \nabla w_3 \times \nabla w_1 F_2 + e_1 e_2 \nabla w_1 \times \nabla w_2 F_3 \qquad (10.41)$$

which is possible because [see Eqs. (10.37a, b, c)]

$$\mathbf{u}_1 = \mathbf{u}_2 \times \mathbf{u}_3 = \nabla w_2 \times \nabla w_3 (e_2 e_3) \qquad (10.42a)$$

$$\mathbf{u}_2 = \mathbf{u}_3 \times \mathbf{u}_1 = \nabla w_3 \times \nabla w_1 (e_3 e_1) \qquad (10.42b)$$

$$\mathbf{u}_3 = \mathbf{u}_1 \times \mathbf{u}_2 = \nabla w_1 \times \nabla w_2 (e_1 e_2) \qquad (10.42c)$$

The divergence of $\mathbf{F}$ can now be written

$$\nabla \cdot \mathbf{F} = \left(\nabla w_1 \frac{\partial}{\partial w_1} + \nabla w_2 \frac{\partial}{\partial w_2} + \nabla w_3 \frac{\partial}{\partial w_3} \right) \cdot$$

$$(e_2 e_3 \nabla w_2 \times \nabla w_3 F_1 + e_3 e_1 \nabla w_3 \times \nabla w_1 F_2 + e_1 e_2 \nabla w_1 \times \nabla w_2 F_3)$$

$$= \frac{1}{e_1 e_2 e_3} \left[\frac{\partial}{\partial w_1} (e_2 e_3 F_1) + \frac{\partial}{\partial w_2} (e_3 e_1 F_2) + \frac{\partial}{\partial w_3} (e_1 e_2 F_3) \right] \qquad (10.43)$$

which is identical to Eq. (10.21). That Eq. (10.43) is correct can be seen by observing the term

$$\nabla w_1 \frac{\partial}{\partial w_1} \cdot (e_2 e_3 \nabla w_2 \times \nabla w_3 F_1 + e_3 e_1 \nabla w_3 \times \nabla w_1 F_2 + e_1 e_2 \nabla w_1 \times \nabla w_2 F_3)$$

$$= \nabla w_1 \cdot \nabla w_2 \times \nabla w_3 \frac{\partial}{\partial w_1} (e_2 e_3 F_1) = \frac{1}{e_1 e_2 e_3} \frac{\partial}{\partial w_1} (e_2 e_3 F_1) \qquad (10.44)$$

because $\nabla w_2 \times \nabla w_3$ is not a function of w_1 and $\nabla w_1 \cdot \nabla w_2 \times \nabla w_3 = 1/e_1 e_2 e_3$; and the other terms can be treated similarly.

The curl of $\mathbf{F}$ is found by writing

$$\nabla \times \mathbf{F} = \left(\nabla w_1 \frac{\partial}{\partial w_1} + \nabla w_2 \frac{\partial}{\partial w_2} + \nabla w_3 \frac{\partial}{\partial w_3} \right)$$

$$\times (e_1 \nabla w_1 F_1 + e_2 \nabla w_2 F_2 + e_3 \nabla w_3 F_3)$$

$$= \frac{\mathbf{u}_3}{e_1 e_2} \frac{\partial (e_2 F_2)}{\partial w_1} - \frac{\mathbf{u}_2}{e_3 e_1} \frac{\partial (e_3 F_3)}{\partial w_1} - \frac{\mathbf{u}_3}{e_1 e_2} \frac{\partial (e_1 F_1)}{\partial w_2}$$

$$+ \frac{\mathbf{u}_1}{e_2 e_3} \frac{\partial (e_3 F_3)}{\partial w_2} + \frac{\mathbf{u}_2}{e_3 e_1} \frac{\partial (e_1 F_1)}{\partial w_3} - \frac{\mathbf{u}_1}{e_2 e_3} \frac{\partial (e_2 F_2)}{\partial w_3}$$

$$= \frac{\mathbf{u}_1}{e_2 e_3} \left[\frac{\partial (e_3 F_3)}{\partial w_2} - \frac{\partial (e_2 F_2)}{\partial w_3} \right] + \frac{\mathbf{u}_2}{e_3 e_1} \left[\frac{\partial (e_1 F_1)}{\partial w_3} - \frac{\partial (e_3 F_3)}{\partial w_1} \right]$$

$$+ \frac{\mathbf{u}_3}{e_1 e_2} \left[\frac{\partial (e_2 F_2)}{\partial w_1} - \frac{\partial (e_1 F_1)}{\partial w_2} \right] \qquad (10.45)$$

where we have taken Eqs. (10.42a, b, and c) into account. Equation (10.45) is seen to be identical to Eq. (10.27).

PROBLEMS

1. For the h and $\mathbf{F}$ expressed in the ellipsoidal coordinate system of Problem 4.1, determine grad h, div $\mathbf{F}$, and curl $\mathbf{F}$.

2. Repeat Problem 10.1 for h and $\mathbf{F}$ expressed in a parabolic coordinate system (see Example 4.2).

3. Repeat Problem 10.1 for h and $\mathbf{F}$ expressed in the ellipsoidal coordinates discussed in Example 4.3.

4. Show that on the surface of a right circular cylinder of radius ρ whose axis is the z-axis, the value of the operator ∇ is

$$\nabla \equiv \frac{\mathbf{u}_\theta}{\rho} \frac{\partial}{\partial \theta} + \mathbf{u}_z \frac{\partial}{\partial z}$$

11

Field Potentials

11.1 Introduction

In nontechnical terminology the word potential connotes "the capability of being but not yet being; possible, but not actual," and is used to express that which is expected. In the study of fields, a field potential or simply potential is an auxiliary field on which prescribed mathematical operations are performed to yield the field which is of primary interest.

There are two types of vector fields — irrotational and solenoidal. The first, as we have seen in Section 5.3, is derivable from a scalar field called the scalar potential; we shall see presently that the latter is derivable from a vector potential.

The utility of potentials and the reason for their consideration are that they provide a convenient way to relate a field to its scalar and/or vector sources and sinks. More specifically, potentials are of interest for these reasons:

1. Field potentials are usually mathematically simpler than the fields which are derivable from them. Consequently, it is generally easier to perform necessary mathematical operations on them than on the primary field. For example, $\mathbf{E}(\mathbf{R})$, the electric field at a point in space, may be written (see Fig. 11.1)

$$\mathbf{E}(\mathbf{R}) = \frac{1}{4\pi\epsilon_0} \iiint_{\substack{\text{all} \\ \text{space}}} \frac{\rho_v(\mathbf{R}')\mathbf{u}_{\mathbf{R}-\mathbf{R}'}\, dV(\mathbf{R}')}{|\mathbf{R}-\mathbf{R}'|^2} \tag{11.1}$$

where $\rho_v(\mathbf{R}')$ is the charge density in an element of volume $dV(\mathbf{R}')$ located by the vector $\mathbf{R}'$, and $\mathbf{u}_{\mathbf{R}-\mathbf{R}'}$ is a unit vector with the sense and direction of the vector $\mathbf{R} - \mathbf{R}'$ which specifies the distance from the source point at $\mathbf{R}'$ to the field point $\mathbf{R}$. In this chapter we shall derive Eq. (11.1) and the scalar field potential $\Phi(\mathbf{R})$, from which $\mathbf{E}(\mathbf{R})$ may be derived. We shall see that $\Phi(\mathbf{R})$ is given by

$$\Phi(\mathbf{R}) = \frac{1}{4\pi\epsilon_0} \iiint_{\substack{\text{all} \\ \text{space}}} \frac{\rho_v(\mathbf{R}')\, dV(\mathbf{R}')}{|\mathbf{R}-\mathbf{R}'|} \tag{11.2}$$

239

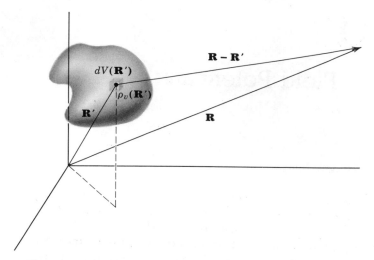

Figure 11.1   The electric field at a point due to a charge element.

Such an expression is simpler and easier to work with than the electric field for two reasons. Equation (11.2) is a scalar relation, whereas Eq. (11.1) is a vector relation requiring the evaluation of three scalar integrals. Furthermore, the integrand of Eq. (11.2) contains $|\mathbf{R} - \mathbf{R}'|$ to the inverse first power and Eq. (11.1) contains it as the inverse square. Very often this difference means that Eq. (11.2) may be evaluated in closed form, whereas Eq. (11.1) may not.

An objection may be raised here that, although Eq. (11.2) is easier to evaluate than Eq. (11.1), it is still necessary to perform some additional operations on the potential to obtain the field which Eq. (11.1) gives directly. However, in this chapter we shall see that the operations which must be performed on a field potential to obtain the field are tantamount to spatial differentiations and such operations are easier to perform than integrations.

2. In many applications of field theory the concept of a field potential may be interpreted in a manner which facilitates and broadens our understanding of the physical situation, the processes or the phenomenon involved. For example, we shall see that the electrostatic potential $\Phi(\mathbf{R})$ given by Eq. (11.2) can be considered as the potential energy of a unit positive charge at $\mathbf{R}$ and, as such, describes the work done by an external agent in moving a unit positive charge from a reference point, usually infinity, to the point $\mathbf{R}$ in the presence of the electric field $\mathbf{E}(\mathbf{R})$.

3. When the scalar and vector source distributions for a vector field are not prescribed as in the situation when a source(s) is to some extent

free to move under the influence of another source(s) to a position of equilibrium, the concept of a field potential is invaluable. It permits us to derive a fundamental differential equation which, when solved, determines the potential and hence the field.

The structure of this chapter will be as follows.

1. We shall begin by discussing the fields and field potentials associated with gravitational, electric, and magnetic forces. The divergence and curl of such fields will be related to field sources.

2. We shall next discuss general irrotational vector fields and show that they are derivable from scalar potentials; then we shall consider solenoidal fields and demonstrate that they may be determined from vector potentials.

3. Then we shall show that a large class of fields, which includes the fields encountered in science and engineering, may be resolved into an irrotational part and a solenoidal part.

4. In Section 9.5 we showed that any vector field **F** is uniquely determined in a region of space V if its divergence and curl are specified for every point of V and if the normal derivative of the field over A, the surface of V, is given. We shall consider the problem of determining the field in a region V once the divergence and curl in V and normal derivative over A for the field are prescribed. In showing how this problem may be solved, we shall demonstrate the usefulness of field potentials in relating the curl and divergence of a field to the field sources and hence to the field itself.

5. We shall derive and discuss the Poisson and Laplace equations. However, to obtain physically acceptable solutions for these two important equations, we must be able to specify appropriate boundary conditions. This topic is intimately associated with field discontinuities and improper integrals. We have neglected the subject of improper integrals up to this point in order not to disturb the continuity of the discussion.

6. Finally, we conclude with a discussion of Green's functions.

11.2 Inverse Square Fields and Their Potentials

Many fields encountered in science and engineering vary inversely as the square of the distance from the source element. As an example of a field of this type, consider a gravitational field (see Fig. 11.2). The force **F(R)** on an element of mass $\Delta m(\mathbf{R})$ located at **R** due to the existence of another element of mass $\Delta m'(\mathbf{R}')$ located at **R'** is directed toward $\Delta m'(\mathbf{R}')$ and is of a magnitude which depends on the product of these masses and is

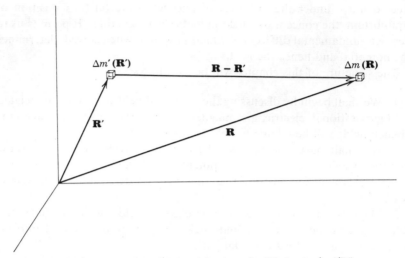

Figure 11.2   The gravitational force on $\Delta m(\mathbf{R})$ due to $\Delta m'(\mathbf{R}')$.

inversely proportional to the square of the distance between the two masses as:

$$F(\mathbf{R}) = \frac{-k\,\Delta m(\mathbf{R})\,\Delta m'(\mathbf{R}')}{4\pi\,|\mathbf{R} - \mathbf{R}'|^{2}}\,\mathbf{u}_{\mathbf{R}-\mathbf{R}'} \qquad (11.3)$$

where k is the gravitational constant whose numerical value depends on the units in which the masses, distance, and force are measured; for example, it is 6.67×10^{-11} newton meters^2/kilogram^2 in the MKS system. Here the spatial extent of $\Delta m(\mathbf{R})$ and $\Delta m'(\mathbf{R}')$ are so small that the distance between the two masses may be specified by a single number $|\mathbf{R} - \mathbf{R}'|$; in other words, Δm and $\Delta m'$ are point masses; that is, one portion of Δm cannot exert any gravitational force on another portion of itself. $\mathbf{u}_{\mathbf{R}-\mathbf{R}'}$ is a unit vector from $\Delta m'(\mathbf{R}')$ to $\Delta m(\mathbf{R})$; the force is attractive so that it has a sense opposite to that of $\mathbf{u}_{\mathbf{R}-\mathbf{R}'}$.

Equation (11.3) may be expressed as a force field $\mathbf{G}(\mathbf{R})$, created by $\Delta m'(\mathbf{R}')$, which acts on $\Delta m(\mathbf{R})$:

$$F(\mathbf{R}) = \mathbf{G}(\mathbf{R})\,\Delta m(\mathbf{R}) \qquad (11.4)$$

where

$$\mathbf{G}(\mathbf{R}) \equiv \frac{F(\mathbf{R})}{\Delta m(\mathbf{R})} = \frac{-k\,\Delta m'(\mathbf{R}')\mathbf{u}_{\mathbf{R}-\mathbf{R}'}}{4\pi\,|\mathbf{R} - \mathbf{R}'|^{2}} \qquad (11.5)$$

As such we see that $\mathbf{G}(\mathbf{R})$ is the force on a unit mass, located at $\mathbf{R}$, which is the result of the presence of another mass $\Delta m'(\mathbf{R}')$. We may consider $\Delta m'(\mathbf{R}')$ to be fixed in space; in other words, $\mathbf{R}'$ is constant and $\Delta m(\mathbf{R})$

may assume any position in space, and $\mathbf{R}$ is a variable. Thus $\Delta m'(\mathbf{R}')$ is the source of the force field.

If we surround $\Delta m'(\mathbf{R}')$ with a closed surface of area A and arbitrary shape (see Fig. 11.3), we see that the surface integral of $\mathbf{G}(\mathbf{R})$ over this surface, the total flux across A, is

$$\oiint_A (\mathbf{R}) \cdot d\mathbf{s}(\mathbf{R}) = -k \oiint_A \frac{\Delta m'(\mathbf{R}')\mathbf{u}_{\mathbf{R}-\mathbf{R}'} \cdot d\mathbf{s}(\mathbf{R})}{4\pi \,|\mathbf{R} - \mathbf{R}'|^2}$$

$$= -k\,\Delta m'(\mathbf{R}') \oiint_A \frac{\mathbf{u}_{\mathbf{R}-\mathbf{R}'} \cdot d\mathbf{s}(\mathbf{R})}{4\pi \,|\mathbf{R} - \mathbf{R}'|^2} \qquad (11.6)$$

because $\Delta m'(\mathbf{R}')$ is not a variable, that is, $\mathbf{R}'$ is fixed. From Gauss's theorem [Eq. (9.58)], Eq. (11.6) becomes

$$\oiint_A \mathbf{G}(\mathbf{R}) \cdot d\mathbf{s}(\mathbf{R}) = -k\,\Delta m'(\mathbf{R}') \qquad (11.7)$$

or

$$\frac{1}{k} \oiint_A \mathbf{G}(\mathbf{R}) \cdot d\mathbf{s}(\mathbf{R}) = -\Delta m'(\mathbf{R}')$$

That is, there is a net flux of gravitational lines of force *into* the volume surrounded by A.

Thus the gravitational field at $\mathbf{R}$ because of several elements of mass

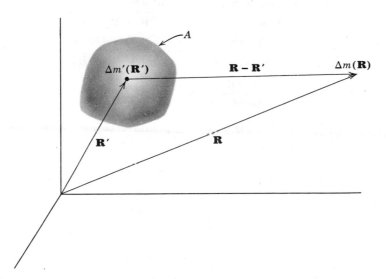

Figure 11.3 Surrounding $\Delta m'(\mathbf{R}')$ with an arbitrary surface A.

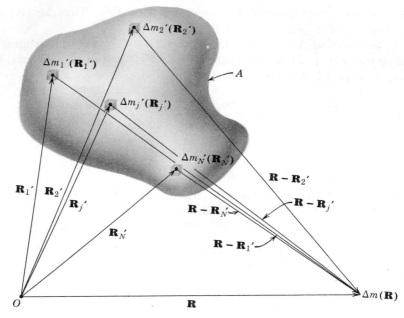

Figure 11.4   Surrounding a group of point masses with an arbitrary surface.

$\Delta m_1'(\mathbf{R}_1')$, $\Delta m_2'(\mathbf{R}_2')$, ..., $\Delta m_j'(\mathbf{R}_j')$, ... $\Delta m_N'(\mathbf{R}_N')$ is (see Fig. 11.4)

$$\mathbf{G}(\mathbf{R}) = \frac{-k\,\Delta m_1'(\mathbf{R}_1')\mathbf{u}_{\mathbf{R}-\mathbf{R}_1'}}{4\pi\,|\mathbf{R} - \mathbf{R}_1'|^2} - \frac{k\,\Delta m_2'(\mathbf{R}_2')\mathbf{u}_{\mathbf{R}-\mathbf{R}_2'}}{4\pi\,|\mathbf{R} - \mathbf{R}_2'|^2}$$

$$\cdots - \cdots \frac{k\,\Delta m_j'(\mathbf{R}_j')\mathbf{u}_{\mathbf{R}-\mathbf{R}_j'}}{4\pi\,|\mathbf{R} - \mathbf{R}_j'|^2} - \cdots \frac{k\,\Delta m_N'(\mathbf{R}_N')\mathbf{u}_{\mathbf{R}-\mathbf{R}_N'}}{|\mathbf{R} - \mathbf{R}_N'|^2}$$

$$= -k\sum_{j=1}^{N} \frac{\Delta m_j'(\mathbf{R}_j')\mathbf{u}_{\mathbf{R}-\mathbf{R}_j'}}{4\pi\,|\mathbf{R} - \mathbf{R}_j'|^2} \tag{11.8}$$

If we surround the N elements of mass with a surface A of arbitrary shape (see Fig. 11.4) and calculate the flux out of A, we obtain

$$\oiint_A \mathbf{G}(\mathbf{R}) \cdot d\mathbf{s}(\mathbf{R}) = -k \oiint_A \sum_{j=1}^{N} \frac{\Delta m_j'(\mathbf{R}_j')\mathbf{u}_{\mathbf{R}-\mathbf{R}_j'}}{4\pi\,|\mathbf{R} - \mathbf{R}_j|^2} \cdot d\mathbf{s}(\mathbf{R})$$

$$= -k\sum_{j=1}^{N} \Delta m_j'(\mathbf{R}_j') \oiint_A \frac{\mathbf{u}_{\mathbf{R}-\mathbf{R}_j'} \cdot d\mathbf{s}(\mathbf{R})}{4\pi\,|\mathbf{R} - \mathbf{R}_j'|^2}$$

$$= -k\sum_{j=1}^{N} \Delta m_j'(\mathbf{R}_j')$$

$$= -k(\text{total mass within } A) \tag{11.9}$$

Again, the minus sign signifies that the force field $\mathbf{G}$ is attractive—that field lines are going into A.

If now we wish to calculate the gravitational field from a continuous distribution of mass, the continuous body may be divided into elements of mass $\Delta m_j'(\mathbf{R}_j') = \rho_v(\mathbf{R}_j')\Delta V(\mathbf{R}_j')$ (see Fig. 11.5), where $\rho_v(\mathbf{R}_j')$ is the volume mass density within $\Delta V(\mathbf{R}_j')$; it is the source density for the field. In the limit, as the number of such mass elements approaches infinity so that all the $\Delta V(\mathbf{R}_j')$ approach zero, Eq. (11.8) becomes

$$\mathbf{G}(\mathbf{R}) = -k \iiint_V \frac{\rho_v(\mathbf{R}')\mathbf{u}_{\mathbf{R}-\mathbf{R}'}\,dV(\mathbf{R}')}{4\pi\,|\mathbf{R}-\mathbf{R}'|^2} \tag{11.10}$$

where V is the volume of the continuous body and $\mathbf{R}'$ is now a variable utilized to locate a source point within V, and $\mathbf{R}$ is a field point.

Since

$$\nabla \times \frac{\mathbf{u}_{\mathbf{R}-\mathbf{R}'}}{|\mathbf{R}-\mathbf{R}'|^2} = 0$$

we observe that the curl of Eq. (11.10) is

$$\begin{aligned}
\nabla \times \mathbf{G}(\mathbf{R}) &= -\nabla \times k \iiint_V \frac{\rho_v(\mathbf{R})\,dV(\mathbf{R}')\mathbf{u}_{\mathbf{R}-\mathbf{R}'}}{4\pi\,|\mathbf{R}-\mathbf{R}'|^2} \\
&= -\frac{k}{4\pi} \iiint \rho_v(\mathbf{R}') \nabla \times \frac{\mathbf{u}_{\mathbf{R}-\mathbf{R}'}}{|\mathbf{R}-\mathbf{R}'|^2}\,dV(\mathbf{R}') \\
&= 0
\end{aligned} \tag{11.11}$$

and we conclude that $\mathbf{G}$ is an irrotational field (see Section 5.2). We see

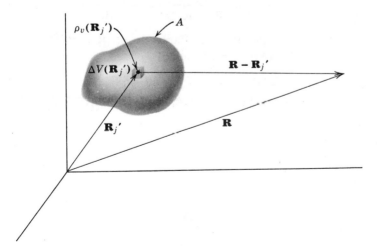

Figure 11.5 The field due to a continuous mass distribution.

that **G** can be written as

$$\mathbf{G(R)} = \nabla g(\mathbf{R}) \tag{11.12}$$

where g, a scalar field, is given by

$$g(\mathbf{R}) = k \iiint \frac{\rho_v(\mathbf{R'})\, dV(\mathbf{R'})}{4\pi\, |\mathbf{R} - \mathbf{R'}|}$$

(See Eq. 8.19.)

Here both **R** and **R'** are variables, but ∇ operates only on the field points located by **R**. We shall meet many situations where we wish to operate on the source points located by **R'**. It is necessary then to develop a notation which distinguishes between these operations. To do so, let us write $|\mathbf{R} - \mathbf{R'}|$ as

$$|\mathbf{R} - \mathbf{R'}| = [(x - x')^2 + (y - y')^2 + (z - z')^2]^{\frac{1}{2}} \tag{11.13}$$

where x, y, z locate $P(\mathbf{R})$ and x', y', and z' locate $P'(\mathbf{R'})$ and adopt the convention

$$\nabla \equiv \mathbf{u}_x \frac{\partial}{\partial x} + \mathbf{u}_y \frac{\partial}{\partial y} + \mathbf{u}_z \frac{\partial}{\partial z} \tag{11.14}$$

and

$$\nabla' \equiv \mathbf{u}_x \frac{\partial}{\partial x'} + \mathbf{u}_y \frac{\partial}{\partial y'} + \mathbf{u}_z \frac{\partial}{\partial z'} \tag{11.15}$$

If these operators operate on $|\mathbf{R} - \mathbf{R'}|^{-\nu}$, we obtain

$$\nabla \frac{1}{|\mathbf{R} - \mathbf{R'}|^\nu} = \frac{-\nu \mathbf{u}_{\mathbf{R}-\mathbf{R'}}}{|\mathbf{R} - \mathbf{R'}|^{\nu+1}} \tag{11.16}$$

and

$$\nabla' \frac{1}{|\mathbf{R} - \mathbf{R'}|^\nu} = \frac{\nu \mathbf{u}_{\mathbf{R}-\mathbf{R'}}}{|\mathbf{R} - \mathbf{R'}|^{\nu+1}} = -\nabla \frac{1}{|\mathbf{R} - \mathbf{R'}|^\nu} \tag{11.17}$$

It should be noted also that the Laplacian of $|\mathbf{R} - \mathbf{R'}|^{-\nu}$ is the same regardless of which variables are treated,

$$\nabla^2 |\mathbf{R} - \mathbf{R'}|^{-\nu} = \nabla'^2 |\mathbf{R} - \mathbf{R'}|^{-\nu} \tag{11.18}$$

By analogy with Eq. (11.9), when A is the surface of the continuous mass distribution having a volume V (see Fig. 11.5), the flux across A is seen to be

$$\oiint_A \mathbf{G(R')} \cdot d\mathbf{s(R')} = -k \oiint_A \left[\iiint_V \rho_v(\mathbf{R'})\, dV(\mathbf{R'}) \right] \frac{\mathbf{u}_{\mathbf{R}-\mathbf{R'}} \cdot d\mathbf{s(R')}}{4\pi\, |\mathbf{R} - \mathbf{R'}|^2}$$

$$= -k \iiint_V \rho_v(\mathbf{R'})\, dV(\mathbf{R'})$$

$$= -k(\text{total mass in } V) \tag{11.19}$$

From Eq. (9.39), the left-hand side of Eq. (11.19) may be changed to a volume integral so that it becomes

$$\iiint\limits_V \nabla' \cdot \mathbf{G}(\mathbf{R}') \, dV(\mathbf{R}') = -k \iiint\limits_V \rho_v(\mathbf{R}') \, dV(\mathbf{R}') \qquad (11.20)$$

Since this is valid for all volumes, the following is true.

$$\nabla' \cdot \mathbf{G}(\mathbf{R}') = -k\rho_v(\mathbf{R}') \qquad (11.21a)$$

This says that the divergence of the gravitational field at any point in space is proportional to the volume mass density at that point. We may therefore write Eq. (11.21a) as

$$\nabla \cdot \mathbf{G}(\mathbf{R}) = -k\rho_v(\mathbf{R}) \qquad (11.21b)$$

where $\mathbf{R}$ locates any point in space. This result, the divergence of a vector field is proportional to the scalar source density, is valid for all vector fields. In fact, we can start to think of the divergence of a field *as* the scalar source density.

As an example of the usefulness of the foregoing ideas, consider dW, the work done by an external agent in moving Δm, a point mass element, to another position in the direction of the field (see Fig. 11.6)

$$dW = \mathbf{F} \cdot d\mathbf{l} = \Delta m \mathbf{G} \cdot d\mathbf{l} \qquad (11.22)$$

[See Eq. (2.21).] Thus the total work done in moving the point mass from a

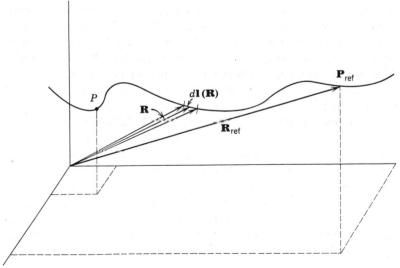

Figure 11.6   The work done by an external agent in moving Δm from P_{ref} to P.

reference point P_{ref} to some other point $P(\mathbf{R})$ along a path Γ is (see Eq. 11.10)

$$W = \int_{\substack{P_{\text{ref}} \\ \Gamma}}^{P} dW$$

$$= -k\,\Delta m \int_{\substack{P_{\text{ref}} \\ \Gamma}}^{P} \iiint_{V} \frac{\rho_v(\mathbf{R}')\,dV(\mathbf{R}')\mathbf{u}_{\mathbf{R}-\mathbf{R}'}}{4\pi\,|\mathbf{R} - \mathbf{R}'|^2} \cdot d\mathbf{l}(\mathbf{R}) \qquad (11.23)$$

It was noted previously (see Eq. 11.12) that $\mathbf{G} = \nabla g$ so that Eq. (11.23) becomes

$$W = \Delta m \int_{\substack{P_{\text{ref}} \\ \Gamma}}^{P} \nabla g \cdot d\mathbf{l}(\mathbf{R}) \qquad (11.24)$$

However, in Eq. (5.30) we saw that such integrals are independent of the path; Eq. (11.24) therefore becomes

$$W = \Delta m \int_{P_{\text{ref}}}^{P} \nabla g \cdot d\mathbf{l}$$

$$= \Delta m \int_{P_{\text{ref}}}^{P} dg = \Delta m[g(P) - g(P_{\text{ref}})]$$

$$= (\Delta m)(\Delta g) \qquad (11.25)$$

where $\Delta g \equiv [g(P) - g(P_{\text{ref}})]$ is the work done per unit mass in moving from a reference point to any point P in the direction of the field.

The fact that $\mathbf{G}$ is derivable from $g(\mathbf{R})$ has led to the name "potential" for $g(\mathbf{R})$; more specifically, $g(\mathbf{R})$ is the gravitational potential.

The foregoing development can be duplicated for the electrostatic field with one small modification caused by the fact that a gravitational field is one of attraction between two elements of matter, whereas the force between two like electrical charges is repulsive. Thus $\mathbf{G}(\mathbf{R})$, $\Delta m(\mathbf{R}')$, $\rho_v(\mathbf{R}')$, and k in Eqs. (11.3) through (11.20) may be replaced respectively by $-\mathbf{E}(\mathbf{R})$ minus the electric field, $\Delta q(\mathbf{R}')$, a positive charge element, $q_v(\mathbf{R}')$, the volume positive charge density, and $1/\epsilon_0$ (MKS), where ϵ_0 is the permittivity of free space. By equations modified in this manner, we can describe the relationship between the electrostatic field, its divergence, and the volume charge density. The electrostatic potential Φ is related to the field by $\mathbf{E}(\mathbf{R}) = -\nabla\Phi$. The symbol Φ represents the work done in moving a unit positive charge from a reference point to a point $P(\mathbf{R})$ in the presence of an electric field $\mathbf{E}$ and is analogous to $g(\mathbf{R})$.

In terms of the gravitational potential, Eq. (11.21b) becomes

$$\nabla^2 g(\mathbf{R}) = -k\rho_v(\mathbf{R}) \qquad (11.26)$$

which is called the Poisson equation. It relates the scalar volume source density to the scalar potential. If it is evaluated at some point(s) where no source(s) or sink(s) exists, then it becomes the Laplace equation

$$\nabla^2 g(\mathbf{R}) = 0 \tag{11.27}$$

These last two equations are extremely important relationships in the study of fields. As a simple example of their applicability, consider the potential Φ between the plates of a capacitor (see Fig. 11.7). For Φ, the electrostatic potential, Eqs. (11.26) and (11.27), take the form

$$\nabla^2 \Phi(\mathbf{R}) = \frac{-q_v}{\epsilon_0} \quad \text{and} \quad \nabla^2 \Phi = 0$$

respectively. Between the plates of a capacitor the volume charge density is zero so that the latter of these two equations becomes

$$\frac{d^2\Phi}{dz^2} = 0 \quad 0 < z < d$$

or

$$\Phi = c_1 z + c_2$$

at

$$z = 0 \quad \Phi = 0 \quad \text{therefore} \quad c_2 = 0$$

$$z = d \quad \Phi = \Phi_0 \quad \text{therefore} \quad c_1 = \frac{\Phi_0}{d}$$

so that $\Phi = z(\Phi_0/d)$ and the field at any point between the plates is

$$\mathbf{E} = -\frac{\partial \Phi}{\partial z} \mathbf{u}_z = -\frac{\Phi_0}{d} \mathbf{u}_z, \quad \text{a constant}$$

where $\mathbf{u}_z$ is a unit vector whose sense is toward $+z$.

As another example of the utility of the Poisson equation, let us determine the gravitational field $\mathbf{G}$ at every point in space as a result of the

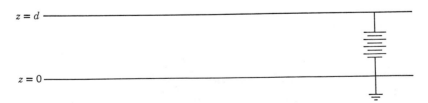

Figure 11.7   A large parallel plate condenser.

presence of a sphere of radius a whose center is at the origin and whose mass density increases linearly from the center, that is,

$$\rho(\mathbf{R}') = \delta_0[1 + b\,|\mathbf{R}'|]$$

Outside the sphere we may write Laplace's equation

$$\nabla^2 g(\mathbf{R}) = 0 \qquad |\mathbf{R}| > a$$

Since the problem is spherically symmetric, we shall use spherical coordinates. Since there is no θ and ϕ dependence, the foregoing equation becomes

$$\frac{1}{|\mathbf{R}|^2}\frac{d}{d\,|\mathbf{R}|}\left[|\mathbf{R}|^2\frac{d}{d\,|\mathbf{R}|}g(\mathbf{R})\right] = 0$$

or

$$|\mathbf{R}|^2\frac{d}{d\,|\mathbf{R}|}g(\mathbf{R}) = c_1$$

where c_1 is a scalar constant which upon integration yields

$$g(\mathbf{R}) = \frac{c_1}{R} + c_2 \qquad R > a$$

Without loss of generality, we can construct the spherical coordinate system so that the point of observation (located by $\mathbf{R}$) is on the $+z$-axis ($\phi = +\pi/2$); thus

$$|\mathbf{R} - \mathbf{R}'| = \left[R^2 + R'^2 - 2RR'\cos\left(\frac{\pi}{2} - \phi\right)\right]^{\frac{1}{2}}$$

$$= (R^2 + R'^2 - 2RR'\sin\phi)^{\frac{1}{2}}$$

and

$$\mathbf{u}_{\mathbf{R}-\mathbf{R}'} = \mathbf{u}_R(\mathbf{u}_{\mathbf{R}-\mathbf{R}'}\cdot\mathbf{u}_R) + \mathbf{u}_\theta(\mathbf{u}_{\mathbf{R}-\mathbf{R}'}\cdot\mathbf{u}_\theta) + \mathbf{u}_\phi(\mathbf{u}_{\mathbf{R}-\mathbf{R}'}\cdot\mathbf{u}_\phi)$$

$$= \mathbf{u}_R[\mathbf{u}_{\mathbf{R}-\mathbf{R}'}\cdot\mathbf{u}_R] + \mathbf{u}_\theta[\mathbf{u}_{\mathbf{R}-\mathbf{R}'}\cdot\mathbf{u}_\theta] + \mathbf{u}_\phi[\mathbf{u}_{\mathbf{R}-\mathbf{R}'}\cdot\mathbf{u}_\phi]$$

$$= \mathbf{u}_R\left[\frac{R - R'\sin\phi'}{|\mathbf{R} - \mathbf{R}'|}\right] + \mathbf{u}_\theta\left[\frac{R'\cos\phi'\sin\theta'}{|\mathbf{R} - \mathbf{R}'|}\right]$$

$$+ \mathbf{u}_\phi\left[\frac{R'\cos\phi'\cos\theta'}{|\mathbf{R} - \mathbf{R}'|^3}\right]$$

Equation (11.10) then yields

$$\mathbf{G}(\mathbf{R}) = -\mathbf{u}_R\frac{k\delta_0}{4\pi}\int_{\theta'=0}^{2\pi} d\theta'\int_{R'=0}^{a} R'^2(1 + bR')\,dR'$$

$$\times \int_{\phi'=-\pi/2}^{\pi/2}\cos\phi'\left[\frac{R - R'\sin\phi'}{|\mathbf{R} - \mathbf{R}'|^3}\right]d\phi'$$

$$= -\mathbf{u}_R\frac{km}{4\pi R^2} \qquad \text{for} \quad |\mathbf{R}| > a$$

or

$$g(\mathbf{R}) = \frac{km}{4\pi R}$$

Thus $c_1 = km/4\pi$ and $c_2 = 0$.

From Eq. (11.26) Poisson's equation within the sphere may be written

$$\frac{1}{R^2}\frac{d}{dR}\left(R^2\frac{dg}{dR}\right) = -k\delta_0[1 + bR] \qquad |\mathbf{R}| < a$$

which yields

$$g = -k\delta_0\left(\frac{R^2}{6} + \frac{bR^3}{12}\right) + \frac{c_3}{R} + c_4$$

At $R = 0$, $g(\mathbf{R})$ is bounded so that $c_3 = 0$. To determine c_4 we observe that at the surface of the sphere, both expressions for g must lead to the same result:

$$g(a) = -k\delta_0\left(\frac{a^2}{6} + \frac{ba^3}{12}\right) + c_4$$

$$= \frac{km}{4\pi a}$$

so that

$$c_4 = k\delta_0\left(\frac{ba^3}{3} + \frac{a^2}{2}\right)$$

The gravitational field within the sphere is

$$\mathbf{G}(\mathbf{R}) = -\frac{k\delta_0}{4\pi}\left(\frac{R}{3} + \frac{bR^2}{4}\right)\mathbf{u_R} \qquad |\mathbf{R}| < a$$

In addition to vector fields which are derivable from a scalar source, there are vector fields which can be derived from vector source(s). An example of a vector field which has a vector source is the magnetic induction field. It is known that there is a force on $d\mathbf{l}(\mathbf{R})$, an element of length of a circuit (see Fig. 11.8) carrying a direct current I which is produced by the presence of $d\mathbf{l}'(\mathbf{R}')$, an element of another circuit carrying a current I'. The magnitude of this force is proportional to the product of the currents and inversely proportional to the square of the distance from $d\mathbf{l}(\mathbf{R})$ to $d\mathbf{l}'(\mathbf{R}')$. The direction of this force is at right angles to $d\mathbf{l}'(\mathbf{R}') \times \mathbf{u_{R-R'}}$ and $d\mathbf{l}(\mathbf{R})$ where $\mathbf{u_{R-R'}}$ is a unit vector in the direction of the vector from $d\mathbf{l}'(\mathbf{R}')$ to $d\mathbf{l}'(\mathbf{R})$. Mathematically, this force may be written

$$d\mathbf{F}(\mathbf{R}) = \frac{\mu_0}{4\pi} II' \frac{d\mathbf{l}(\mathbf{R}) \times [d\mathbf{l}'(\mathbf{R}') \times \mathbf{u_{R-R'}}]}{|\mathbf{R} - \mathbf{R}'|^2} \qquad (11.28)$$

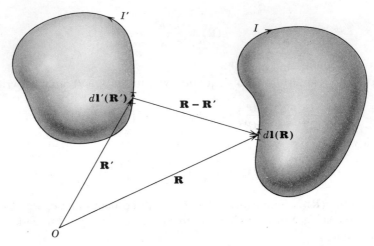

Figure 11.8   The force on one current element due to the presence of another current element.

where $\mu_0/4\pi$ is the constant of proportionality and μ_0 is the permeability of free space; its value is $4\pi 10^{-7}$ newtons/amp². Equation (11.28) could have been written in terms of a force field $\mathbf{B}(\mathbf{R})$, which is defined to be the force per unit current element $I\,d\mathbf{l}(\mathbf{R})$:

$$dF(\mathbf{R}) = I\,d\mathbf{l}(\mathbf{R}) \times d\mathbf{B}(\mathbf{R}) \tag{11.29}$$

where

$$d\mathbf{B}(\mathbf{R}) \equiv \frac{\mu_0}{4\pi}\frac{I'[d\mathbf{l}'(\mathbf{R}') \times \mathbf{u}_{\mathbf{R}-\mathbf{R}'}]}{|\mathbf{R} - \mathbf{R}'|^2}$$

is the element of the magnetic induction field at $d\mathbf{l}(\mathbf{R})$ due to the current element $I'\,d\mathbf{l}'(\mathbf{R}')$. Then the total magnetic induction field at $d\mathbf{l}(\mathbf{R})$ resulting from the other entire circuit is

$$\mathbf{B}(\mathbf{R}) = \frac{\mu_0 I'}{4\pi} \oint_\Gamma \frac{d\mathbf{l}'(\mathbf{R}') \times \mathbf{u}_{\mathbf{R}-\mathbf{R}'}}{|\mathbf{R} - \mathbf{R}'|^2} \tag{11.30}$$

where Γ is the space curve representing the circuit of which $d\mathbf{l}'$ is an element. This equation is usually called the Biot-Savart law.

By analogy with Eq. (11.21), where the divergence of a vector field is related to the scalar source density, we now wish to show that

$$\nabla \times \mathbf{B}(\mathbf{R}) = \mu_0 \mathbf{J}(\mathbf{R}) \tag{11.31}$$

for all space where $\mathbf{J}(\mathbf{R})$, the current density, plays the role of the vector source density for the field. The demonstration of Eq. (11.31) in general

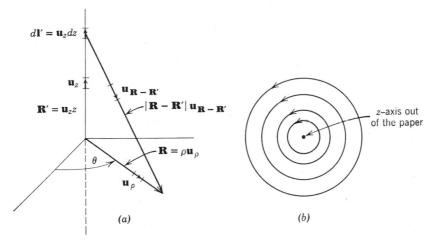

Figure 11.9 (a) The **B** field around an infinitely long straight wire.

terms is somewhat tedious, and we shall therefore devote our discussion to a certain geometry in order to reduce the amount of mathematics involved.

Let us apply Eq. (11.30) to a circuit which is a very long straight wire carrying a current I' (see Fig. 11.9a). Integrating Eq. (11.30) for such a situation, we can use cylindrical coordinates so that $|\mathbf{R} - \mathbf{R}'|\, \mathbf{u}_{\mathbf{R}-\mathbf{R}'} = \mathbf{u}_\rho \rho - \mathbf{u}_z z$, $d\mathbf{l}' = \mathbf{u}_z\, dz$, $|\mathbf{R} - \mathbf{R}'|^{-2} = (z^2 + \rho^2)^{-1}$, and

$$d\mathbf{l}' \times \mathbf{u}_{\mathbf{R}-\mathbf{R}'} = (\rho \mathbf{u}_\theta\, dz)/(z^2 + \rho^2)^{1/2}$$

Then

$$\mathbf{B(R)} = \frac{\mu_0 I' \mathbf{u}_\theta}{4\pi} \int_{-\infty}^{\infty} \frac{\rho\, dz}{(z^2 + \rho^2)^{3/2}} = \frac{\mu_0 I' \mathbf{u}_\theta}{2\pi\rho} \tag{11.32}$$

where ρ is the distance from the wire to the point of observation. Here we see that the magnetic induction is in the direction of increasing azimuth when the current is out of the page in Fig. 11.9b.

If we now calculate the circulation of **B** around a closed circular path surrounding the wire, we obtain (see Fig. 11.10)

$$\oint_\Gamma \mathbf{B} \cdot d\mathbf{l} = \int_0^{2\pi} \mathbf{B} \cdot \rho \mathbf{u}_\theta\, d\theta = \mu_0 I' \tag{11.33}$$

Equation (11.33) is Ampere's circuital law. Like Gauss's law, it can be very useful when there is a large degree of symmetry.

Since $I' = \iint_A \mathbf{J(R')} \cdot d\mathbf{s(R')}$, where A is the cross-sectional area of the

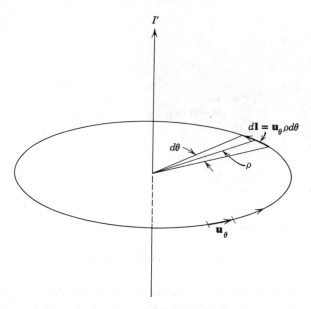

Figure 11.10   The **B** field around an infinitely long straight wire.

wire, Eq. (11.33) becomes

$$\oint_{\Gamma} \mathbf{B} \cdot d\mathbf{l} = \mu_0 \iint_{A} \mathbf{J}(\mathbf{R}') \cdot d\mathbf{s}(\mathbf{R}') \tag{11.34}$$

If the path Γ lies on the surface of the wire, Eq. (11.34) becomes

$$\oint_{\Gamma} \mathbf{B}(\mathbf{R}') \cdot d\mathbf{l}(\mathbf{R}') = \mu_0 \iint_{A} \mathbf{J}(\mathbf{R}') \cdot d\mathbf{s}(\mathbf{R}') \tag{11.35}$$

But by Stokes's theorem, Eq. (9.2), the left-hand side of Eq. (11.35) becomes a surface integral,

$$\iint_{A} \nabla' \times \mathbf{B}(\mathbf{R}') \cdot d\mathbf{s} = \mu_0 \iint_{A} \mathbf{J}(\mathbf{R}') \cdot d\mathbf{s}(\mathbf{R}') \tag{11.36}$$

For this to be true for all areas, the integrands must be equal,

$$\nabla' \times \mathbf{B}(\mathbf{R}') = \mu_0 \mathbf{J}(\mathbf{R}') \tag{11.37}$$

so that at any point the curl of **B** is proportional to the current density $\mathbf{J}(\mathbf{R}')$ when $\mathbf{J}(\mathbf{R}')$ does not vary with time. Since this is true for all space, Eq. (11.31) is true.

To see that **B** has a potential from which it can be derived, we must first show that $\nabla \cdot \mathbf{B(R)} = 0$. To do so, we note that $d\mathbf{B(R')}$ can be expressed in terms of the current density, where $I' = J(R') \cdot d\mathbf{s}(R')$ and $dV = d\mathbf{l} \cdot d\mathbf{s}$ because $d\mathbf{l}$ and $d\mathbf{s}$ have the same direction in the wire. Thus

$$\mathbf{B(R)} = \frac{\mu_0}{4\pi} \iiint_V \frac{\mathbf{J(R')} \times \mathbf{u}_{R-R'} \, dV(R')}{|\mathbf{R} - \mathbf{R'}|^2} \tag{11.38}$$

$\mathbf{J(R')}$ does not depend on **R**, so that when we apply Eq. (8.22h) to Eq. (11.38), we obtain

$$\nabla \cdot \mathbf{B(R)} = \frac{-\mu_0}{4\pi} \iiint_V \mathbf{J(R')} \cdot \nabla \times \left(\frac{\mathbf{u}_{R-R'}}{|\mathbf{R} - \mathbf{R'}|^2} \right) dV(R') \tag{11.39}$$

However,

$$\frac{\mathbf{u}_{R-R'}}{|\mathbf{R} - \mathbf{R'}|^2} = -\nabla \frac{1}{|\mathbf{R} - \mathbf{R'}|}$$

Since the curl of any gradient is zero (see Eq. 8.22r), we see that the right-hand side of Eq. (11.39) is zero:

$$\nabla \cdot \mathbf{B(R)} = 0 \tag{11.40}$$

A field which satisfies Eq. (11.40) is said to be solenoidal. From Eq. (8.22q), we see that Eq. (11.40) can be satisfied if

$$\mathbf{B(R)} = \nabla \times \mathbf{A(R)} \tag{11.41}$$

where $\mathbf{A(R)}$ is the magnetic potential field. If we take the curl of Eq. (11.41) and recall Eq. (11.37), we obtain

$$\nabla \times \mathbf{B(R)} = \nabla \times \nabla \times \mathbf{A(R)} = \mu_0 \mathbf{J(R)} \tag{11.42}$$

But the curl of the curl of a vector field is given by Eq. (8.22s) so that Eq. (11.42) becomes

$$\nabla[\nabla \mathbf{A(R)}] - \nabla^2 \mathbf{A(R)} = \mu_0 \mathbf{J(R)} \tag{11.43}$$

We have established (see Section 9.5) that to define uniquely a vector field in a region V, its divergence, curl, and normal derivative over the surface of V must be given. Observing Eq. (11.41), we see that only the curl of **A** has been specified and consequently **A** has not been uniquely determined. In view of Eq. (11.43), it behooves us to choose the divergence of **A** to be zero. Then Eq. (11.43) is

$$\nabla^2 \mathbf{A(R)} = -\mu_0 \mathbf{J(R)} \tag{11.44}$$

which is a vector equation whose component equations are similar to Eq. (11.26); in other words, they are Poisson equations. If at **R**, $\mathbf{J(R)}$ is zero, we see that Eq. (11.44) becomes a vector equation whose component equations satisfy the Laplace equation. However, if, for every $\mathbf{R}$ in a simply connected region, $\mathbf{J}(\mathbf{R})$ is zero, we see from Eq. (11.37) that within that region the curl of $\mathbf{B}(\mathbf{R})$ is zero, which, according to Eq. (8.22r), implies that $\mathbf{B}(\mathbf{R})$ can be written as the gradient of a magnetic scalar potential U^*, that is,

$$\mathbf{B} = -\mu_0 \nabla U^* \tag{11.45}$$

But the divergence of $\mathbf{B}$ has been shown to be zero, so that the divergence of Eq. (11.45) becomes a Laplace equation

$$\nabla^2 U^* = 0 \tag{11.46}$$

Thus in this case the magnetic induction can be determined from a scalar potential which satisfies the Laplace equation.

In this section we have treated typical inverse square fields encountered in science and engineering. The purpose of the following sections is to treat a more general vector field and demonstrate certain fundamental relationships which describe it and its influence.

11.3 Irrotational Fields and Scalar Potentials

In addition to the gravitational and electric fields already discussed there is a large group of vector fields each of which can be derived from its associated auxiliary scalar field, called its scalar potential. These fields, as we saw in Section 5.2, are referred to as irrotational fields.

A vector field $\mathbf{I}(\mathbf{R})$ is called irrotational in a region of space if its circulation vanishes, that is,

$$\oint_\Gamma \mathbf{I} \cdot d\mathbf{l} = 0 \tag{11.47}$$

for every reducible closed path Γ in that region of space. In our discussion of the gradient in Chapter 5, we showed that in a simply connected region where a vector field satisfies Eq. (11.47), where the vector field was irrotational and continuous, the line integral of $\mathbf{I} \cdot d\mathbf{l}$ between a fixed reference point P_{ref}, located by $\mathbf{R}_0$, and a variable point P, located by the vector $\mathbf{R}$, is independent of the path taken between P_{ref} and P (see Eq. 5.29). We then concluded that since such a line integral depends only on the end point $P(\mathbf{R})$, it defines a scalar function $\Phi(\mathbf{R})$ which depends on $\mathbf{R}$ alone. On the basis of this reasoning, we can write (see Eq. 5.30)

$$\Phi(\mathbf{R}) = \int_{\mathbf{R}_{\text{ref}}}^{\mathbf{R}} \mathbf{I}(\mathbf{R}) \cdot d\mathbf{l}(\mathbf{R}) + c \tag{11.48}$$

where c is a constant scalar. We also concluded that if $\mathbf{I(R)}$ is defined by Eq. (11.47), $\mathbf{I(R)}$ could be related to the negative of the gradient of a scalar field,

$$\mathbf{I} = -\nabla\Phi \tag{11.49}$$

Since $\mathbf{I(R)}$ is derivable from $\Phi(\mathbf{R})$, $\Phi(\mathbf{R})$ is called the scalar potential for $\mathbf{I(R)}$.

Another property of irrotational vector fields used to characterize them is that their curl is identically zero. To demonstrate this fact, let us apply Stokes's theorem to Eq. (11.47) which we may do if $\mathbf{I(R)}$ and its first derivatives are continuous; then

$$\oint_{\Gamma} \mathbf{I} \cdot d\mathbf{l} = \iint_{A} \mathrm{curl}\ \mathbf{I} \cdot d\mathbf{s} = 0 \tag{11.50}$$

where Γ is the space curve which is the periphery of the surface of area A. For Eq. (11.50) to be true for all surfaces in a region of space, the integrand must be identically zero:

$$\mathrm{curl}\ \mathbf{I(R)} = 0 \tag{11.51}$$

We might have anticipated this result, since we may observe in Eq. (8.22r) that the curl of the gradient of a scalar field is identically zero.

For irrotational vector fields which are continuous and possess continuous derivatives, we may then state the following.

1. Its circulation is zero.
2. It is the gradient of a scalar field called its scalar potential.
3. Its curl is identically zero.

If $\mathbf{I}$ is an irrotational force field, it is called a *conservative* field and, as we have shown (see Eq. 11.23), $\mathbf{I} \cdot d\mathbf{l}$ represents the work done by an external agent in moving a distance $d\mathbf{l}$ in that field. It follows from Eq. (11.47) that the work done by moving around in a closed path in such a field is zero. Furthermore, the potential energy at a point located by a vector $\mathbf{R}$ is given by Eq. (11.48), that is, Φ is the scalar potential of $\mathbf{I}$.

11.4 Solenoidal Fields and Vector Potentials

Solenoidal fields constitute another large group of vector fields. A field in this category is derivable from another vector field called a vector potential.

A vector field $\mathbf{S}$ is called solenoidal in a region of space if the net flux of that field emerging from any and every closed area A in that region (see

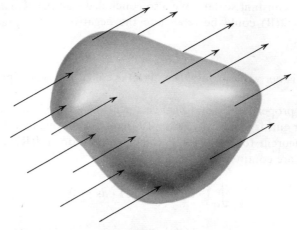

Figure 11.11   Number of field lines entering equal the number leaving.

Fig. 11.11) is zero:

$$\oiint_A \mathbf{S} \cdot ds = 0 \tag{11.52}$$

When $\mathbf{S}$ is differentiable, we may apply Gauss's divergence theorem to Eq. (11.52) and obtain

$$\oiint_A \mathbf{S} \cdot ds = \iiint_V \text{div } \mathbf{S} \, dV = 0 \tag{11.53}$$

where V is the volume enclosed by the surface of area A. For this relationship to be valid for any and all simply connected volumes, the integrand of the volume integral must be identically zero, that is,

$$\text{div } \mathbf{S} = 0 \tag{11.54}$$

By Eq. (8.22q) we know that the divergence of the curl of any vector field must be identically zero. It follows that if $\mathbf{S}$ were the curl of another vector field $\mathbf{T}$,

$$\text{curl } \mathbf{T} = \mathbf{S} \tag{11.55}$$

then $\mathbf{S}$ would satisfy (11.54).

Thus far we have not shown that if $\mathbf{S}$ satisfies Eq. (11.54), it is the curl of another vector field. To prove this, we must first show that if $\mathbf{S}$ is solenoidal, it can only be expressible as the vector product of two gradients, $\mathbf{S} = \nabla\psi_1 \times \nabla\psi_2$, where ψ_1 and ψ_2 are scalar fields. To show that this is true consider the vector field $\mathbf{S}$ to be

$$\mathbf{S} = \mathbf{u}_x S_x + \mathbf{u}_y S_y + \mathbf{u}_z S_z$$

We have seen in Eq. (4.64) that the flow lines for such a field are expressible in the following differential equations:

$$\frac{dx}{S_x} = \frac{dy}{S_y} = \frac{dz}{S_z} \tag{11.56}$$

which can be succinctly stated as

$$d\mathbf{l} \times \mathbf{S} = 0 \tag{11.57}$$

Since $\mathbf{S}$ is assumed to be continuously differentiable, these three differential equations may be solved to obtain two independent solutions which we shall designate as

$$S_{x_1}(x, y, z) = c_1 \quad \text{and} \quad S_{x_2}(x, y, z) = c_2 \tag{11.58}$$

where c_1 and c_2 are constant scalars. Both these solutions represent surfaces tangent to the vector field $\mathbf{S}$ at every point. The gradients of S_{x_1} and S_{x_2} are then everywhere perpendicular to $\mathbf{S}$, so that the vector product of the gradients of S_{x_1} and S_{x_2} is a vector field which at every point has the same direction and sense as $\mathbf{S}$:

$$\mathbf{S} = \eta[\nabla S_{x_1}] \times [\nabla S_{x_2}] \tag{11.59}$$

where η is a scale factor. Suppose S_{x_1} and S_{x_2}, together with another function S_{x_3}, form a system of curvilinear coordinates so that η may depend on S_{x_1}, S_{x_2}, and S_{x_3}. By considering $\mathbf{F}$ in Eq. (10.43) to be replaced by $\mathbf{S}$ as defined in Eq. (11.59) and by replacing w_1, w_2, and w_3 by S_{x_1}, S_{x_2}, and S_{x_3}, respectively, Eq. (10.43) becomes

$$\nabla \cdot \mathbf{S} = \frac{\partial \eta}{\partial S_{x_3}} \nabla S_{x_3} \cdot \nabla S_{x_1} \times \nabla S_{x_2} \tag{11.60}$$

But if $\mathbf{S}$ is solenoidal, this is zero and therefore $\partial \eta / \partial S_{x_3}$ is zero. We then conclude that η depends on S_{x_1} and S_{x_2} only. We can then define ξ to be the integration of η along the S_{x_1} coordinate:

$$\xi = \int \eta \, dS_{x_1} \tag{11.61}$$

Then

$$\nabla \xi = \frac{\partial \xi}{\partial S_{x_1}} \nabla S_{x_1} + \frac{\partial \xi}{\partial S_{x_2}} \nabla S_{x_2}$$

$$= \eta \nabla S_{x_1} + \frac{\partial \xi}{\partial S_{x_2}} \nabla S_{x_2} \tag{11.62}$$

or

$$\eta \nabla S_{x_1} = \nabla \xi - \frac{\partial \xi}{\partial S_{x_2}} \nabla S_{x_2}$$

Forming the vector product of this with ∇S_{x_2}, we obtain

$$\eta \nabla S_{x_1} \times \nabla S_{x_2} = \nabla \xi \times \nabla S_{x_2} \tag{11.63}$$

which is just the form required for **S**. We see therefore that if div **S** is zero, **S** may be represented by

$$\mathbf{S} = \nabla \psi_1 \times \nabla \psi_2 \tag{11.64}$$

Expanding this according to Eq. (8.22k), we obtain

$$\mathbf{S} = \nabla \psi_1 \times \nabla \psi_2 = \operatorname{curl} [\psi_1 \nabla \psi_2] - \psi_1 \operatorname{curl} [\nabla \psi_2] = \operatorname{curl} [\psi_1 \nabla \psi_2] \tag{11.65}$$

because the curl of the gradient of a scalar field is identically zero. If we designate the vector field $\psi_1 \nabla \psi_2$ as **T**, we see that

$$\mathbf{S} = \operatorname{curl} \mathbf{T} \tag{11.66}$$

We conclude that if div **S** = 0, it follows that **S** is the curl of a vector field. The field **T** is then called the vector potential for **S**.

Again we make the point that Eq. (11.66) cannot serve to specify **T** uniquely. If, for example, we were to add the gradient of a scalar field Θ to **T**,

$$\mathbf{T} + \nabla \Theta$$

this new vector would also satisfy Eq. (11.66) because the curl of the gradient of a scalar field is identically zero. If a vector potential **T** is transformed into a new vector potential $\mathbf{T} + \nabla \Theta$, the transformation is called a *gauge transformation* and the fact that the field **S** is not changed by such a transformation is referred to as gauge invariance. As was pointed out in Eq. (9.81), we must specify the curl and divergence of **T** and its normal derivative before it is uniquely determined. In applying the idea of vector potential to observed phenomena, we must remove this ambiguity through additional physical argument. For time-independent fields, we usually take $\nabla \cdot \mathbf{T} = 0$, which is called the Coulomb gauge, because **T** will then satisfy a Poisson equation quite analogous to that satisfied by the scalar potential. We shall return to this in the next section.

For a solenoidal vector field which is continuous and possesses continuous derivatives, we may then state the following.

1. Its net flux is zero over any closed surface.
2. It is the curl of a vector field called its vector potential.
3. Its divergence is identically zero.

We have said that if a vector field is solenoidal, that is, div **S** = 0 for every point in a region of space, the *net* flux passing through any closed surface in that region is zero (see Fig. 11.11). This is interpreted to mean that the field lines of a solenoidal field always form closed curves (see

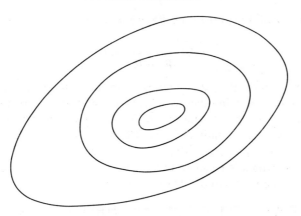

Figure 11.12   Field lines which are closed curves.

Fig. 11.12). The field surrounding a bar magnet is of this type. The fact that div **F** = 0 at a single point does not mean that the field is everywhere solenoidal; all it means is that in the neighborhood of that point, as many F-lines begin as end. In other words, there are no *net* scalar sources at that point.

11.5 The General Vector Field

We have discussed two classes of vector fields: irrotational and solenoidal. Here we intend to show that any vector field which, together with its first derivatives is continuous in a simply connected region, may be resolved into an irrotational portion and a solenoidal portion:

$$\mathbf{F(R)} = \mathbf{I(R)} + \mathbf{S(R)} \qquad (11.67)$$

Equation (11.67) is a statement of the Helmholtz theorem. To prove it, we will first show that any vector field **F(R)** which is continuous and whose derivatives are continuous may be represented as

$$\mathbf{F(R)} = -\frac{\nabla^2}{4\pi} \iiint_{\substack{\text{all} \\ \text{space}}} \frac{\mathbf{F(R')}\, dV(\mathbf{R'})}{|\mathbf{R} - \mathbf{R'}|} \qquad (11.68)$$

where **R'** locates all points in space and **R** locates the point at which **F** is to be determined, that is, **R** locates the point of observation.

The reader will recall from Eq. (8.20) that

$$\nabla^2 \frac{1}{|\mathbf{R} - \mathbf{R}'|} = 0$$

at all points where $|\mathbf{R} - \mathbf{R}'|$ remains finite, i.e., all space except for the point where $\mathbf{R} = \mathbf{R}'$. In other words, as the point located by the vector $\mathbf{R}'$ moves toward the point located by $\mathbf{R}$ during the integration process, $|\mathbf{R} - \mathbf{R}'|$ approaches infinity. Since $\mathbf{F}(\mathbf{R}')$ is a continuous function of $\mathbf{R}'$, we may choose a sphere of radius ϵ and volume V_ϵ, centered at the point located by $\mathbf{R}$, which is so small that $\mathbf{F}(\mathbf{R}')$ is essentially equal to $\mathbf{F}(\mathbf{R})$, its value at $\mathbf{R}$. The right-hand side of Eq. (11.68) becomes

$$-\iiint_{V_\epsilon} \frac{\mathbf{F}(\mathbf{R}')}{4\pi} \nabla^2 \frac{1}{|\mathbf{R} - \mathbf{R}'|} \, dV(\mathbf{R}') = - \frac{\mathbf{F}(\mathbf{R})}{4\pi} \iiint_{V_\epsilon} \nabla^2 \frac{1}{|\mathbf{R} - \mathbf{R}'|} \, dV(\mathbf{R}')$$

$$(11.69)$$

Since

$$\nabla^2 \frac{1}{|\mathbf{R} - \mathbf{R}'|} = \nabla'^2 \frac{1}{|\mathbf{R} - \mathbf{R}'|}$$

we may utilize Eq. (9.39) to write Eq. (11.69) as

$$- \frac{\mathbf{F}(\mathbf{R})}{4\pi} \iiint_{V_\epsilon} \nabla' \cdot \nabla' \frac{1}{|\mathbf{R} - \mathbf{R}'|} \, dV(\mathbf{R}') = \frac{-\mathbf{F}(\mathbf{R})}{\pi 4} \oiint_{A_\epsilon} \nabla' \frac{1}{|\mathbf{R} - \mathbf{R}'|} \cdot d\mathbf{s}(\mathbf{R}')$$

$$(11.70)$$

where A_ϵ is the surface area of the very small sphere surrounding the point located by $\mathbf{R}$. We note that $\nabla' |\mathbf{R} - \mathbf{R}'|^{-1} = \mathbf{u}_{\mathbf{R}-\mathbf{R}'} |\mathbf{R} - \mathbf{R}'|^{-2}$, where $\mathbf{u}_{\mathbf{R}-\mathbf{R}'}$ is a unit vector pointing from the surface of the very small sphere inward toward the center of the sphere (see Fig. 11.13). Then, since $d\mathbf{s}(\mathbf{R}') = -\mathbf{u}_{\mathbf{R}-\mathbf{R}'} |\mathbf{R} - \mathbf{R}'|^2 \cos \phi \, d\theta \, d\phi$ [$d\mathbf{s}(\mathbf{R}')$ points outward from V_ϵ, i.e., with a sense opposite to $\mathbf{u}_{\mathbf{R}-\mathbf{R}'}$], we may write Eq. (11.70) as

$$- \frac{\mathbf{F}(\mathbf{R})}{4\pi} \iiint_{V_\epsilon} \nabla' \cdot \nabla' \frac{1}{|\mathbf{R} - \mathbf{R}'|} \, dV(\mathbf{R}')$$

$$= \frac{\mathbf{F}(\mathbf{R})}{4\pi} \int_{\theta=0}^{2\pi} \int_{\phi=-\pi/2}^{\pi/2} \frac{\mathbf{u}_{\mathbf{R}-\mathbf{R}'} \cdot \mathbf{u}_{\mathbf{R}-\mathbf{R}'}}{|\mathbf{R} - \mathbf{R}'|^2} |\mathbf{R} - \mathbf{R}'|^2 \cos \phi \, d\theta \, d\phi \quad \text{(see Eq. 9.57)}$$

$$= \mathbf{F}(\mathbf{R}) \tag{11.71}$$

and Eq. (11.68) is established.

To rewrite Eq. (11.68) in a way that shows the Helmholtz theorem is true, we recall from Eq. (8.22s) that

$$\nabla^2 = \nabla \nabla \cdot - \nabla \times \nabla \times$$

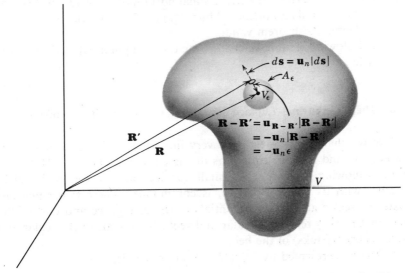

Figure 11.13 Surrounding a field point with a small sphere of radius $|\mathbf{R}' - \mathbf{R}| \equiv \epsilon$.

Then, because ∇ operates on $\mathbf{R}$ and the indicated integration is over $\mathbf{R}'$, Eq. (11.68) becomes

$$\mathbf{F}(\mathbf{R}) = -\nabla^2 \iiint_{\substack{\text{all} \\ \text{space}}} \frac{\mathbf{F}(\mathbf{R}') \, dV(\mathbf{R}')}{4\pi \, |\mathbf{R} - \mathbf{R}'|}$$

$$= -\nabla\nabla \cdot \iiint_{\substack{\text{all} \\ \text{space}}} \frac{\mathbf{F}(\mathbf{R}') \, dV(\mathbf{R}')}{4\pi \, |\mathbf{R} - \mathbf{R}'|} + \nabla \times \nabla \times \iiint_{\substack{\text{all} \\ \text{space}}} \frac{\mathbf{F}(\mathbf{R}') \, dV(\mathbf{R}')}{4\pi \, |\mathbf{R} - \mathbf{R}'|} \tag{11.72}$$

By defining a scalar field Φ and a vector field $\mathbf{T}$ to be

$$\Phi \equiv \nabla \cdot \iiint_{\substack{\text{all} \\ \text{space}}} \frac{\mathbf{F}(\mathbf{R}') \, dV(\mathbf{R}')}{4\pi \, |\mathbf{R} - \mathbf{R}'|} \tag{11.73}$$

$$\mathbf{T} \equiv \nabla \times \iiint_{\substack{\text{all} \\ \text{space}}} \frac{\mathbf{F}(\mathbf{R}') \, dV(\mathbf{R}')}{4\pi \, |\mathbf{R} - \mathbf{R}'|} \tag{11.74}$$

we see that Eq. (11.72) may be written in the form

$$\mathbf{F}(\mathbf{R}) = -\nabla\Phi + \nabla \times \mathbf{T} = \mathbf{I}(\mathbf{R}) + \mathbf{S}(\mathbf{R}) \tag{11.75}$$

where $I(R) \equiv -\nabla\Phi(R)$ is the irrotational portion of the field and $S(R) \equiv \nabla \times T$ is the solenoidal portion. Thus Eq. (11.67) is shown to be correct and the Helmholtz theorem valid.

In the following section we shall relate the field potential to the sources of the field.

11.6 The Poisson and Laplace Equations for the Field Potentials

Here we shall rederive the two very important differential equations, the Poisson and Laplace equations discussed in Section 11.2. However, in the following derivation we shall consider any vector field which, together with its first derivatives, is continuous. These two equations relate the scalar and vector potentials to the divergence and curl of the field, that is, they relate the scalar and vector potentials to the scalar and vector sources (sinks) of the field.

If $F(R)$ is represented by Eq. (11.75), we may write

$$\text{div } F(R) = \nabla \cdot [I(R) + S(R)] = \nabla \cdot I(R) \tag{11.76}$$

because $\nabla \cdot S = 0$, that is, S is solenoidal. Since $I(R) = -\nabla\Phi(R)$, Eq. (11.76) becomes the Poisson equation for any field $F(R)$:

$$\nabla^2\Phi(R) = -\text{div } F(R)$$

but we associate the divergence of a field with the scalar source density; thus

$$\nabla^2\Phi(R) = -\rho_v(R) \tag{11.77}$$

When the divergence of the vector field is zero, that is, when there are no scalar sources, Eq. (11.77) becomes the Laplace equation

$$\nabla^2\Phi(R) = 0 \tag{11.78}$$

where $\Phi(R)$, a solution of either Eq. (11.77) or (11.78), is given by Eq. (11.73). Equation (11.73), however, does not relate $\Phi(R)$ to the divergence of the field; to do this, let us consider Eq. (11.73) further (see Eq. 8.22g):

$$\Phi(R) = \nabla \cdot \iiint_{\substack{\text{all} \\ \text{space}}} \frac{F(R')\, dV(R')}{4\pi\, |R - R'|} = \iiint_{\substack{\text{all} \\ \text{space}}} \frac{F(R') \cdot \nabla}{4\pi} \frac{1}{|R - R'|}\, dV(R')$$

$$= -\iiint_{\substack{\text{all} \\ \text{space}}} \frac{F(R') \cdot \nabla'}{4\pi} \frac{1}{|R - R'|}\, dV(R') \tag{11.79}$$

Utilizing Eq. (8.22g) again

$$\nabla' \cdot \frac{\mathbf{F}(\mathbf{R}')}{|\mathbf{R} - \mathbf{R}'|} = \mathbf{F}(\mathbf{R}') \cdot \nabla' \frac{1}{|\mathbf{R} - \mathbf{R}'|} + \frac{1}{|\mathbf{R} - \mathbf{R}'|} \nabla' \cdot \mathbf{F}(\mathbf{R}') \quad (11.80)$$

we may write Eq. (11.79) as

$$\Phi(\mathbf{R}) = \frac{1}{4\pi} \iiint_{\substack{\text{all} \\ \text{space}}} \frac{1}{|\mathbf{R} - \mathbf{R}'|} \nabla' \cdot \mathbf{F}(\mathbf{R}') \, dV(\mathbf{R}')$$

$$- \frac{1}{4\pi} \iiint_{\substack{\text{all} \\ \text{space}}} \nabla' \cdot \frac{\mathbf{F}(\mathbf{R}')}{|\mathbf{R} - \mathbf{R}'|} \, dV(\mathbf{R}') \quad (11.81)$$

We now wish to show that the last integral vanishes. From Gauss's divergence theorem we may write

$$\frac{1}{4\pi} \iiint_{V} \frac{1}{|\mathbf{R} - \mathbf{R}'|} \nabla' \cdot \mathbf{F}(\mathbf{R}') \, dV(\mathbf{R}') = \frac{1}{4\pi} \oiint_{A} \frac{\mathbf{F}(\mathbf{R}') \cdot d\mathbf{s}(\mathbf{R}')}{|\mathbf{R} - \mathbf{R}'|}$$

$$(11.82)$$

where A is the area of the surface of the volume V. If the volume V increases to include all space, the surface A moves to infinity, and if the field $\mathbf{F}(\mathbf{R}')$ on A decreases faster than $|\mathbf{R} - \mathbf{R}'|^{-1}$, the surface integral vanishes and we obtain

$$\Phi(\mathbf{R}) = \frac{1}{4\pi} \iiint_{\substack{\text{all} \\ \text{space}}} \frac{1}{|\mathbf{R} - \mathbf{R}'|} \nabla' \cdot \mathbf{F}(\mathbf{R}') \, dV(\mathbf{R}')$$

$$= \frac{1}{4\pi} \iiint_{\substack{\text{all} \\ \text{space}}} \frac{\rho_v(\mathbf{R}') \, dV(\mathbf{R}')}{|\mathbf{R} - \mathbf{R}'|} \quad (11.83)$$

Equation (11.83) relates the scalar potential Φ at the point of observation located by $\mathbf{R}$ to the divergence of the field at all points in space located by $\mathbf{R}'$, that is, at all possible source points. If the divergence is not known for all points of space but only within an arbitrary volume V, then Eq. (11.83) must be modified. To accomplish this, let us consider Green's theorem [Eq. (9.73)]

$$\iiint_{V} [g \nabla^2 h - h \nabla^2 g] \, dV = \oiint_{A} [g \nabla h - h \nabla g] \cdot d\mathbf{s} \quad (9.73)$$

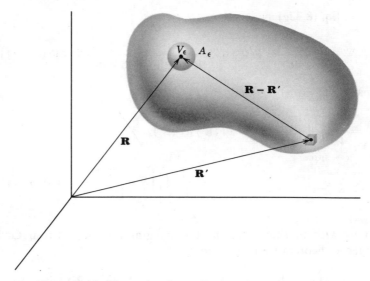

Figure 11.14   Illustrating the application of Green's theorem.

where g and h are continuous and twice differentiable scalar fields. If we now let g correspond to $\Phi(\mathbf{R}')$ and h to $|\mathbf{R} - \mathbf{R}'|^{-1}$, we may then write Eq. (9.73) as

$$\iiint_V \left[\Phi(\mathbf{R}') \nabla'^2 \frac{1}{|\mathbf{R} - \mathbf{R}'|} - \frac{1}{|\mathbf{R} - \mathbf{R}'|} \nabla'^2 \Phi(\mathbf{R}') \right] dV(\mathbf{R}')$$

$$= \oiint_A \left[\Phi(\mathbf{R}') \nabla' \frac{1}{|\mathbf{R} - \mathbf{R}'|} - \frac{1}{|\mathbf{R} - \mathbf{R}'|} \nabla' \Phi(\mathbf{R}') \right] \cdot d\mathbf{s}(\mathbf{R}') \quad (11.84)$$

Since $|\mathbf{R} - \mathbf{R}'|^{-1}$ is not continuous when the observation point and the point located by $\mathbf{R}'$ are coincident, the point of observation cannot be included within V. If the observation point is not within V, there is no difficulty. If the observation point is within V (which is simply connected), we must exclude it from V by surrounding the point with a very small sphere of volume V_ϵ and area A_ϵ (see Fig. 11.14). Now Eq. (11.84) becomes

$$\iiint_{V'} \left[\Phi(\mathbf{R}') \nabla'^2 \frac{1}{|\mathbf{R} - \mathbf{R}'|} - \frac{1}{|\mathbf{R} - \mathbf{R}'|} \nabla'^2 \Phi(\mathbf{R}') \right] dV(\mathbf{R}')$$

$$= \iint_{A'} \left[\Phi(\mathbf{R}') \nabla' \frac{1}{|\mathbf{R} - \mathbf{R}'|} - \frac{1}{|\mathbf{R} - \mathbf{R}'|} \nabla' \Phi(\mathbf{R}') \right] \cdot d\mathbf{s}(\mathbf{R}')$$

$$+ \iint_{A_\epsilon} \left[\Phi(\mathbf{R}') \nabla' \frac{1}{|\mathbf{R} - \mathbf{R}'|} - \frac{1}{|\mathbf{R} - \mathbf{R}'|} \nabla' \Phi(\mathbf{R}') \right] \cdot d\mathbf{s}(\mathbf{R}') \quad (11.85)$$

where $V' = V - V_\epsilon$ and $A' + A_\epsilon$ are the surface of V'. In the volume V', the quantity $\nabla'^2 |\mathbf{R} - \mathbf{R}'|^{-1}$ vanishes.

Since V_ϵ is very small and since $\Phi(\mathbf{R}')$ and $\nabla'\Phi(\mathbf{R}')$ are continuous within V_ϵ, these quantities in the surface integral over A_ϵ may be replaced by their values at the center of the sphere. Thus

$$\iint\limits_{A_\epsilon} \left[\Phi(\mathbf{R}') \nabla' \frac{1}{|\mathbf{R} - \mathbf{R}'|} - \frac{1}{|\mathbf{R} - \mathbf{R}'|} \nabla'\Phi(\mathbf{R}') \right] \cdot d\mathbf{s}(\mathbf{R}')$$

$$= \Phi(\mathbf{R}) \iint\limits_{A_\epsilon} \frac{\mathbf{u}_{\mathbf{R}-\mathbf{R}'}}{|\mathbf{R} - \mathbf{R}'|^2} \cdot d\mathbf{s}(\mathbf{R}') - \frac{\partial \Phi}{\partial n} \iint\limits_{A_\epsilon} \frac{|d\mathbf{s}(\mathbf{R}')|}{|\mathbf{R} - \mathbf{R}'|} \quad (11.86)$$

However, $d\mathbf{s}(\mathbf{R}') = \mathbf{u}_{\mathbf{R}-\mathbf{R}'} |\mathbf{R} - \mathbf{R}'|^2 \cos \phi \, d\theta \, d\phi$ (the sense of $d\mathbf{s}$ is outward from V') so that in the limit as $|\mathbf{R} - \mathbf{R}'|$, the radius of the sphere, approaches zero Eq. (11.86) becomes

$$\iint\limits_{A_\epsilon} \left[\Phi(\mathbf{R}') \nabla' \frac{1}{|\mathbf{R} - \mathbf{R}'|} - \frac{1}{|\mathbf{R} - \mathbf{R}'|} \nabla'\Phi(\mathbf{R}') \right] \cdot d\mathbf{s}(\mathbf{R}') = 4\pi\Phi(\mathbf{R})$$

Thus if the observation point is within V, Eq. (11.85) can be solved for $\Phi(\mathbf{R})$. [Remember that as $|\mathbf{R} - \mathbf{R}'| \to 0$, $V' \to V$ and $A' \to A$ (the external surface area of V).]

$$4\pi\Phi(\mathbf{R}) = \iiint\limits_V \frac{\rho_v(\mathbf{R}')}{|\mathbf{R} - \mathbf{R}'|} \, dV(\mathbf{R}')$$

$$+ \iint\limits_A \left[\frac{1}{|\mathbf{R} - \mathbf{R}'|} \nabla'\Phi(\mathbf{R}') - \Phi(\mathbf{R}') \nabla' \frac{1}{|\mathbf{R} - \mathbf{R}'|} \right] \cdot d\mathbf{s}(\mathbf{R}')$$

$$= \iiint\limits_V \frac{\rho_v(\mathbf{R}') \, dV(\mathbf{R}')}{|\mathbf{R} - \mathbf{R}'|} + \iint\limits_A \frac{1}{|\mathbf{R} - \mathbf{R}'|} \frac{\partial \Phi(\mathbf{R}')}{\partial n} |d\mathbf{s}|$$

$$- \iint\limits_A \Phi\nabla' \frac{1}{|\mathbf{R} - \mathbf{R}'|} \cdot d\mathbf{s}(\mathbf{R}') \quad (11.87a)$$

where $\nabla'\Phi(\mathbf{R}') \cdot d\mathbf{s} = (\partial\Phi/\partial n) |d\mathbf{s}|$, where $\partial\Phi/\partial n$ is the derivative of Φ in a direction normal to the surface.

If the observation point is not within V, the creation of V_ϵ and A_ϵ is not necessary and Eq. (11.85) becomes

$$\iiint\limits_V \frac{\rho_v(\mathbf{R}') \, dV(\mathbf{R}')}{|\mathbf{R} - \mathbf{R}'|} = \iint\limits_A \left[\Phi(\mathbf{R}') \nabla' \frac{1}{|\mathbf{R} - \mathbf{R}'|} - \frac{1}{|\mathbf{R} - \mathbf{R}'|} \nabla'\Phi(\mathbf{R}') \right] \cdot d\mathbf{s}(\mathbf{R}')$$

$$(11.87b)$$

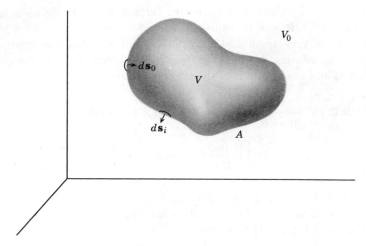

Figure 11.15 Dividing all space into two regions V and V_0.

If there are discontinuities within V as a result of discrete (point) sources, the results of the previous discussion are unchanged. We merely surround such source points with spheres to exclude them from V. It turns out that the resulting surface integrals associated with these point sources are zero.

The surface integrals in Eqs. (11.87a) and (11.87b) represent the contribution to the potential at the observation point by the scalar sources outside V. To see this we consider Eq. (11.83):

$$\Phi(\mathbf{R}) = \frac{1}{4\pi} \iiint\limits_{\substack{\text{all} \\ \text{space}}} \frac{\rho_v(\mathbf{R}')}{|\mathbf{R} - \mathbf{R}'|} \, dV(\mathbf{R}') \qquad (11.83)$$

where $\rho_v(\mathbf{R}')$ is continuous. If we divide all space into two volumes V and V_0 (see Fig. 11.15), Eq. (11.83) may be written

$$\Phi(\mathbf{R}) = \frac{1}{4\pi} \iiint\limits_{V} \frac{\rho_v(\mathbf{R}') \, dV(\mathbf{R}')}{|\mathbf{R} - \mathbf{R}'|} + \frac{1}{4\pi} \iiint\limits_{V_0} \frac{\rho_v(\mathbf{R}') \, dV(\mathbf{R}')}{|\mathbf{R} - \mathbf{R}'|} \qquad (11.88)$$

If we assume that the observation point is within V, we may use Eq. (11.87a) which yields

$$\Phi(\mathbf{R}) = \frac{1}{4\pi} \iiint\limits_{V} \frac{\rho_v(\mathbf{R}') \, dV(\mathbf{R}')}{|\mathbf{R} - \mathbf{R}'|}$$

$$+ \frac{1}{4\pi} \iint\limits_{A} \left[\frac{1}{|\mathbf{R} - \mathbf{R}'|} \nabla'\Phi(\mathbf{R}') - \Phi(\mathbf{R}') \nabla' \frac{1}{|\mathbf{R} - \mathbf{R}'|} \right] \cdot d\mathbf{s}_i(\mathbf{R}') \qquad (11.89)$$

where the sense of $d\mathbf{s}_i(\mathbf{R}')$ is outward from V.

If we apply Eq. (11.87b) to V_0, we obtain (remember that the surface A forms the common surface for V and V_0 and that the observation point is not within V_0)

$$\iiint_{V_0} \frac{\rho_v(\mathbf{R}')\, dV(\mathbf{R}')}{|\mathbf{R} - \mathbf{R}'|}$$

$$= \iint_A \left[\Phi(\mathbf{R}')\, \nabla' \frac{1}{|\mathbf{R} - \mathbf{R}'|} - \frac{1}{|\mathbf{R} - \mathbf{R}'|} \nabla'\Phi(\mathbf{R}') \right] \cdot ds_0(\mathbf{R}') \quad (11.90)$$

The sense of $ds_0(\mathbf{R}')$ is outward from V_0, that is, into V; thus $d\mathbf{s}_0 = -d\mathbf{s}_i$ and (11.88) becomes

$$\Phi(\mathbf{R}) = \frac{1}{4\pi} \iiint_V \frac{\rho_v(\mathbf{R}')\, dV(\mathbf{R}')}{|\mathbf{R} - \mathbf{R}'|}$$

$$+ \frac{1}{4\pi} \iint_A \left[\frac{1}{|\mathbf{R} - \mathbf{R}'|} \nabla'\Phi(\mathbf{R}') - \Phi(\mathbf{R}')\, \nabla' \frac{1}{|\mathbf{R} - \mathbf{R}'|} \right] \cdot ds(\mathbf{R}') \quad (11.91)$$

where $d\mathbf{s}_i = d\mathbf{s}$, or, $d\mathbf{s}$ is considered outward from V. We see that Eqs. (11.91) and (11.87a) are identical. Thus the surface integrals over A represent the influence of the sources outside of A on the potential at a point within A.

Equations (11.87a) and (11.87b) can also be derived heuristically by assuming that it is not necessary to exclude the observation point from V [see the discussion concerning Eqs. (9.58), (9.61), and (9.62)]. Then the term

$$\iiint_V \Phi(\mathbf{R}')\, \nabla'^2 \frac{1}{|\mathbf{R} - \mathbf{R}'|}\, dV(\mathbf{R}') = -4\pi\Phi(\mathbf{R})$$

if the observation point is within V so that $\mathbf{R}'$ can assume the value $\mathbf{R}$; similarly, this volume integral is zero if the observation point is external to V. Now there is no need to create V_e and A_e, so that Eq. (11.84) becomes

$$\iiint_V \left[\Phi(\mathbf{R}')\, \nabla'^2 \frac{1}{|\mathbf{R} - \mathbf{R}'|} - \frac{1}{|\mathbf{R} - \mathbf{R}'|} \nabla'^2\Phi(\mathbf{R}') \right] dV(\mathbf{R}')$$

$$= \oiint_A \left[\Phi(\mathbf{R}')\, \nabla' \frac{1}{\mathbf{R} - \mathbf{R}'} - \frac{1}{\mathbf{R} - \mathbf{R}'} \nabla'\Phi(\mathbf{R}') \right] \cdot ds(\mathbf{R}')$$

$$= \begin{cases} -4\pi\Phi(\mathbf{R}) - \iiint_V \dfrac{1}{|\mathbf{R} - \mathbf{R}'|} \nabla'^2\Phi(\mathbf{R}')\, dV(\mathbf{R}') & \text{if the observation point is within } V \\[3mm] -\iiint_V \dfrac{1}{|\mathbf{R} - \mathbf{R}'|} \nabla'^2\Phi(\mathbf{R}')\, dV(\mathbf{R}') & \text{if the observation point is outside } V \end{cases}$$

which is the same result given in Eqs. (11.87a) and (11.87b). We shall return to a discussion of the physical significance of Eq. (11.87a) in Section 11.8, where we will treat surface discontinuities in Φ and $\partial\Phi/\partial n$.

The fundamental problem of static irrotational fields is to determine $\Phi(\mathbf{R})$, that is, determine solutions to the Poisson equation. To obtain physically reasonable solutions, we must be able first to specify appropriate boundary conditions. It is not obvious that a set of boundary conditions is necessary or even consistent. For example, it appears from Eq. (11.87a) that if the point of observation is within V, and V is a source-free region, the potential is given by

$$\Phi(\mathbf{R}) = \frac{1}{4\pi} \iint_A \left[\frac{1}{|\mathbf{R} - \mathbf{R'}|} \nabla'\Phi(\mathbf{R'}) - \Phi(\mathbf{R'}) \nabla' \frac{1}{|\mathbf{R} - \mathbf{R'}|} \right] \cdot ds(\mathbf{R'}) \quad (11.92)$$

Thus to determine Φ within V, we must know Φ and $\partial\Phi/\partial n$ on A. However, both these quantities cannot be specified independently since $\Phi(\mathbf{R'})$ must be a solution of the Laplace equation. It is well to remember then that Φ can be determined within V if the correct values of Φ and $\partial\Phi/\partial n$ are known on A. However, we shall show in Section 11.8 that knowledge concerning either Φ or (not and) $\partial\Phi/\partial n$ on A is sufficient to determine Φ within a closed, simply connected region V.

In a discussion analogous to that just given for the scalar field potential and its Poisson equation, we shall now treat the vector field potential. We shall see that under certain conditions the vector field potential must also be a solution of the Poisson or Laplace equation. The relationship of the curl of a vector field to the vector potential will be seen to be similar to that between the divergence of a vector field and the scalar potential.

If $\mathbf{F}(\mathbf{R})$ is represented by Eq. (11.75), its curl is

$$\text{curl } \mathbf{F}(\mathbf{R}) = \nabla \times [\mathbf{I}(\mathbf{R}) + \mathbf{S}(\mathbf{R})] = \nabla \times \mathbf{S}(\mathbf{R}) \quad (11.93)$$

because the curl of an irrotational field vanishes. Since $\mathbf{S} = \nabla \times \mathbf{T}$, where $\mathbf{T}$ is the vector field potential, Eq. (11.93) becomes

$$\text{curl } \mathbf{F}(\mathbf{R}) = \nabla \times \nabla \times \mathbf{T} \quad (11.94)$$

Recalling that $\nabla \times \nabla \times = \nabla\nabla \cdot -\nabla^2$ [Eq. (8.22s)], we may write Eq. (11.94) as

$$\nabla(\nabla \cdot \mathbf{T}) - \nabla^2\mathbf{T} = \text{curl } \mathbf{F}(\mathbf{R}) \quad (11.95)$$

As we have argued previously, $\mathbf{T}$ has not been uniquely specified until its divergence is given. Since we have the choice, it is reasonable to choose $\mathbf{T}$ to be solenoidal,

$$\nabla \cdot \mathbf{T} = 0$$

Then Eq. (11.95) is

$$\nabla^2 \mathbf{T} = -\text{curl } \mathbf{F(R)}$$

However, we associate the curl of a vector field with $\mathbf{K}_s$, the vector source density; thus

$$\nabla^2 \mathbf{T} = -\mathbf{K}_s \tag{11.96}$$

which is the Poisson equation for the vector field potential. Analogous to Eq. (11.78), if curl $\mathbf{F(R)}$ is zero, the Poisson equation becomes the Laplace equation

$$\nabla^2 \mathbf{T} = 0 \tag{11.97}$$

where $\mathbf{T}$, a solution of either Eq. (11.96) or (11.97), is given by Eq. (11.74). The magnitude of each component of $\mathbf{T}$ also satisfies the scalar Laplace equation. In Eq. (11.74), $\mathbf{T}$ is not yet related to the curl of $\mathbf{F}$, but by considering Eq. (11.74) further, we can determine how $\mathbf{T}$ depends on the curl of $\mathbf{F}$. From Eq. (11.74) we obtain (using Eq. 8.22k)

$$\mathbf{T(R)} = \nabla \times \iiint_{\substack{\text{all} \\ \text{space}}} \frac{\mathbf{F(R')}\, dV(\mathbf{R'})}{4\pi \, |\mathbf{R} - \mathbf{R'}|} = \iiint_{\substack{\text{all} \\ \text{space}}} \frac{\mathbf{F(R')}}{4\pi} \times \nabla \frac{1}{|\mathbf{R} - \mathbf{R'}|} \, dV(\mathbf{R'}) \tag{11.98}$$

If we integrate both sides of Eq. (8.22k) over a volume V, we obtain

$$\iiint_V \nabla' \times \frac{\mathbf{F(R')}}{|\mathbf{R} - \mathbf{R'}|} \, dV(\mathbf{R'}) = \iiint_V \frac{1}{|\mathbf{R} - \mathbf{R'}|} \nabla' \times \mathbf{F(R')} \, dV(\mathbf{R'})$$
$$- \iiint_V \mathbf{F(R')} \times \nabla' \frac{1}{|\mathbf{R} - \mathbf{R'}|} \, dV(\mathbf{R'}) \tag{11.99}$$

By means of Eq. (2.40) we may transform the left-hand side of Eq. (11.99) to a surface integral. Solving the result for the integral containing $\nabla' \times \mathbf{F(R')}$, we obtain

$$\iiint_V \frac{1}{|\mathbf{R} - \mathbf{R'}|} \nabla' \times \mathbf{F(R')} \, dV(\mathbf{R'}) = \iiint_V \mathbf{F(R')} \times \nabla' \frac{1}{|\mathbf{R} - \mathbf{R'}|} \, dV(\mathbf{R'})$$
$$- \oiint_A \frac{\mathbf{F(R')} \times d\mathbf{s(R')}}{|\mathbf{R} - \mathbf{R'}|} \tag{11.100}$$

If V expands to include all space, then the surface integral will approach zero if $\mathbf{F(R')}$ decreases faster than $|\mathbf{R} - \mathbf{R'}|^{-1}$ on A. Thus Eq. (11.100) becomes

$$\iiint_{\substack{\text{all} \\ \text{space}}} \frac{1}{|\mathbf{R} - \mathbf{R'}|} \nabla' \times \mathbf{F(R')} \, dV(\mathbf{R'}) = \iiint_{\substack{\text{all} \\ \text{space}}} \mathbf{F(R')} \times \nabla' \frac{1}{|\mathbf{R} - \mathbf{R'}|} \, dV(\mathbf{R'}) \tag{11.101}$$

and Eq. (11.98) may be written

$$\mathbf{T} = \iiint_{\substack{\text{all} \\ \text{space}}} \frac{\nabla' \times \mathbf{F}(\mathbf{R}')}{4\pi|\mathbf{R} - \mathbf{R}'|} \, dV(\mathbf{R}') \tag{11.102a}$$

However, the curl of a field is related to vector sources $\mathbf{K}_s$ of the field so that Eq. (11.102a) may also be written

$$\mathbf{T} = \iiint_{\substack{\text{all} \\ \text{space}}} \frac{\mathbf{K}_s(\mathbf{R}')}{4\pi|\mathbf{R} - \mathbf{R}'|} \, dV(\mathbf{R}') \tag{11.102b}$$

Equations (11.102a) and (11.102b) specify the relationship between the vector potential $\mathbf{T}$ and the curl of $\mathbf{F}$ at all points in space. If curl $\mathbf{F} = \mathbf{K}_s$ is not known for all points in space but in a finite volume V only, we may still determine $\mathbf{T}(\mathbf{R})$ by means of Green's theorem. With this theorem we can develop an expression which will yield the vector potential at every point within V in terms of the curl of the field, that is, the value of $\mathbf{T}$ and its normal derivative of $\mathbf{T}$ on A.

If, in Eq. (9.73), we associate g with $T_x(\mathbf{R}')$, the magnitude of the x-component of $\mathbf{T}(\mathbf{R}')$, and h with $|\mathbf{R} - \mathbf{R}'|^{-1}$, then Eq. (9.73) becomes

$$\iiint_V \left[T_x(\mathbf{R}') \nabla'^2 \frac{1}{|\mathbf{R} - \mathbf{R}'|} - \frac{1}{|\mathbf{R} - \mathbf{R}'|} \nabla'^2 T_x(\mathbf{R}') \right] dV(\mathbf{R}')$$

$$= \oiint_A \left[T_x(\mathbf{R}') \nabla' \frac{1}{|\mathbf{R} - \mathbf{R}'|} - \frac{1}{|\mathbf{R} - \mathbf{R}'|} \nabla' T_x(\mathbf{R}') \right] \cdot d\mathbf{s}(\mathbf{R}') \tag{11.103}$$

Proceeding as in the discussion preceding Eqs. (11.87a) and (11.87b), we obtain

$$T_x(\mathbf{R}) = \frac{1}{4\pi} \iiint_V \frac{[\nabla' \times \mathbf{F}(\mathbf{R}')]_x}{|\mathbf{R} - \mathbf{R}'|} \, dV(\mathbf{R}')$$

$$+ \frac{1}{4\pi} \oiint_A \left[\frac{1}{|\mathbf{R} - \mathbf{R}'|} \nabla' T_x(\mathbf{R}') - T_x(\mathbf{R}') \nabla' \frac{1}{|\mathbf{R} - \mathbf{R}'|} \right] \cdot d\mathbf{s}(\mathbf{R}') \tag{11.104}$$

if the observation point is within V; and if the observation point is outside of V,

$$\iiint_V \frac{[\nabla' \times \mathbf{F}(\mathbf{R}')]_x}{|\mathbf{R} - \mathbf{R}'|} \, dV(\mathbf{R}') = \oiint_A \left[T_x(\mathbf{R}') \nabla' \frac{1}{|\mathbf{R} - \mathbf{R}'|} \right.$$

$$\left. - \frac{1}{|\mathbf{R} - \mathbf{R}'|} \nabla' T_x(\mathbf{R}') \right] \cdot d\mathbf{s}(\mathbf{R}') \tag{11.105}$$

If we repeat the foregoing procedure for T_y and T_z, then multiply each equation by $\mathbf{u}_x$, $\mathbf{u}_y$, and $\mathbf{u}_z$, respectively, and sum the resulting equations, we obtain

$$\mathbf{T}(\mathbf{R}) = \frac{1}{4\pi} \iiint_V \frac{K_s(\mathbf{R}')\,dV(\mathbf{R}')}{|\mathbf{R} - \mathbf{R}'|} - \frac{1}{4\pi} \oiint_A \mathbf{T}\left[\nabla'\frac{1}{|\mathbf{R} - \mathbf{R}'|}\right] \cdot d\mathbf{s}(\mathbf{R}')$$

$$+ \frac{1}{4\pi} \oiint_A \frac{[d\mathbf{s}(\mathbf{R}') \cdot \nabla']\mathbf{T}(\mathbf{R}')}{|\mathbf{R} - \mathbf{R}'|} \quad (11.106a)$$

if $\mathbf{R}$ locates a point within V. If, conversely, the observation point is external to V, the result is

$$\iiint_V \frac{K_s(\mathbf{R}')}{|\mathbf{R} - \mathbf{R}'|}\,dV(\mathbf{R}') = -\oiint_A \frac{(d\mathbf{s} \cdot \nabla')\mathbf{T}(\mathbf{R}')}{|\mathbf{R} - \mathbf{R}'|}$$

$$+ \oiint_A \mathbf{T}\left[\nabla'\frac{1}{|\mathbf{R} - \mathbf{R}'|}\right] \cdot d\mathbf{s}(\mathbf{R}') \quad (11.106b)$$

where

$$(d\mathbf{s} \cdot \nabla')\mathbf{T}(\mathbf{R}') = \mathbf{u}_x[\nabla'T_x(\mathbf{R}') \cdot d\mathbf{s}] + \mathbf{u}_y[\nabla'T_y(\mathbf{R}') \cdot d\mathbf{s}] + \mathbf{u}_z[\nabla'T_z(\mathbf{R}') \cdot d\mathbf{s}]$$

In a manner analogous to that employed when discussing the vector potential, it can be shown that the surface integrals in Eqs. (11.106a) and (11.106b) represent the vector sources external to V.

In a region where there are no vector sources, only the surface integrals of Eq. (11.106a) would remain. However, this would only constitute an integral equation because $\mathbf{T}$ and $\partial \mathbf{T}/\partial n$ cannot be specified independently if $\mathbf{T}$ is a solution of Poisson's equation.

If div $\mathbf{F}(\mathbf{R}) = 0$ in certain regions of space, then in those regions the field $\mathbf{F}(\mathbf{R}) = \mathbf{S}(\mathbf{R})$ is completely solenoidal and may be uniquely described by a vector potential satisfying the Poisson equation. If, in addition, curl $\mathbf{F} = $ curl $\mathbf{S} = 0$, $\mathbf{S}$ may be derived from a scalar potential satisfying the Laplace equation. That is, if $K_s(\mathbf{R}) = 0$, then $\nabla \times \mathbf{S}(\mathbf{R}) = 0$; but this implies that

$$\mathbf{S}(\mathbf{R}) = -\nabla\Phi^* \quad (11.107)$$

[see Eq. (8.22r)], where Φ^* is a scalar field.
Since div $\mathbf{S}(\mathbf{R}) = 0$, we see that

$$\nabla^2\Phi^* = 0 \quad (11.108)$$

That is, the field is derivable from a scalar potential which satisfies the Laplace equation.

11.7   Improper Integrals

Upon superficial examination of the equations for the potentials and fields appearing in this chapter, it may appear that because of the presence of $|\mathbf{R} - \mathbf{R}'|$ in the denominator, these quantities are discontinuous at the point $\mathbf{R} = \mathbf{R}'$. We have seen in the previous section that this discontinuity presents no difficulty to the discussion. Let us emphasize this point by reexamining the volume integral involved in the scalar potential:

$$\frac{1}{4\pi} \iiint\limits_V \frac{\rho_v(\mathbf{R}') \, dV(\mathbf{R}')}{|\mathbf{R} - \mathbf{R}'|} \tag{11.109}$$

When V does not contain the field point located by $\mathbf{R}$, the integral is proper and no difficulty is experienced. If the field point is located within V, then we surround that point by a sphere of radius ϵ and volume V_ϵ. Then Eq. (11.109) may be written

$$\frac{1}{4\pi} \iiint\limits_V \frac{\rho_v(\mathbf{R}') \, dV(\mathbf{R}')}{|\mathbf{R} - \mathbf{R}'|} = \frac{1}{4\pi} \iiint\limits_{V - V_\epsilon} \frac{\rho_v(\mathbf{R}') \, dV(\mathbf{R}')}{|\mathbf{R} - \mathbf{R}'|}$$
$$+ \frac{1}{4\pi} \iiint\limits_{V_\epsilon} \frac{\rho_v(\mathbf{R}') \, dV(\mathbf{R}')}{|\mathbf{R} - \mathbf{R}'|} \tag{11.110}$$

The first integral on the right-hand side presents no difficulty. In the second integral the volume element of the sphere may be taken as a shell so that $dV = 4\pi |\mathbf{R} - \mathbf{R}'|^2 \, d|\mathbf{R} - \mathbf{R}'|$. If $\rho_v(\mathbf{R}')$ is bounded, single-valued, and continuous within V_ϵ and its maximum value within V_ϵ is $\rho_{v\mathrm{max}}$, then

$$\frac{1}{4\pi} \iiint \frac{\rho_v(\mathbf{R}') \, dV(\mathbf{R}')}{|\mathbf{R} - \mathbf{R}'|} \leq \rho_{v\mathrm{max}} \int_{|\mathbf{R} - \mathbf{R}'| = 0}^{\epsilon} |\mathbf{R} - \mathbf{R}'| \, d|\mathbf{R} - \mathbf{R}'| \tag{11.111}$$

Since the right-hand side of Eq. (11.111) approaches zero as $\epsilon \to 0$, that is, as the sphere shrinks down on the point $\mathbf{R}' = \mathbf{R}$, the value of (11.109) converges and is twice differentiable.

What the foregoing means is that even though the contribution to the potential integral from the volume element containing the observation point is very large, the size of that volume element can be made to approach zero so that the net influence to the potential is negligible, that is, $dV(\mathbf{R}')/|\mathbf{R} - \mathbf{R}'|$ approaches zero as $\mathbf{R}' \to \mathbf{R}$.

11.8   Field Discontinuities and Boundary Conditions

The value of a field or potential may suffer a discontinuity across a surface. Let us now examine the nature of these discontinuities.

Consider the surface A shown in Fig. 11.16. Let us suppose that there are surface scalar sources on A, where $\mathbf{R}'$ locates points on A. As illustrated in Fig. 11.16, imagine a small pill box having a top and bottom of area $ds(\mathbf{R}')$ and placed so that half of the pill box is on one side of the surface A and the other half is on the other side. By applying Gauss's divergence theorem to the pill box, we obtain

$$\iiint_V \nabla' \cdot \mathbf{F}(\mathbf{R}') \, dV(\mathbf{R}') = \oiint_A \mathbf{F}(\mathbf{R}') \cdot ds(\mathbf{R}') \tag{11.112}$$

Since $\nabla' \cdot \mathbf{S} = 0$, Eq. (11.112) becomes

$$\iiint_V \nabla' \cdot \mathbf{I}(\mathbf{R}') \, dV(\mathbf{R}') = \oiint_A \mathbf{I}(\mathbf{R}') \cdot ds(\mathbf{R}') + \oiint_A \mathbf{S}(\mathbf{R}') \cdot ds(\mathbf{R}')$$

However, we know that

$$\iiint_V \nabla' \cdot \mathbf{I}(\mathbf{R}') \, dV(\mathbf{R}') = \oiint_A \mathbf{I}(\mathbf{R}') \cdot ds(\mathbf{R}') \tag{11.113}$$

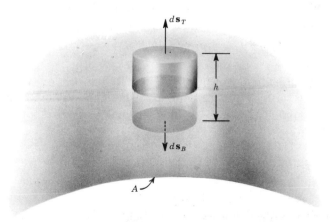

Figure 11.16   For the discussion of boundary conditions for vector fields.

so that

$$\oiint_A \mathbf{S}(\mathbf{R}') \cdot d\mathbf{s}(\mathbf{R}') = 0 \tag{11.114}$$

We may write Eq. (11.113) as

$$\iiint_V \rho_v(\mathbf{R}') \, dV(\mathbf{R}') = \iint_{sides} \mathbf{I}(\mathbf{R}') \cdot d\mathbf{s}(\mathbf{R}') + \iint_{top} \mathbf{I}(\mathbf{R}') \cdot d\mathbf{s}(\mathbf{R}')$$

$$+ \iint_{bottom} \mathbf{I}(\mathbf{R}') \cdot d\mathbf{s}(\mathbf{R}') \tag{11.115}$$

We now require the altitude of the pill box to decrease in such a way that the top and bottom of the pill box approach coincidence with A. The left-hand side of Eq. (11.115) is the net scalar source strength within the pill box, which is just $\iint \rho_s(\mathbf{R}') \, |d\mathbf{s}(\mathbf{R}')|$, where $\rho_s(\mathbf{R}')$ is the scalar surface source density on the surface A. As $h \to 0$ the area of the sides of the pill box approach zero and the first integral on the right-hand side of Eq. (11.115) is negligible. Equation (11.115) then becomes

$$\iint \rho_s(\mathbf{R}') \, |d\mathbf{s}(\mathbf{R}')| = \iint_{top} \mathbf{I}_T \cdot d\mathbf{s}_T + \iint_{bottom} \mathbf{I}_B \cdot d\mathbf{s}_B$$

$$= \iint (I_{T_n} - I_{B_n}) \, |d\mathbf{s}(\mathbf{R}')| \tag{11.116}$$

where $d\mathbf{s}_B = \mathbf{u}_{n_B} |d\mathbf{s}_B| = -\mathbf{u}_{n_T} |d\mathbf{s}_B| = -\mathbf{u}_n |d\mathbf{s}|$ and I_{T_n}, I_{B_n} are the normal components of the irrotational part of $\mathbf{F}$ on the top and bottom of A, respectively. We may conclude from Eq. (11.116) that

$$I_{T_n} - I_{B_n} = \rho_s = \left. \frac{\partial \Phi}{\partial n} \right|_{bottom} - \left. \frac{\partial \Phi}{\partial n} \right|_{top} \tag{11.117}$$

that is, the normal component of the irrotational portion of the field is discontinuous across A by the amount ρ_s. This is equivalent to the negative of the discontinuity across A of the normal derivatives of the scalar potential.

From Eq. (11.114) we can conclude that the normal component of the solenoidal portion of the field is continuous across A:

$$S_{T_n} = S_{B_n} \tag{11.118}$$

To determine the influence on the field of a surface vector source density $\mathbf{K}_s(\mathbf{R}')$, consider Γ the rectangular path 1, 2, 3, 4 shown in Fig.

11.17. Applying Stokes's theorem to this path yields

$$\iint_{A'} \nabla' \times \mathbf{F(R')} \cdot ds(\mathbf{R'}) = \oint_{\Gamma} \mathbf{F} \cdot d\mathbf{l(R')} \qquad (11.119)$$

where A' is the area enclosed by Γ.

Since $\nabla' \times \mathbf{I} = 0$, Eq. (11.119) becomes

$$\iint_{A'} \nabla' \times \mathbf{S(R')} \cdot ds(\mathbf{R'}) = \oint_{\Gamma} \mathbf{I} \cdot d\mathbf{l} + \oint_{\Gamma} \mathbf{S} \cdot d\mathbf{l} \qquad (11.120)$$

We may also write

$$\iint_{A'} \nabla' \times \mathbf{S(R')} \cdot ds(\mathbf{R'}) = \oint_{\Gamma} \mathbf{S} \cdot d\mathbf{l} \qquad (11.121)$$

so that

$$\oint_{\Gamma} \mathbf{I} \cdot d\mathbf{l} = 0$$

In other words, the tangential component of $\mathbf{I}$ is continuous across A,

$$I_{T_t} = I_{B_t} \qquad (11.122)$$

We may write Eq. (11.121) as

$$\iint_{A} \mathbf{K_s(R')} \cdot ds(\mathbf{R'}) = \int_{1}^{2} \mathbf{S} \cdot d\mathbf{l} + \int_{2}^{3} \mathbf{S} \cdot d\mathbf{l} + \int_{3}^{4} \mathbf{S} \cdot d\mathbf{l} + \int_{4}^{1} \mathbf{S} \cdot d\mathbf{l} \qquad (11.123)$$

If we require that the lengths of the sides 2, 3 and 1, 4 decrease in such a way that the paths of integration 1 to 2 and 3 to 4 approach the surface A from top and bottom respectively, the left-hand side of Eq. (11.123), which is the number of source lines through A', is $\int |\mathbf{K}_l \times d\mathbf{l}_t| = |\mathbf{K}_l \times \mathbf{u}_t| \, |d\mathbf{l}_t|$, where $d\mathbf{l}_t$ is an elemental line segment tangent to the surface A. $\mathbf{K}_l$, defined to be the line vector source density, is just that vector which will make $|\mathbf{K}_l \times \mathbf{u}_t| \, |d\mathbf{l}_t|$ equal to the number of lines passing perpendicular to $d\mathbf{l}_t$ on A. It is the vector source strength per unit length on the surface.

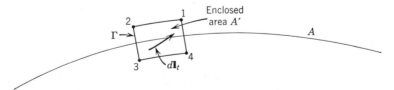

Figure 11.17   For discussion of boundary conditions for vector fields.

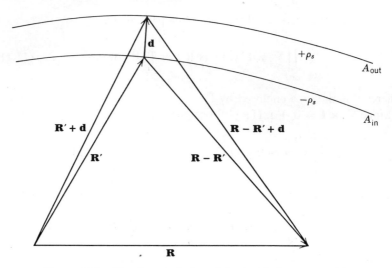

Figure 11.18   For the calculation of the double-layer potential.

Equation (11.123) then becomes

$$|\mathbf{K}_l \times \mathbf{u}_t| = S_{T_t} - S_{B_t} \qquad (11.124a)$$

Since this is true for any $d\mathbf{l}_t$ tangent to A, Eq. (11.124a) may be written as

$$\mathbf{K}_l = \mathbf{u}_n \times (\mathbf{S}_T - \mathbf{S}_B) \qquad (11.124b)$$

That is, the tangential component of the solenoidal part of a field suffers a discontinuity across a surface on which there is the line vector source density.

We have seen that a scalar surface source density will result in a discontinuity in the normal component of the irrotational part of a field, that is, the normal derivative of the scalar potential (see Fig. 11.18). A scalar surface source density does not lead to a discontinuity in the scalar potential across a surface. However, a distribution of dipoles (sometimes called a double or doublet layer) on a surface will lead to a discontinuity in Φ. To see what a double layer is and how it leads to a potential discontinuity, consider two surfaces A_{out} and A_{in} on each of which reside scalar surface source densities $+\rho_s$ and $-\rho_s$, respectively; then the potential at $\mathbf{R}$ is given by

$$\Phi_d(\mathbf{R}) = +\frac{1}{4\pi} \iint\limits_{A_{\text{out}}} \frac{\rho_s(\mathbf{R}') \, |d\mathbf{s}(\mathbf{R}')|}{|\mathbf{R} - \mathbf{R}' + \mathbf{d}|} - \frac{1}{4\pi} \iint\limits_{A_{\text{in}}} \frac{[\rho_s(\mathbf{R}')] \, |d\mathbf{s}(\mathbf{R}')|}{|\mathbf{R} - \mathbf{R}'|} \qquad (11.125)$$

where **d** is the normal distance from A_{in} to A_{out} as measured from A_{in} to A_{out}. If $|d|$ is small compared to $|R - R'|$,

$$|R - R' + d|^{-1} = [(x - x')^2 + (y - y')^2 + (z - z')^2 - 2(R - R') \cdot d]^{-\frac{1}{2}}$$

$$= |R - R'|^{-1}\left[1 - \frac{2(R - R') \cdot d}{|R - R'|^2}\right]^{-\frac{1}{2}}$$

$$= |R - R'|^{-1}\left[1 + \frac{(R - R') \cdot d}{|R - R'|^2}\right]$$

$$= \frac{1}{|R - R'|} + \frac{u_{R-R'} \cdot d}{|R - R'|} = \frac{1}{|R - R'|} + \nabla'\frac{1}{|R - R'|} \cdot d$$

where we have used a Taylor expansion of $\{1 + [2(R - R')]/|R - R'|\}^{-\frac{1}{2}}$ and neglected the higher order terms.

As A_{out} approaches A_{in}, that is, as $d \to 0$, Eq. (11.125) becomes

$$\Phi_d = \frac{1}{4\pi}\iint_A \tau \cdot \nabla' \frac{1}{|R - R'|}\,|ds(R')| \qquad (11.126)$$

where $\tau \equiv \rho_s d$ is called the dipole or double layer density on A. Since **d**, and hence τ, has the same sense as $ds(R')$, Eq. (11.126) may be written

$$\Phi_d = \frac{1}{4\pi}\iint_A |\tau|\,\nabla'\frac{1}{|R - R'|} \cdot ds(R') = -\frac{1}{4\pi}\iint_A |\tau|\,d\Omega \qquad (11.127a)$$

where $d\Omega$ is the solid angle subtended by $ds(R')$ at **R**.

Thus if **R** locates an observation point on the inside of a closed surface, Eq. (11.127a) yields

$$\Phi_{d_{in}} = -|\tau| \qquad (11.127b)$$

and if **R** locates an observation point on the outside of a closed surface, Eq. (11.127a) gives

$$\Phi_{d_{out}} = 0 \qquad (11.127c)$$

Thus when traversing a surface A on which resides a dipole distribution, the potential suffers a discontinuity of

$$\Phi_+ - \Phi_- = \Phi_{d_{out}} - \Phi_{d_{in}} = |\tau| \qquad (11.128)$$

By utilizing Eqs. (11.117) and (11.127), we are now in a position to present a "physical" interpretation of the surface integrals in Eq. (11.87a):

$$\Phi = \frac{1}{4\pi}\iiint_V \frac{\rho_v(R')\,dV(R')}{|R - R'|} + \frac{1}{4\pi}\iint_A \frac{1}{|R - R'|}\frac{\partial\Phi}{\partial n}\,|ds(R')|$$

$$- \frac{1}{4\pi}\iint_A \Phi(R)\,\nabla'\frac{1}{|R - R'|} \cdot ds(R) \qquad (11.87a)$$

In light of Eq. (11.117), it is reasonable to associate the term $\partial\Phi/\partial n$ (which is evaluated just on the inside of A since this is the only portion belonging to V) with ρ_s, the scalar source density on A:

$$\left.\frac{\partial\Phi}{\partial n}\right|_{\text{in}} = \rho_s \tag{11.129}$$

Here we consider the inside of the surface to be equivalent to the bottom of the surface discussed in connection with Eq. (11.117). Equations (11.126) and (11.127) lead us to associate the potential $\Phi(\mathbf{R}')$ (which is evaluated just on the inside of A since we are concerned with quantities within V) with $|\boldsymbol{\tau}|$, the magnitude of the dipole layer density on A

$$\Phi_{\text{in}} = |\boldsymbol{\tau}| \tag{11.130}$$

Thus we are led to believe that the two surface integrals in Eq. (11.87a) represent the surface scalar-source density and the dipole-layer density we must place on A to simulate the contribution to the potential within A due to sources outside of A. It is interesting to note that this surface scalar-source density and dipole-layer density that we place on A to simulate the sources external to A are just those necessary to make the potential and the irrotational portion of the field zero at every point outside of A. To see this, we note from Eqs. (11.117), (11.127), (11.129), and (11.130) that

$$\left.\frac{\partial\Phi}{\partial n}\right|_{\text{out}} = 0 \tag{11.131}$$

and

$$\Phi(\mathbf{R}')_{\text{out}} = 0 \tag{11.132}$$

If we now apply Eq. (11.90) to V_0 the region outside of V, we see that

$$\iiint\limits_{V_0} \frac{\rho_v(\mathbf{R}')\,dV(\mathbf{R}')}{|\mathbf{R} - \mathbf{R}'|} = \iint\limits_{A} \Phi(\mathbf{R}')\,\nabla' \frac{1}{|\mathbf{R} - \mathbf{R}'|} \cdot d\mathbf{s}_0$$
$$- \iint\limits_{A} \frac{1}{|\mathbf{R} - \mathbf{R}'|}\frac{\partial\Phi}{\partial n}(\mathbf{R}')\,|d\mathbf{s}_0|$$

where A is the common surface between V and V_0. However, the quantities $\Phi(\mathbf{R}')$ and $\partial\Phi/\partial n$ are to be evaluated just on the inside of V_0, that is, just on the outside of V. These quantities were shown to be zero in Eqs. (11.131) and (11.132). Thus $\rho_v(\mathbf{R}')$ is zero at all points of V_0. Since Φ and $\partial\Phi/\partial n$ are zero on the surface of V_0, on A, Φ must be zero everywhere in V_0. Since Φ in Eq. (11.87a), together with its derivatives is continuous, $\mathbf{I}$ is zero outside of V.

We have stated that before we can obtain solutions to the Poisson or Laplace equation in a particular region, we must have some knowledge concerning the value of Φ or of $\partial\Phi/\partial n$, but not both. We now wish to show that unique solutions (except for an additive constant) can be obtained for the Poisson equation within a region V if

1. The potential is specified on A, the surface of V (this is called the Dirichlet condition). As we have seen in Eq. (11.127b), this condition is equivalent to specifying the double-layer distribution on A.

2. The normal derivative of the potential on A, that is, the normal component of the field, is specified (this is called the Neumann condition); as we have seen in Eq. (11.117), this condition is equivalent to specifying the scalar source surface density on A.

To prove this, let g and h in Eq. (9.71) be equal to each other and to the difference $\Phi_2 - \Phi_1$, where Φ_2 and Φ_1 are different solutions to the same Poisson equation with the same boundary conditions. Thus $\nabla^2 g = 0$ in V, and either $\partial g/\partial n$ or $g = 0$ on A, the surface of V. Equation (9.71) then yields

$$\iiint\limits_V (\Phi_2 - \Phi_1)\,\nabla^2(\Phi_2 - \Phi_1)\,dV + \iiint\limits_V [\nabla(\Phi_2 - \Phi_1)]^2\,dV$$

$$= \oiint\limits_A (\Phi_2 - \Phi_1)\frac{\partial}{\partial n}(\Phi_2 - \Phi_1)\,ds$$

$$= 0 \tag{11.133}$$

This implies that $[\nabla(\Phi_2 - \Phi_1)]^2 = 0$; thus inside V, $\Phi_2 - \Phi_1$ is a constant. For Dirichlet conditions $\Phi_2 - \Phi_1 = 0$ on A, so $\Phi_2 = \Phi_1$ throughout V. For Neumann conditions $[\partial(\Phi_2 - \Phi_1)]/\partial n = 0$ so that the two solutions can differ by an additive constant only. We have shown, therefore, that imposing Dirichlet or Neumann conditions on a potential leads to unique solutions for the Poisson equation.

11.9 Green's Functions

As we have stated previously, attempts to find solutions to the Poisson equation

$$\nabla^2\Phi(\mathbf{R}) = -\rho_v(\mathbf{R}) \tag{11.77}$$

for a particular set of boundary conditions constitute an extremely important aspect of science and engineering. A very productive approach, involving the use of Green's functions, has been devised to facilitate the process of obtaining such solutions.

Before discussing Green's functions in more detail, it is of value at this point to introduce the concept of the Dirac delta function, which is defined by the relationships

$$\delta(\mathbf{R} - \mathbf{R'}) = 0 \qquad \mathbf{R'} \neq \mathbf{R}$$

and

$$\iiint\limits_{\substack{\text{all values} \\ \text{of } \mathbf{R'}}} \delta(\mathbf{R} - \mathbf{R'}) \, dV(\mathbf{R'}) = 1 \tag{11.134}$$

It is seen that $\delta(\mathbf{R} - \mathbf{R'})$ is a function which is zero for all values of $\mathbf{R'}$ except in an infinitesimally small region in the neighborhood of the point $\mathbf{R'} = \mathbf{R}$.

It follows from these defining relations that

$$\iiint\limits_{\substack{\text{all values} \\ \text{of } \mathbf{R'}}} f(\mathbf{R'}) \, \delta(\mathbf{R} - \mathbf{R'}) \, dV(\mathbf{R'}) = f(\mathbf{R}) \tag{11.135}$$

To demonstrate the validity of Eq. (11.135), we observe that only for those values of $\mathbf{R'}$ which are nearly equal to $\mathbf{R}$ is $\delta(\mathbf{R} - \mathbf{R'})$ different from zero; we may then write

$$\iiint\limits_{\substack{\text{all} \\ \text{values} \\ \text{of } \mathbf{R'}}} f(\mathbf{R'}) \, \delta(\mathbf{R} - \mathbf{R'}) \, dV(\mathbf{R'}) = \lim_{\Delta \mathbf{R} \to 0} \iiint\limits_{\substack{\text{those} \\ \text{values} \\ \text{of } \mathbf{R'} \\ \text{which lie} \\ \text{between} \\ \mathbf{R} \pm \Delta \mathbf{R}}} f(\mathbf{R'}) \, \delta(\mathbf{R} - \mathbf{R'}) \, dV(\mathbf{R'}) \tag{11.136}$$

However, in the small interval $\mathbf{R'} = \mathbf{R} \pm \Delta \mathbf{R}$, $f(\mathbf{R'})$ has essentially the value $f(\mathbf{R})$. Then Eq. (11.136) becomes

$$\iiint\limits_{\substack{\text{all} \\ \text{values} \\ \text{of } R'}} f(\mathbf{R'}) \, \delta(\mathbf{R} - \mathbf{R'}) \, dV(\mathbf{R'}) = f(\mathbf{R}) \lim_{\Delta \mathbf{R} \to 0} \iiint\limits_{\substack{\text{values of} \\ \mathbf{R'} \text{ which lie} \\ \text{within the} \\ \text{interval} \\ \mathbf{R} \pm \Delta \mathbf{R}}} \delta(\mathbf{R} - \mathbf{R'}) \, dV(\mathbf{R'})$$

$$= f(\mathbf{R}) \iiint\limits_{\substack{\text{all} \\ \text{values} \\ \text{of } \mathbf{R'}}} \delta(\mathbf{R} - \mathbf{R'}) \, dV(\mathbf{R'})$$

$$= f(\mathbf{R}) \tag{11.137}$$

by virtue of Eq. (11.134).

Before examining some of the fundamental aspects of Green's functions, let us discuss their utility in a superficial manner. If, instead of solving Eq. (11.77), we solve the equation

$$\nabla^2 G(\mathbf{R}, \mathbf{R'}) = -\delta(\mathbf{R} - \mathbf{R'}) \tag{11.138}$$

where $G(\mathbf{R}, \mathbf{R}')$ is called the Green function, then $\Phi(\mathbf{R})$, the solution to Eq. (11.77), may be written

$$\Phi = \iiint_{\substack{\text{all} \\ \text{values} \\ \text{of } \mathbf{R}'}} G(\mathbf{R}, \mathbf{R}')\rho_v(\mathbf{R}') \, dV(\mathbf{R}') \qquad (11.139)$$

To see that Eq. (11.139) is a solution to Eq. (11.77), we take the Laplacian (with respect to the field coordinates) of Eq. (11.134),

$$\nabla^2\Phi = \nabla^2 \iiint_{\substack{\text{all} \\ \text{values} \\ \text{of } \mathbf{R}'}} G(\mathbf{R}, \mathbf{R}')\rho_v(\mathbf{R}') \, dV(\mathbf{R}')$$

$$= \iiint_{\substack{\text{all} \\ \text{values} \\ \text{of } \mathbf{R}'}} \nabla^2 G(\mathbf{R}, \mathbf{R}')\rho_v(\mathbf{R}') \, dV(\mathbf{R}')$$

$$= -\iiint \delta(\mathbf{R} - \mathbf{R}')\rho_v(\mathbf{R}') \, dV(\mathbf{R}')$$

$$= -\rho_v(\mathbf{R}) \qquad (11.140)$$

[See Eqs. (11.135) and (11.138).]

Thus we are led to believe that Eq. (11.139) is at least a partial solution of the Poisson equation.

To treat Green's functions more thoroughly, let us review specifically what we are attempting to accomplish.

We shall now show that if we can obtain solutions to Eq. (11.138) under either of the two boundary conditions, then we can state solutions to the Poisson equation in terms of $G(\mathbf{R}, \mathbf{R}')$. To do this we note that

$$\nabla'^2\left[\frac{1}{|\mathbf{R} - \mathbf{R}'|}\right] = -4\pi \, \delta(\mathbf{R} - \mathbf{R}') \qquad (11.141)$$

See, for example, Eq. (11.71).

Thus $G(\mathbf{R}, \mathbf{R}') = 1/4\pi[\mathbf{R} - \mathbf{R}']$ is a function which satisfies Eq. (11.138). In general, we may say

$$\nabla'^2 G(\mathbf{R}, \mathbf{R}') = -\delta(\mathbf{R} - \mathbf{R}') \qquad (11.142)$$

where $G(\mathbf{R}, \mathbf{R}') = (1/4\pi)[|\mathbf{R} - \mathbf{R}'|^{-1} + \psi(\mathbf{R}, \mathbf{R}')]$ \qquad (11.143)

where $\nabla^2\psi(\mathbf{R}, \mathbf{R}') = 0$ within V.

With the existence of a function $\psi(\mathbf{R}, \mathbf{R}')$ there is a possibility that we can use it in Green's theorem, Eq. (9.68) [which was used to derive

(11.87a)] to eliminate either of the surface integrals. Let $g = \Phi$ and $h = G(\mathbf{R}, \mathbf{R}')$; we obtain from Eq. (9.68)

$$\iiint\limits_V (\Phi \, \nabla^2 G - G \, \nabla^2 \Phi) \, dV = \oiint\limits_A (\Phi \, \nabla G - G \, \nabla \Phi) \cdot d\mathbf{s} \qquad (11.144)$$

which leads to

$$\Phi(R) = \iiint\limits_V \rho_v G(\mathbf{R}, \mathbf{R}') \, dV + \oiint\limits_A G \frac{\partial \Phi}{\partial n} \, |ds| - \oiint\limits_A \Phi \frac{\partial G}{\partial n} \, |ds| \qquad (11.145)$$

If we must satisfy the Dirichlet boundary conditions, $G(\mathbf{R}, \mathbf{R}')$ must be chosen to be $G_D(\mathbf{R}, \mathbf{R}') = 0$. We can make this choice because we are free to choose $\psi(\mathbf{R}, \mathbf{R}')$. Thus we choose $\psi(\mathbf{R}, \mathbf{R}')$ to be a scalar source distribution outside of V which is just sufficient to make G zero on A. Then Eq. (11.145) becomes

$$\Phi(\mathbf{R}) = \iiint\limits_V \rho(\mathbf{R}')G_D(\mathbf{R}, \mathbf{R}') \, dV - \oiint\limits_A \Phi(\mathbf{R}') \frac{\partial G_D(\mathbf{R}, \mathbf{R}') \, |ds|}{\partial n} \qquad (11.146)$$

Similarly, to satisfy the Neumann conditions, we would like to choose $G(\mathbf{R}, \mathbf{R}') = G_N(\mathbf{R}, \mathbf{R}')$ so that the second surface integral of Eq. (11.145) vanishes. It would at first appear that the choice would be $\partial G_N/\partial n = 0$; however, this is not permitted because applying Gauss's theorem [Eq. (9.39)] to Eq. (11.142) yields

$$\iiint\limits_V \nabla'^2 G(\mathbf{R}, \mathbf{R}') \, dV = -\iiint\limits_V \delta(\mathbf{R} - \mathbf{R}') \, dV = -1$$

$$= \oiint\limits_A \nabla' G(\mathbf{R}, \mathbf{R}') \cdot d\mathbf{s}(\mathbf{R}') = \oiint\limits_A \frac{\partial G}{\partial n} \, |ds| \qquad (11.147)$$

We see that $\partial G/\partial n$ cannot be zero on A. Thus if we choose $\partial G_N/\partial n$ to be $-1/A$, Eq. (11.145) becomes

$$\Phi = \iiint\limits_V \rho_v G_N(\mathbf{R}, \mathbf{R}') \, dV + \oiint\limits_A G_N \frac{\partial \Phi}{\partial n} \, |ds| + \frac{1}{A} \oiint\limits_A \Phi \, |ds| \qquad (11.148)$$

Now the quantity

$$\frac{1}{A} \oiint\limits_A \Phi \, |ds| \quad \text{is} \quad \langle \Phi \rangle$$

the average value of Φ over the surface A. Then Eq. (11.148) may be written

$$\Phi - \langle \Phi \rangle = \iiint\limits_V \rho_v G_N \, dV + \oiint\limits_A G_N \frac{\partial \Phi}{\partial n} \, |ds| \qquad (11.149)$$

Thus the deviation of Φ from its average value on the surface A is given by Eq. (11.149).

By comparing Eq. (11.145) with Eq. (11.87a), we see that the development given in Sections 11.5 to 11.6 is essentially a discussion utilizing Green's functions where $G(\mathbf{R}, \mathbf{R}') = \dfrac{1}{4\pi \, |\mathbf{R} - \mathbf{R}'|}$.

PROBLEMS

1. Show that all analytic functions of a complex variable are solutions of the two-dimensional Laplace equation.
2. If a field is given by $\mathbf{F} = kr^{-v}\mathbf{u}_r$, calculate div $\mathbf{F}$ and curl $\mathbf{F}$.
3. Determine the equation of the lines of forces on the plane $z = 0$ for a point dipole oriented along the x-axis whose potential is

$$U(\mathbf{R}) = \frac{1}{4\pi\epsilon_0} \frac{\mathbf{p} \cdot \mathbf{u}_{\mathbf{R}-\mathbf{R}'}}{|\mathbf{R} - \mathbf{R}'|}$$

4. What is the electrostatic potential at a point external to an infinitely long charged cylinder?
5. Is the field

$$\mathbf{F} = \mathbf{u}_x y - \mathbf{u}_y x$$

irrotational or solenoidal?
6. Prove the following statement encountered in electrostatics: Any excess electrical charge placed on a conductor must reside entirely on its surface.
7. If the gravitational potential in a medium is of the form e^{-r^2}, show, by using the Poisson equation, that the volume mass density of the medium varies as

$$\rho = 2e^{-r^2} \{3 - 2r^2\}$$

8. Consider an infinite plane with points P_1, P_2, each located a distance d on a straight line normal to the plane. On the plane there is a movable point Q; r_1 and r_2 are the distances P_1Q and P_2Q, respectively. Show, by considering the plane as the limiting case of a sphere, that a Green's function on one side of the infinite plane is

$$G[P_1 Q] = \frac{1}{r_1} - \frac{1}{r_2}$$

9. Show that the surface integrals

$$\oiint_A \left[\Phi(\mathbf{R}') \nabla' \frac{1}{|\mathbf{R} - \mathbf{R}'|} - \frac{1}{|\mathbf{R} - \mathbf{R}'|} \nabla' \Phi(\mathbf{R}') \right] \cdot d\mathbf{s}(\mathbf{R}')$$

just cancel each other for a small sphere surrounding a point charge where $\Phi(\mathbf{R}')$ is given by $-q/4\pi \, |\mathbf{R}'|$.

12

Time-Dependent Fields

12.1 Introduction

Thus far we have discussed fields which have been functions of position only. In this chapter we intend to extend our discussion to include those fields that depend on time as well as position. In addition, we shall consider situations where the volumes and surfaces, discussed previously, move relative to the fields.

To unify our discussion, let us first consider the following experiment. Suppose we are on a boat on a lake and we are asked to determine the vector field which represents the time rate of change of the wind velocity (as measured relative to the boat) at the surface of the water. The wind velocity will appear to change for one or more of the following reasons:

1. The wind velocity relative to the earth at any single point on the lake is changing, say, because it is a gusty day; then, even if the boat were stationary with respect to the earth, its occupants observe that the velocity of the wind is changing with time.

2. The velocity of the wind, as measured relative to the earth, is constant in time but varies from position to position; then, as the boat moves on the surface of the water, its occupants observe that the wind velocity is changing.

3. The velocity of the wind, as measured relative to the earth, is a constant in time and position, but the boat is changing its velocity, that is, is accelerating, and the occupants experience a changing wind velocity.

To state these ideas mathematically, let us calculate the total time derivative of $\mathbf{v}_w$, remembering that $\mathbf{v}_w$ (the velocity of the wind as observed by occupants of a boat) is a function of time, position, and boat velocity.

$$\frac{d\mathbf{v}_w}{dt} = \frac{\partial \mathbf{v}_w}{\partial t} + \frac{\partial \mathbf{v}_w}{\partial x}\frac{dx}{dt} + \frac{\partial \mathbf{v}_w}{\partial y}\frac{dy}{dt} + \frac{\partial \mathbf{v}_w}{\partial z}\frac{dz}{dt}$$

$$+ \frac{\partial \mathbf{v}_w}{\partial v_{Bx}}\frac{dv_{Bx}}{dt} + \frac{\partial \mathbf{v}_w}{\partial v_{By}}\frac{dv_{By}}{dt} + \frac{\partial \mathbf{v}_w}{\partial v_{Bz}}\frac{dv_{Bz}}{dt}$$

$$= \frac{\partial \mathbf{v}_w}{\partial t} + (\mathbf{v}_B \cdot \mathrm{grad})\mathbf{v}_w + (\mathbf{a}_B \cdot \mathrm{grad}_{\mathbf{v}_B})\mathbf{v}_w \qquad (12.1)$$

where $\mathbf{a}_B$, $\mathbf{v}_B$, and x, y, and z are the boat acceleration velocity and position coordinates, respectively, relative to the earth; $\mathrm{grad}_{\mathbf{v}_B}$ can be thought of as the gradient operator in a space where the coordinates are v_{Bx}, v_{By}, and v_{Bz}, that is,

$$
\mathbf{a}_B \cdot \mathrm{grad}_{\mathbf{v}_B} = \left(\mathbf{u}_{Bx} \frac{\partial v_{Bx}}{\partial t} + \mathbf{u}_{By} \frac{\partial v_{By}}{\partial t} + \mathbf{u}_{Bz} \frac{\partial v_{Bz}}{\partial t} \right)
$$

$$
\cdot \left(\mathbf{u}_{Bx} \frac{\partial}{\partial v_{Bx}} + \mathbf{u}_{By} \frac{\partial}{\partial v_{By}} + \mathbf{u}_{Bz} \frac{\partial}{\partial v_{Bz}} \right)
$$

where $\mathbf{u}_{Bx}$, $\mathbf{u}_{By}$, and $\mathbf{u}_{Bz}$ are unit vectors in the instantaneous directions of $\mathbf{v}_{Bx}$, $\mathbf{v}_{By}$, and $\mathbf{v}_{Bz}$. By analogy with Eq. (5.35), $(\mathbf{a}_B \cdot \mathrm{grad}_{\mathbf{v}_B}) = |\mathbf{a}_B| \, \mathbf{u}_{a_B} \cdot \mathrm{grad}_{\mathbf{v}_B}$ represents $|\mathbf{a}_B|$ times the directional derivative in $\mathbf{v}_B$ space in the direction of $\mathbf{a}_B$.

We call dv_w/dt the substantial or total derivative, whereas $\partial v_w/\partial t$ describes the rate of change of the wind velocity relative to the earth and is called the local acceleration; $(\mathbf{v}_B \cdot \mathrm{grad})\mathbf{v}_w$ is termed the convective acceleration.

The first term on the right-hand side of Eq. (12.1) represents the time rate of change of the wind velocity as experienced by the observers in the boat when it is not moving (item 1); the second term on the right-hand side represents the influence of the velocity of the boat on the rate of change of the wind as seen by the occupants of the boat; and the last term of Eq. (12.1) indicates the manner in which the vector acceleration of the boat influences the rate of change of the wind velocity as experienced by the people riding in the boat.

The ideas expressed in Eq. (12.1) can be generalized for any vector field $\mathbf{F}$:

$$
\frac{d\mathbf{F}}{dt} = \frac{\partial \mathbf{F}}{\partial t} + (\mathbf{v} \cdot \mathrm{grad})\mathbf{F} + (\mathbf{a} \cdot \mathrm{grad}_\mathbf{v})\mathbf{F} \qquad (12.3)
$$

where $\mathbf{v}$ and $\mathbf{a}$ are considered to be the velocity and acceleration, relative to the earth, of the observer who is experiencing the rate of change of the vector field.

If $\mathbf{a} = 0$ or if $\mathbf{F}$ is not a function of $\mathbf{v}$, Eq. (12.3) becomes

$$
\frac{d\mathbf{F}}{dt} = \frac{\partial \mathbf{F}}{\partial t} + (\mathbf{v} \cdot \mathrm{grad})\mathbf{F} \qquad (12.4)
$$

A similar expression can be developed for a scalar field. Consider, for example, the temperature inside an automobile. The time rate of change of the temperature inside an automobile is determined by the temperature rate of change at one position as well as by the motion of the automobile from one point to another point where the temperature is different; then

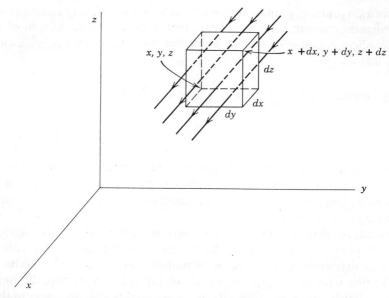

Figure 12.1   Illustration for the derivation of the Euler hydrodynamic equation.

by analogy with Eq. (12.4), we may write

$$\frac{dg}{dt} = \frac{\partial g}{\partial t} + \mathbf{v} \cdot \operatorname{grad} g \qquad (12.5)$$

If the vector or scalar fields represented in Eqs. (12.4) and (12.5) do not change as the observer moves along with the field, then $d/dt = 0$ and $\partial/\partial t = -\mathbf{v} \cdot \operatorname{grad}$. The operator $\partial/\partial t + \mathbf{v} \cdot \operatorname{grad}$ is sometimes called the convective derivative.

To illustrate the utility of these ideas, let us apply Eq. (12.4) to the flow of a perfect fluid and, by so doing, derive Euler's hydrodynamical equations.

In Eq. (12.4) we take as the vector field the momentum of a certain mass of a perfect fluid. Suppose at the instant in time that we observe this unit volume it has a cubic form (see Fig. 12.1). Then the momentum of this mass of fluid is [see Eq. (12.4)]

$$\rho \, dx \, dy \, dz \, \frac{d\mathbf{v}}{dt} = \rho \left[\frac{\partial \mathbf{v}}{\partial t} + (\mathbf{v} \cdot \operatorname{grad})\mathbf{v} \right] dx \, dy \, dz \qquad (12.6)$$

This, according to Newton's second law, must equal the total force acting on this element of the fluid. The net force in the $+x$-direction acting on the elemental volume is just the difference of the force acting in the $+x$-direction on the face $dy\ dz$ located at x and the force acting in the $-x$-direction on the face $dy\ dz$ located at $x + dx$, that is,

$$F_x = \left[p - \left(p + \frac{\partial p}{\partial x}\, dx \right) \right] dy\ dz + f_x\, dx\ dy\ dz$$

$$= \left(f_x - \frac{\partial p}{\partial x} \right) dx\ dy\ dz$$

where p is the pressure and f_x is the x-component of any external force due to, say, gravitational or electrostatic forces. Similar equations can be established for the y- and z-components. We may then write for the force

$$\mathbf{F} = \mathbf{f} - \operatorname{grad} p$$

so that Eq. (12.6) becomes

$$\frac{\partial \mathbf{v}}{\partial t} + (\mathbf{v} \cdot \operatorname{grad})\mathbf{v} = \frac{1}{\rho}(\mathbf{f} - \operatorname{grad} p) \tag{12.7}$$

This is the Euler hydrodynamic equation. It may be rewritten in another way if we note that

$$\tfrac{1}{2}\nabla v^2 = \mathbf{v} \times (\nabla \times \mathbf{v}) + (\mathbf{v} \cdot \nabla)\mathbf{v}$$

Then Eq. (12.7) becomes

$$\frac{\partial \mathbf{v}}{\partial t} + \tfrac{1}{2}\nabla v^2 - \mathbf{v} \times (\nabla \times \mathbf{v}) = \frac{1}{\rho}(\mathbf{f} - \operatorname{grad} p) \tag{12.8a}$$

This equation is called the second form of Euler's equation. If $\mathbf{f}$ is conservative, that is, if $\mathbf{f} = \nabla h$, then Eq. (12.8a) becomes

$$\frac{\partial \mathbf{v}}{\partial t} + \tfrac{1}{2}\nabla v^2 - \mathbf{v} \times (\nabla \times \mathbf{v}) = \frac{1}{\rho}\nabla\{h - p\} \tag{12.8b}$$

12.2 Bodies Moving Relative to the Field

Let us now calculate the rate of change of the flux across the surface A when the value of the field at any point is changing with time and the area A is moving in space. We have defined the flux across any surface to be

$$\Phi = \iint_A \mathbf{F} \cdot d\mathbf{s} \tag{12.9}$$

(see Eq. 3.84). The time rate of change of Φ is then

$$\frac{d\Phi}{dt} = \frac{d}{dt} \iint_A \mathbf{F} \cdot d\mathbf{s} \qquad (12.10)$$

We would like to express this quantity in terms of the surface integral of F and its time rate of change and when the surface A is moving (see Fig. 12.2). Equation (12.10) may be written

$$\lim_{\Delta t \to 0} \frac{\Delta \iint_A \mathbf{F} \cdot d\mathbf{s}}{\Delta t} = \lim_{\Delta t \to 0} \frac{\left(\iint_A \mathbf{F} \cdot d\mathbf{s} \right)_{t+\Delta t} - \left(\iint_A \mathbf{F} \cdot d\mathbf{s} \right)_t}{\Delta t} \qquad (12.11)$$

In the time Δt the surface A will have suffered a displacement $\mathbf{v}\,\Delta t$, where $\mathbf{v}$ is the velocity with which A is moving. If we designate the surface element at the time t as $d\mathbf{s}_T$ and at $t + \Delta t$ as $d\mathbf{s}_B$, we may write Eq. (12.11) as

$$\lim_{\Delta t \to 0} \frac{\left[\iint_A \mathbf{F}(t + \Delta t) \cdot d\mathbf{s}_B \right] - \left[\iint_A \mathbf{F}(t) \cdot d\mathbf{s}_T \right]}{\Delta t} \qquad (12.12)$$

Since, by Taylor's expansion theorem, we may write

$$\mathbf{F}(t + \Delta t) = \mathbf{F}(t) + \frac{\partial \mathbf{F}}{\partial t}\,\Delta t + \cdots \text{ higher order terms in } \Delta t$$

Eq. (12.12) may be written

$$\frac{d\Phi}{dt} = \lim_{\Delta t \to 0} \left[\iint_A \mathbf{F}(t) \cdot d\mathbf{s}_B + \iint_A \frac{\partial \mathbf{F}}{\partial t}\,\Delta t \cdot d\mathbf{s}_B - \iint_A \mathbf{F}(t) \cdot d\mathbf{s}_T \right] \frac{1}{\Delta t} \qquad (12.13)$$

Now, if at time t we apply Gauss's divergence theorem to a volume identical to that through which A moved in the time Δt, we obtain

$$\iiint_V \nabla \cdot \mathbf{F}\, dV = \oiint_{A'} \mathbf{F} \cdot d\mathbf{s}$$

$$= \iint_A \mathbf{F} \cdot d\mathbf{s}_B - \iint_A \mathbf{F} \cdot d\mathbf{s}_T$$

$$+ \iint_{\text{sides}} \mathbf{F} \cdot d\mathbf{s}_S \qquad (12.14)$$

where A' is the surface area of the volume V. Solving Eq. (12.14) for the difference between the integrals over the top and bottom, substituting the result into Eq. (12.13), and letting $\Delta t \to 0$ yields

$$\frac{d\Phi}{dt} = \iint\limits_{\text{bottom}} \frac{\partial \mathbf{F}}{\partial t} \cdot d\mathbf{s}_B + \iiint\limits_{V} \nabla \cdot \mathbf{F} \frac{dV}{dt} - \iint\limits_{\text{sides}} \mathbf{F} \cdot \frac{d\mathbf{s}_S}{dt} \qquad (12.15)$$

An element of area of the sides $d\mathbf{s}_B$ is just (see Fig. 12.2)

$$d\mathbf{s}_S = \mathbf{v}\, dt \times d\mathbf{l}_T = -\mathbf{v}\, dt \times d\mathbf{l}_B \qquad (12.15)$$

since $d\mathbf{s}_B$ is pointing outward; and

$$dV = \mathbf{v} \cdot d\mathbf{s}_T\, dt = -\mathbf{v} \cdot d\mathbf{s}_B\, dt \qquad (12.17)$$

where $d\mathbf{l}_B$ is an element of the curve Γ_B which is the periphery of the bottom area A. Since

$$\iint \mathbf{F} \cdot \frac{d\mathbf{s}_S}{dt} = -\oint_{\Gamma_B} \mathbf{F} \cdot \mathbf{v} \times d\mathbf{l}_B = -\oint_{\Gamma_B} \mathbf{F} \times \mathbf{v} \cdot d\mathbf{l}_B$$

$$= -\iint\limits_{\text{bottom}} \nabla \times (\mathbf{F} \times \mathbf{v}) \cdot d\mathbf{s}_B \qquad (12.18)$$

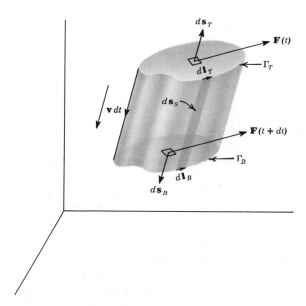

Figure 12.2   The flux through A moving surface.

[See Eqs. (2.44) and (9.2).] Equation (12.15) becomes

$$\frac{d\Phi}{dt} = \iint_{\text{bottom}} \frac{\partial \mathbf{F}}{\partial t} \cdot d\mathbf{s}_B + \iint_{\text{bottom}} \nabla \times (\mathbf{F} \times \mathbf{v}) \cdot d\mathbf{s} + \iint_{\text{bottom}} (\nabla \cdot \mathbf{F})\mathbf{v} \cdot d\mathbf{s}$$

$$= \iint_{\text{bottom}} \left[\frac{\partial \mathbf{F}}{\partial t} + \nabla \times (\mathbf{F} \times \mathbf{v}) + (\nabla \cdot \mathbf{F})\mathbf{v} \right] \cdot d\mathbf{s} \qquad (12.19)$$

We can define an operator D/Dt by

$$\frac{D\mathbf{F}}{Dt} = \frac{\partial \mathbf{F}}{\partial t} + \nabla \times (\mathbf{F} \times \mathbf{v}) + (\nabla \cdot \mathbf{F})\mathbf{v} \qquad (12.20)$$

so that Eq. (12.19) may be written

$$\frac{d\Phi}{dt} = \iint \frac{D\mathbf{F}}{Dt} \cdot d\mathbf{s} \qquad (12.21)$$

Substituting the value of $\partial\mathbf{F}/\partial t$ in Eq. (12.4) into Eq. (12.21) yields

$$\frac{D\mathbf{F}}{Dt} = \frac{d\mathbf{F}}{dt} - (\mathbf{v} \cdot \text{grad})\mathbf{F} + \nabla \times (\mathbf{F} \times \mathbf{v}) + \mathbf{v}(\nabla \cdot \mathbf{F}) \qquad (12.22)$$

Utilizing Eq. (8.22l), we see that this can be written

$$\frac{D\mathbf{F}}{Dt} = \frac{d\mathbf{F}}{dt} + \mathbf{F}\nabla \cdot \mathbf{v} - (\mathbf{F} \cdot \text{grad})\mathbf{v} \qquad (12.23)$$

The operator D/Dt is of value when dealing with vector quantities in a moving media.

12.3   Retarded Potentials

In Section 12.1 we described an experiment whose goal was to determine the rate of change of the wind velocity relative to a boat. Suppose, in the course of this experiment, a large explosion is set off in the vicinity of the boat. After a time sufficiently long that the disturbance can reach the boat, the occupants of the boat notice a change in the wind velocity. For many physically important cases an occurrence at a source point (located by $\mathbf{R}'$), causing the source density at that point to change with time, does not immediately produce an effect at the field point (located by $\mathbf{R}$). This is because the effect induced by a changing source usually propagates with a finite velocity. In other words, the value of the field at a field point at a time t has been determined by the values of the sources (or sinks) at earlier times t' given by

$$t' = t - \frac{|\mathbf{R} - \mathbf{R}'|}{v} \tag{12.24}$$

where $|\mathbf{R} - \mathbf{R}'|$ is the distance from the source point to the field point, and v is the speed with which the disturbance moves, that is, $|\mathbf{R} - \mathbf{R}'|/v$ is the time for the disturbance to go from a source point to the field point.

We now wish to describe the value of a field at a particular point and at a particular time t in terms of the values of the field potentials or sources not at the time t but at the time t' when the disturbances were taking place. By analogy with Eq. (11.68), we may write for a time-dependent field

$$\mathbf{F}(\mathbf{R}, t) = -\frac{1}{4\pi} \iiint_{\substack{\text{all} \\ \text{space}}} \mathbf{F}(\mathbf{R}', t') \nabla^2 \frac{1}{|\mathbf{R} - \mathbf{R}'|} dV(\mathbf{R}') \tag{12.25}$$

To demonstrate that this is valid, we recall that $\nabla^2 1/|\mathbf{R} - \mathbf{R}'| = 0$ except at that point where $\mathbf{R} = \mathbf{R}'$. As discussed in connection with Eqs. (11.68) and (11.131), we can consider $\nabla^2 1/|\mathbf{R} - \mathbf{R}'|$ as related to the delta function

$$\nabla^2 \frac{1}{|\mathbf{R} - \mathbf{R}'|} = -4\pi\, \delta(\mathbf{R} - \mathbf{R}') \tag{12.26}$$

Equation (12.25) then becomes

$$\mathbf{F}(\mathbf{R}, t) = \iiint_{\substack{\text{all} \\ \text{space}}} \mathbf{F}(\mathbf{R}', t')\, \delta(\mathbf{R} - \mathbf{R}')\, dV(\mathbf{R}') \tag{12.27}$$

because at $\mathbf{R}' = \mathbf{R}$, $t' = t$ (see Eq. 12.24).

By considering Eq. (12.25), we shall be led to the concept of retarded potentials. In the following discussion of retarded potentials, it will be important to note that this equation is valid:

$$\nabla^2 \left[\frac{\mathbf{F}(\mathbf{R}', t')}{|\mathbf{R} - \mathbf{R}'|}\right] = \left[\mathbf{F}(\mathbf{R}', t') + \frac{|\mathbf{R} - \mathbf{R}'|}{v}\frac{\partial \mathbf{F}(\mathbf{R}', t')}{\partial t'}\right] \nabla^2 \frac{1}{|\mathbf{R} - \mathbf{R}'|}$$
$$+ \frac{1}{v^2}\frac{\partial^2}{\partial t'^2}\left[\frac{\mathbf{F}(\mathbf{R}', t')}{|\mathbf{R} - \mathbf{R}'|}\right] \tag{12.28}$$

To demonstrate that Eq. (12.28) is true, let us examine the Laplacian of the magnitude of the x-component $F_x(\mathbf{R}', t')/|\mathbf{R} - \mathbf{R}'|$.

$$\nabla^2 \frac{F_x(\mathbf{R}', t')}{|\mathbf{R} - \mathbf{R}'|} = \nabla \cdot \nabla \frac{F_x(\mathbf{R}', t')}{|\mathbf{R} - \mathbf{R}'|}$$

$$= \nabla \cdot \left[\frac{1}{|\mathbf{R} - \mathbf{R}'|} \nabla F_x(\mathbf{R}', t') + F_x(\mathbf{R}', t') \nabla \frac{1}{|\mathbf{R} - \mathbf{R}'|} \right] \quad (12.29)$$

[See Eq. (8.22c).] However,

$$\nabla F_x(\mathbf{R}', t') = \left(\mathbf{u}_x \frac{\partial}{\partial x} + \mathbf{u}_y \frac{\partial}{\partial y} + \mathbf{u}_z \frac{\partial}{\partial z} \right) F_x(\mathbf{R}', t')$$

$$= \left(\mathbf{u}_x \frac{\partial}{\partial t'} \frac{\partial t'}{\partial x} + \mathbf{u}_y \frac{\partial}{\partial t'} \frac{\partial t'}{\partial y} + \mathbf{u}_z \frac{\partial}{\partial t'} \frac{\partial t'}{\partial z} \right) F_x(\mathbf{R}', t') \quad (12.30)$$

Since

$$\frac{\partial t'}{\partial x} = \frac{\partial}{\partial x} \left(t - \frac{|\mathbf{R} - \mathbf{R}'|}{v} \right) = \frac{\partial}{\partial x} \left\{ t - \frac{[(x - x')^2 + (y - y')^2 + (z - z')^2]^{\frac{1}{2}}}{v} \right\}$$

$$= - \frac{x - x'}{v\,|\mathbf{R} - \mathbf{R}'|}$$

with similar equations for $\partial t'/\partial y$ and $\partial t'/\partial z$, we may write Eq. (12.30) as

$$\nabla F_x(\mathbf{R}', t') = - \frac{\mathbf{u}_{\mathbf{R}-\mathbf{R}'}}{v} \frac{\partial F_x(\mathbf{R}', t')}{\partial t'} = - \frac{1}{v} \frac{\partial F_x(\mathbf{R}', t')}{\partial t'} \nabla |\mathbf{R} - \mathbf{R}'|$$

$$= \frac{|\mathbf{R} - \mathbf{R}'|^2}{v} \frac{\partial F_x(\mathbf{R}', t')}{\partial t'} \nabla \frac{1}{|\mathbf{R} - \mathbf{R}'|} \quad (12.31)$$

Then Eq. (12.29) becomes

$$\nabla^2 \left[\frac{F_x(\mathbf{R}', t')}{|\mathbf{R} - \mathbf{R}'|} \right] = \nabla \cdot \left\{ \left[F_x(\mathbf{R}', t') + \frac{|\mathbf{R} - \mathbf{R}'|}{v} \frac{\partial F_x(\mathbf{R}', t')}{\partial t'} \right] \nabla \frac{1}{|\mathbf{R} - \mathbf{R}'|} \right\}$$

$$= \left[F_x(\mathbf{R}', t') + \frac{|\mathbf{R} - \mathbf{R}'|}{v} \frac{\partial F_x(\mathbf{R}', t')}{\partial t'} \right] \nabla^2 \frac{1}{|\mathbf{R} - \mathbf{R}'|}$$

$$+ \left[\nabla \frac{1}{|\mathbf{R} - \mathbf{R}'|} \right] \cdot \left[\frac{-\mathbf{u}_{\mathbf{R}-\mathbf{R}'}}{v} \frac{\partial F_x(\mathbf{R}', t')}{\partial t'} \right.$$

$$\left. + \frac{\mathbf{u}_{\mathbf{R}-\mathbf{R}'}}{v} \frac{\partial F_x(\mathbf{R}', t')}{\partial t'} - \frac{|\mathbf{R} - \mathbf{R}'|}{v^2} \frac{\partial^2 F_x(\mathbf{R}', t')}{\partial t'^2} \mathbf{u}_{\mathbf{R}-\mathbf{R}'} \right]$$

$$= \left[F_x(\mathbf{R}', t') + \frac{|\mathbf{R} - \mathbf{R}'|}{v} \frac{\partial F_x(\mathbf{R}', t')}{\partial t'} \right] \nabla^2 \frac{1}{|\mathbf{R} - \mathbf{R}'|}$$

$$+ \frac{1}{v^2} \frac{\partial^2}{\partial t'^2} \left[\frac{F_x(\mathbf{R}', t')}{|\mathbf{R} - \mathbf{R}'|} \right] \quad (12.32)$$

A similar equation can be written for $F_y(\mathbf{R}', t')$ and $F_z(\mathbf{R}', t')$ so that we may write Eq. (12.25) as

$$\mathbf{F}(\mathbf{R}, t) = -\left\{\nabla^2 \iiint_{\substack{\text{all} \\ \text{space}}} \frac{\mathbf{F}(\mathbf{R}', t')}{4\pi |\mathbf{R} - \mathbf{R}'|} \, dV(\mathbf{R}')\right.$$

$$- \iiint_{\substack{\text{all} \\ \text{space}}} \frac{|\mathbf{R} - \mathbf{R}'|}{v} \frac{\partial \mathbf{F}}{\partial t'} \nabla^2 \frac{1}{4\pi |\mathbf{R} - \mathbf{R}'|} \, dV(\mathbf{R}')$$

$$\left. - \frac{1}{v^2} \iiint_{\substack{\text{all} \\ \text{space}}} \frac{\partial^2}{\partial t'^2} \left[\frac{\mathbf{F}(\mathbf{R}', t')}{4\pi |\mathbf{R} - \mathbf{R}'|}\right] dV(\mathbf{R}')\right\} \qquad (12.33)$$

The second term on the right-hand side of this equation is zero because $\nabla^2 \, 1/|\mathbf{R} - \mathbf{R}'|$ is zero except at those points where $\mathbf{R} = \mathbf{R}'$, but at those points $|\mathbf{R} - \mathbf{R}'| = 0$. Equation (12.33) then becomes

$$\mathbf{F}(\mathbf{R}, t) = -\nabla^2 \iiint_{\substack{\text{all} \\ \text{space}}} \frac{\mathbf{F}(\mathbf{R}', t')}{4\pi |\mathbf{R} - \mathbf{R}'|} \, dV(\mathbf{R}') + \frac{1}{v^2} \frac{\partial^2}{\partial t^2} \iiint_{\substack{\text{all} \\ \text{space}}} \frac{\mathbf{F}(\mathbf{R}', t')}{4\pi |\mathbf{R} - \mathbf{R}'|} \, dV(\mathbf{R}')$$

$$= -\nabla \nabla \cdot \iiint_{\substack{\text{all} \\ \text{space}}} \frac{\mathbf{F}(\mathbf{R}', t')}{4\pi |\mathbf{R} - \mathbf{R}'|} \, dV(\mathbf{R}')$$

$$+ \nabla \times \nabla \times \iiint_{\substack{\text{all} \\ \text{space}}} \frac{\mathbf{F}(\mathbf{R}', t')}{4\pi |\mathbf{R} - \mathbf{R}'|} \, dV(\mathbf{R}')$$

$$+ \frac{1}{v^2} \frac{\partial^2}{\partial t^2} \iiint_{\substack{\text{all} \\ \text{space}}} \frac{\mathbf{F}(\mathbf{R}', t')}{4\pi |\mathbf{R} - \mathbf{R}'|} \, dV(\mathbf{R}') \qquad (12.34)$$

[See Eq. (8.22s).]

We have changed the partial differentiation with respect to t' to partial differentiation with respect to t because a change in t' is equal to a change in t at any point.

If, by analogy with Eqs. (11.73) and (11.74), we define the scalar and vector potentials for time-dependent fields to be

$$\Phi(\mathbf{R}, t) \equiv \nabla \cdot \iiint_{\substack{\text{all} \\ \text{space}}} \frac{\mathbf{F}(\mathbf{R}', t') \, dV(\mathbf{R}')}{4\pi |\mathbf{R} - \mathbf{R}'|} \qquad (12.35)$$

$$\mathbf{T}(\mathbf{R}, t) \equiv \nabla \times \iiint_{\substack{\text{all} \\ \text{space}}} \frac{\mathbf{F}(\mathbf{R}', t') \, dV(\mathbf{R}')}{4\pi |\mathbf{R} - \mathbf{R}'|} \qquad (12.36)$$

We may then write Eq. (12.34) as

$$\mathbf{F}(\mathbf{R}, t) = -\nabla\Phi(\mathbf{R}, t) + \nabla \times \mathbf{T} + \frac{1}{v^2}\frac{\partial^2}{\partial t^2} \iiint_{\substack{\text{all}\\\text{space}}} \frac{\mathbf{F}(\mathbf{R}', t')\, dV(\mathbf{R}')}{4\pi\,|\mathbf{R} - \mathbf{R}'|} \qquad (12.37)$$

To derive the fundamental differential equation for $\Phi(\mathbf{R}, t)$, we take the divergence of Eq. (12.37) [use Eq. (12.35)], and obtain

$$\nabla \cdot \mathbf{F}(\mathbf{R}, t) = -\nabla^2\Phi + \frac{1}{v^2}\frac{\partial^2\Phi}{\partial t^2} \qquad (12.38)$$

If, as we have done previously, we associate the divergence of a field with ρ_v, the scalar source density, Eq. (12.38) becomes the *inhomogeneous scalar wave equation*

$$\nabla^2\Phi(\mathbf{R}, t) - \frac{1}{v^2}\frac{\partial^2\Phi(\mathbf{R}, t)}{\partial t^2} = -\rho_v(\mathbf{R}, t) \qquad (12.39)$$

Similarly, the curl of Eq. (12.37) is

$$\nabla \times \mathbf{F}(\mathbf{R}, t) = \nabla \times \nabla \times \mathbf{T} + \frac{1}{v^2}\frac{\partial^2\mathbf{T}}{\partial t^2} \qquad (12.40)$$

Using Eq. (8.22s) again, we obtain

$$\nabla \times \mathbf{F}(\mathbf{R}, t) = \nabla(\nabla \cdot \mathbf{T}) - \nabla^2\mathbf{T} + \frac{1}{v^2}\frac{\partial^2\mathbf{T}}{\partial t^2} \qquad (12.41)$$

where $\nabla^2\mathbf{T} \equiv \partial^2\mathbf{T}/\partial x^2 + \partial^2\mathbf{T}/\partial y^2 + \partial^2\mathbf{T}/\partial z^2$.

If we utilize a Coulomb gauge, $\nabla \cdot \mathbf{T} = 0$ [see the discussions concerning Eqs. (11.44) and (11.95)], Eq. (12.41) becomes

$$-\mathbf{K}_S(\mathbf{R}, t) = \nabla^2\mathbf{T} - \frac{1}{v^2}\frac{\partial^2\mathbf{T}}{\partial t^2} \qquad (12.42)$$

where we have equated the curl of a vector field to $\mathbf{K}_S(\mathbf{R}, t)$, the surface vector source density (see Eq. 11.96). Equation (12.42) is called the inhomogeneous vector wave equation. Equations (12.39) and (12.42) are sometimes called d'Alembert's equations.

To show the integral form of the scalar wave equation, we shall examine Eq. (12.35) and arrive at the concept of a retarded potential. We know that any change in the volume scalar source density will propagate from the source point to the observation point $\mathbf{R}$ with the velocity v; thus the scalar potential at $\mathbf{R}$ at the time t is determined from the value of ρ_v not at the time t but at an earlier time, $t - |\mathbf{R} - \mathbf{R}'|/v$. To obtain this result, we operate on Eq. (12.35), remembering that t' is a function of $|\mathbf{R} - \mathbf{R}'|$.

$$\Phi(\mathbf{R}, t) \equiv \nabla \cdot \iiint_{\substack{\text{all} \\ \text{space}}} \frac{\mathbf{F}(\mathbf{R}', t')\, dV(\mathbf{R}')}{4\pi\,|\mathbf{R} - \mathbf{R}'|}$$

$$= \frac{1}{4\pi} \iiint_{\substack{\text{all} \\ \text{space}}} \mathbf{F}(\mathbf{R}', t') \cdot \nabla \frac{1}{|\mathbf{R} - \mathbf{R}'|}\, dV(\mathbf{R}')$$

$$+ \frac{1}{4\pi} \iiint_{\substack{\text{all} \\ \text{space}}} \frac{1}{|\mathbf{R} - \mathbf{R}'|} \nabla \cdot \mathbf{F}(\mathbf{R}', t')\, dV(\mathbf{R}')$$

$$= -\frac{1}{4\pi} \iiint_{\substack{\text{all} \\ \text{space}}} \mathbf{F}(\mathbf{R}', t') \cdot \nabla' \frac{1}{|\mathbf{R} - \mathbf{R}'|}\, dV(\mathbf{R}')$$

$$+ \frac{1}{4\pi} \iiint_{\substack{\text{all} \\ \text{space}}} \frac{1}{|\mathbf{R} - \mathbf{R}'|} \frac{1}{v} \frac{\partial \mathbf{F}}{\partial t'} \cdot \nabla'\, |\mathbf{R} - \mathbf{R}'|\, dV(\mathbf{R}') \quad \text{(see Eq. 12.31)}$$

$$= -\frac{1}{4\pi} \iiint_{\substack{\text{all} \\ \text{space}}} \mathbf{F}(\mathbf{R}', t') \cdot \nabla' \frac{1}{|\mathbf{R} - \mathbf{R}'|}\, dV(\mathbf{R}')$$

$$- \frac{1}{4\pi} \iiint_{\substack{\text{all} \\ \text{space}}} \frac{|\mathbf{R} - \mathbf{R}'|}{v} \frac{\partial \mathbf{F}}{\partial t'} \cdot \nabla' \frac{1}{|\mathbf{R} - \mathbf{R}'|}\, dV(\mathbf{R}') \quad \text{using (11.16)}$$

$$= -\frac{1}{4\pi} \iiint_{\substack{\text{all} \\ \text{space}}} \left[\mathbf{F}(\mathbf{R}', t') + \frac{|\mathbf{R} - \mathbf{R}'|}{v} \frac{\partial \mathbf{F}}{\partial t'} \right] \cdot \nabla' \frac{1}{|\mathbf{R} - \mathbf{R}'|}\, dV(\mathbf{R}')$$

$$\tag{12.43}$$

Since

$$\nabla' \cdot \left[\frac{\mathbf{F}(\mathbf{R}', t') + \dfrac{|\mathbf{R} - \mathbf{R}'|}{v} \dfrac{\partial \mathbf{F}}{\partial t'}}{|\mathbf{R} - \mathbf{R}'|} \right]$$

$$= \frac{1}{|\mathbf{R} - \mathbf{R}'|} \nabla' \cdot \left[\mathbf{F}(\mathbf{R}', t') + \frac{|\mathbf{R} - \mathbf{R}'|}{v} \frac{\partial \mathbf{F}}{\partial t'} \right]$$

$$+ \left(\nabla' \frac{1}{|\mathbf{R} - \mathbf{R}'|} \right) \cdot \left[\mathbf{F}(\mathbf{R}', t') + \frac{|\mathbf{R} - \mathbf{R}'|}{v} \frac{\partial \mathbf{F}}{\partial t'} \right] \tag{12.44}$$

Equation (12.43) may be written

$$\Phi(\mathbf{R}, t) = \frac{1}{4\pi} \iiint_{\substack{\text{all} \\ \text{space}}} \frac{1}{|\mathbf{R} - \mathbf{R}'|} \nabla' \cdot \left[\mathbf{F}(\mathbf{R}', t') + \frac{|\mathbf{R} - \mathbf{R}'|}{v} \frac{\partial \mathbf{F}}{\partial t'} \right] dV(\mathbf{R}')$$

$$- \frac{1}{4\pi} \iiint_{\substack{\text{all} \\ \text{space}}} \nabla' \cdot \left[\frac{\mathbf{F}(\mathbf{R}', t') + \dfrac{|\mathbf{R} - \mathbf{R}'|}{v} \dfrac{\partial \mathbf{F}}{\partial t'}}{|\mathbf{R} - \mathbf{R}'|} \right] dV(\mathbf{R}')$$

Thus

$$\Phi(\mathbf{R}, t) = \frac{1}{4\pi} \iiint_{\substack{\text{all} \\ \text{space}}} \frac{\nabla' \cdot \mathbf{F}(\mathbf{R}', t')\, dV(\mathbf{R}')}{|\mathbf{R} - \mathbf{R}'|}$$

$$+ \frac{1}{4\pi v} \iiint_{\substack{\text{all} \\ \text{space}}} \frac{1}{|\mathbf{R} - \mathbf{R}'|} \nabla' \cdot \left(\frac{|\mathbf{R} - \mathbf{R}'|}{v} \frac{\partial \mathbf{F}}{\partial t'} \right) dV(\mathbf{R}')$$

$$- \frac{1}{4\pi} \iiint_{\substack{\text{all} \\ \text{space}}} \nabla' \cdot \left[\frac{\mathbf{F}(\mathbf{R}', t')}{|\mathbf{R} - \mathbf{R}'|} \right] dV(\mathbf{R}') - \frac{1}{4\pi v} \iiint_{\substack{\text{all} \\ \text{space}}} \nabla' \cdot \frac{\partial \mathbf{F}}{\partial t'}\, dV(\mathbf{R}') \tag{12.45}$$

We now observe that

$$\nabla' \cdot \mathbf{F}(\mathbf{R}', t') = \nabla'_{t'} \cdot \mathbf{F}(\mathbf{R}', t') + \frac{\partial \mathbf{F}}{\partial t'} \cdot \nabla' t'$$

Here $\nabla'_{t'}$ denotes differentiation with respect to the source coordinates while t' is held constant, that is, at some specific time. Since

$$t' = t - \frac{|\mathbf{R} - \mathbf{R}'|}{v}$$

Then

$$\nabla' t' = - \frac{\nabla' |\mathbf{R} - \mathbf{R}'|}{v}$$

so that we may write

$$\nabla' \cdot \mathbf{F}(\mathbf{R}', t') = \nabla'_{t'} \cdot \mathbf{F}(\mathbf{R}', t') - \frac{\nabla' |\mathbf{R} - \mathbf{R}'|}{v} \cdot \frac{\partial \mathbf{F}(\mathbf{R}', t')}{\partial t'} \tag{12.46}$$

The integrand of the first integral on the right-hand side of Eq. (12.45) is then

$$\frac{\nabla' \cdot \mathbf{F}(\mathbf{R}', t')}{|\mathbf{R} - \mathbf{R}'|} = \frac{1}{|\mathbf{R} - \mathbf{R}'|} \left\{ [\nabla'_{t'} \cdot \mathbf{F}(\mathbf{R}', t')] - \frac{\nabla' |\mathbf{R} - \mathbf{R}'|}{v} \cdot \frac{\partial \mathbf{F}(\mathbf{R}', t')}{\partial t'} \right\}$$

and the integrand of the second integral on the right-hand side of Eq. (12.45) is

$$\frac{1}{|\mathbf{R} - \mathbf{R}'|} \nabla' \cdot \left[\frac{|\mathbf{R} - \mathbf{R}'|}{v} \frac{\partial \mathbf{F}(\mathbf{R}', t')}{\partial t'} \right]$$

$$= \frac{1}{v} \nabla' \cdot \frac{\partial \mathbf{F}(\mathbf{R}', t')}{\partial t'} + \frac{1}{v} \frac{\partial \mathbf{F}(\mathbf{R}', t')}{\partial t'} \cdot \frac{\nabla' |\mathbf{R} - \mathbf{R}'|}{|\mathbf{R} - \mathbf{R}'|}$$

Equation (12.45) then becomes

$$\Phi(\mathbf{R}, t) = \frac{1}{4\pi} \iiint\limits_{\substack{\text{all} \\ \text{space}}} \frac{[\nabla'_{t'} \cdot \mathbf{F}(\mathbf{R}', t')]}{|\mathbf{R} - \mathbf{R}'|} \, dV(\mathbf{R}')$$

$$- \frac{1}{4\pi} \iiint\limits_{\substack{\text{all} \\ \text{space}}} \nabla' \cdot \left[\frac{\mathbf{F}(\mathbf{R}', t')}{|\mathbf{R} - \mathbf{R}'|} \right] dV(\mathbf{R}') \quad (12.47)$$

The second volume integral vanishes. This can be seen by considering Eq. (9.39) in the situation when t' is held constant:

$$\iiint\limits_V \nabla'_{t'} \cdot \left[\frac{\mathbf{F}(\mathbf{R}', t')}{|\mathbf{R} - \mathbf{R}'|} \right] dV(\mathbf{R}') = \oiint\limits_A \frac{\mathbf{F}(\mathbf{R}', t')}{|\mathbf{R} - \mathbf{R}'|} \cdot d\mathbf{s}(\mathbf{R}') \quad (12.48)$$

If, as V expands to include all space, $\mathbf{F}(\mathbf{R}', t')$ on A, the surface of V, decreases faster than $|\mathbf{R} - \mathbf{R}'|^{-1}$, then the surface integral approaches zero. This Eq. (12.47) becomes

$$\Phi(\mathbf{R}, t) = \frac{1}{4\pi} \iiint\limits_{\substack{\text{all} \\ \text{space}}} \frac{\rho_v(\mathbf{R}', t')}{|\mathbf{R} - \mathbf{R}'|} \, dV(\mathbf{R}') \quad (12.49)$$

In many instances, $\rho_v(\mathbf{R}', t')$ is not known over all space. It turns out again, as in the static case, that we can determine the scalar potential within a finite volume when the scalar source density is known within that volume only if the potential and its normal derivative over the surface of the volume are also specified.

In order to relate $\Phi(\mathbf{R}, t)$ to the scalar source density within V and to boundary conditions on A, we proceed from Green's theorem (Eq. 9.73):

$$\iiint\limits_V \left[\frac{1}{|\mathbf{R} - \mathbf{R}'|} \nabla'^2 \Phi(\mathbf{R}', t') - \Phi(\mathbf{R}', t') \nabla'^2 \frac{1}{|\mathbf{R} - \mathbf{R}'|} \right] dV(\mathbf{R}')$$

$$= \oiint\limits_A \left[\frac{1}{|\mathbf{R} - \mathbf{R}'|} \nabla' \Phi(\mathbf{R}', t') - \Phi(\mathbf{R}', t') \nabla' \frac{1}{|\mathbf{R} - \mathbf{R}'|} \right] \cdot d\mathbf{s}(\mathbf{R}') \quad (12.50)$$

By a derivation analogous with that performed to obtain Eq. (12.46), we may obtain

$$\nabla'\Phi(\mathbf{R}', t') = \nabla'_{t'}\Phi(\mathbf{R}', t') - \frac{\nabla'\,|\mathbf{R} - \mathbf{R}'|}{v}\frac{\partial\Phi(\mathbf{R}', t')}{\partial t'}$$

so that

$$\nabla'_{t'}\Phi(\mathbf{R}', t') = \nabla'\Phi(\mathbf{R}', t') + \frac{\nabla'\,|\mathbf{R} - \mathbf{R}'|}{v}\frac{\partial\Phi(\mathbf{R}', t')}{\partial t'} \qquad (12.51)$$

The divergence of this is then

$$\nabla'\cdot\nabla'_{t'}\Phi(\mathbf{R}', t') = \nabla'^{2}\Phi(\mathbf{R}', t') + \frac{\nabla'^{2}\,|\mathbf{R} - \mathbf{R}'|}{v}\frac{\partial\Phi(\mathbf{R}', t')}{\partial t'}$$

$$+ \frac{\nabla'\,|\mathbf{R} - \mathbf{R}'|}{v}\cdot\nabla'\frac{\partial\Phi(\mathbf{R}', t')}{\partial t'} \qquad (12.52)$$

Since

$$\nabla'\cdot\nabla'_{t'}\Phi(\mathbf{R}', t') = \left(\nabla'_{t'} - \frac{\nabla'\,|\mathbf{R} - \mathbf{R}'|}{v}\frac{\partial}{\partial t'}\right)\cdot\nabla'_{t'}\Phi(\mathbf{R}', t')$$

$$= \nabla'^{2}_{t'}\Phi(\mathbf{R}', t') - \frac{\nabla'\,|\mathbf{R} - \mathbf{R}'|}{v}\cdot\frac{\partial}{\partial t'}\,[\nabla'_{t'}\Phi(\mathbf{R}', t')]$$

$$= \nabla'^{2}_{t'}\Phi(\mathbf{R}', t') - \frac{\nabla'\,|\mathbf{R} - \mathbf{R}'|}{v}\cdot$$

$$\frac{\partial}{\partial t'}\left[\nabla'\Phi(\mathbf{R}', t') + \frac{\nabla'\,|\mathbf{R} - \mathbf{R}'|}{v}\frac{\partial\Phi(\mathbf{R}', t')}{\partial t'}\right]$$

we may rearrange Eq. (12.52) to yield

$$\nabla'^{2}\Phi(\mathbf{R}', t') = \nabla'^{2}_{t'}\Phi(\mathbf{R}', t') - \frac{2\nabla'\,|\mathbf{R} - \mathbf{R}'|}{v}\cdot\nabla'\frac{\partial\Phi(\mathbf{R}', t')}{\partial t'}$$

$$- \frac{1}{v^{2}}\frac{\partial^{2}\Phi(\mathbf{R}', t')}{\partial t'^{2}} - \frac{\nabla'^{2}\,|\mathbf{R} - \mathbf{R}'|}{v}\frac{\partial\Phi(\mathbf{R}', t')}{\partial t'} \qquad (12.53)$$

We observe that (see Eq. 8.21c)

$$\frac{2\,|\mathbf{R} - \mathbf{R}'|}{v}\nabla'\cdot\left[\frac{\mathbf{R} - \mathbf{R}'}{|\mathbf{R} - \mathbf{R}'|^{2}}\frac{\partial\Phi(\mathbf{R}', t')}{\partial t'}\right]$$

$$= \frac{-6}{v\,|\mathbf{R} - \mathbf{R}'|}\frac{\partial\Phi(\mathbf{R}', t')}{\partial t'} + \frac{4}{v\,|\mathbf{R} - \mathbf{R}'|}\frac{\partial\Phi(\mathbf{R}', t')}{\partial t'}$$

$$+ \frac{2(\mathbf{R} - \mathbf{R}')}{v\,|\mathbf{R} - \mathbf{R}'|}\cdot\nabla'\frac{\partial\Phi(\mathbf{R}', t')}{\partial t'}$$

$$= \frac{-2}{v\,|\mathbf{R} - \mathbf{R}'|}\frac{\partial\Phi(\mathbf{R}', t')}{\partial t'} - \frac{2\nabla'\,|\mathbf{R} - \mathbf{R}'|}{v}\cdot\nabla'\frac{\partial\Phi(\mathbf{R}', t')}{\partial t'} \qquad (12.54)$$

Equation (12.53) may then be written (using Eq. 11.16)

$$\nabla'^2 \Phi(\mathbf{R}', t') = \nabla'^2_{t'} \Phi(\mathbf{R}', t') - \frac{1}{v^2} \frac{\partial^2 \Phi(\mathbf{R}', t')}{\partial t'^2}$$

$$+ \frac{2 |\mathbf{R} - \mathbf{R}'|}{v} \nabla' \cdot \left[\frac{\mathbf{R} - \mathbf{R}'}{|\mathbf{R} - \mathbf{R}'|^2} \frac{\partial \Phi(\mathbf{R}', t')}{\partial t'} \right] \quad (12.55)$$

Substituting Eq. (12.55) into Eq. (12.50) yields

$$\iiint_V \left\{ \frac{1}{|\mathbf{R} - \mathbf{R}'|} \left[\nabla'^2_{t'} \Phi(\mathbf{R}', t') - \frac{1}{v^2} \frac{\partial^2 \Phi}{\partial t^2} + \frac{2 |\mathbf{R} - \mathbf{R}'|}{v} \nabla' \right. \right.$$

$$\left. \left. \cdot \left(\frac{\mathbf{R} - \mathbf{R}'}{|\mathbf{R} - \mathbf{R}'|^2} \frac{\partial \Phi(\mathbf{R}', t')}{\partial t'} \right) \right] - \Phi \nabla'^2 \frac{1}{|\mathbf{R} - \mathbf{R}'|} \right\} dV(\mathbf{R}')$$

$$= \oiint_A \left\{ \frac{1}{|\mathbf{R} - \mathbf{R}'|} \nabla' \Phi(\mathbf{R}', t') - \Phi(\mathbf{R}', t') \nabla' \frac{1}{|\mathbf{R} - \mathbf{R}'|} \right\} \cdot d\mathbf{s}(\mathbf{R}')$$

$$= \oiint_A \left\{ \frac{1}{|\mathbf{R} - \mathbf{R}'|} \left[\nabla'_{t'} \Phi(\mathbf{R}', t') - \frac{\nabla' |\mathbf{R} - \mathbf{R}'|}{c} \frac{\partial \Phi(\mathbf{R}', t')}{\partial t'} \right] \right.$$

$$\left. - \Phi(\mathbf{R}', t') \nabla' \frac{1}{|\mathbf{R} - \mathbf{R}'|} \right\} \cdot d\mathbf{s}(\mathbf{R}') \quad \text{[see Eq. (12.51)]} \quad (12.56)$$

Solving Eq. (12.56) for

$$- \iiint_V \Phi(\mathbf{R}', t') \nabla'^2 \frac{1}{|\mathbf{R} - \mathbf{R}'|} dV(\mathbf{R}')$$

yields

$$- \iiint_V \Phi(\mathbf{R}', t') \nabla'^2 \frac{1}{|\mathbf{R} - \mathbf{R}'|} dV(\mathbf{R}')$$

$$= \begin{cases} 4\pi \Phi(\mathbf{R}, t) & \text{when observation point within } A \\ 0 & \text{when observation point outside of } A \end{cases}$$

$$= - \iiint_V \left[\frac{\nabla'^2_{t'} \Phi(\mathbf{R}', t') - \frac{1}{v^2} \frac{\partial^2 \Phi}{\partial t^2}}{|\mathbf{R} - \mathbf{R}'|} \right] dV(\mathbf{R}')$$

$$- \frac{2}{v} \iiint_V \nabla' \cdot \left[\frac{\mathbf{R} - \mathbf{R}'}{|\mathbf{R} - \mathbf{R}'|^2} \frac{\partial \Phi(\mathbf{R}', t')}{\partial t'} \right] dV(\mathbf{R}')$$

$$+ \oiint_A \left\{ \frac{1}{|\mathbf{R} - \mathbf{R}'|} \left[\nabla'_{t'} \Phi(\mathbf{R}', t') - \frac{\nabla' |\mathbf{R} - \mathbf{R}'|}{v} \frac{\partial \Phi(\mathbf{R}', t')}{\partial t'} \right] \right.$$

$$\left. - \Phi(\mathbf{R}', t') \nabla' \frac{1}{|\mathbf{R} - \mathbf{R}'|} \right\} \cdot d\mathbf{s}(\mathbf{R}') \quad (12.57)$$

Applying Eq. (9.39) to the last term on the left-hand side of Eq. (12.57) and then subtracting the result from both sides of Eq. (12.56) yields

$$-\iiint\limits_{V} \Phi(\mathbf{R}', t') \nabla'^2 \frac{1}{|\mathbf{R} - \mathbf{R}'|} \, dV(\mathbf{R}')$$

$$= -\iiint\limits_{V} \left[\frac{\nabla_{t'}'^2 \Phi(\mathbf{R}', t') - \dfrac{1}{v^2} \dfrac{\partial^2 \Phi(\mathbf{R}', t')}{\partial t'^2}}{|\mathbf{R} - \mathbf{R}'|} \right] dV(\mathbf{R}')$$

$$+ \oiint\limits_{A} \left[\frac{\nabla_{t'}' \Phi(\mathbf{R}', t')}{|\mathbf{R} - \mathbf{R}'|} - \frac{2(\mathbf{R} - \mathbf{R}')}{v |\mathbf{R} - \mathbf{R}'|^2} \frac{\partial \Phi(\mathbf{R}', t')}{\partial t'} \right.$$

$$+ \frac{1}{v} \frac{(\mathbf{R} - \mathbf{R}')}{|\mathbf{R} - \mathbf{R}'|^2} \frac{\partial \Phi(\mathbf{R}', t')}{\partial t'} - \left. \Phi(\mathbf{R}', t') \nabla' \frac{1}{|\mathbf{R} - \mathbf{R}'|} \right] \cdot d\mathbf{s}(\mathbf{R}')$$

$$= -\iiint\limits_{V} \left[\frac{\nabla_{t'}'^2 \Phi(\mathbf{R}', t') - \dfrac{1}{v^2} \dfrac{\partial^2 \Phi(\mathbf{R}', t')}{\partial t'^2}}{|\mathbf{R} - \mathbf{R}'|} \right] dV(\mathbf{R}')$$

$$+ \oiint\limits_{A} \frac{1}{|\mathbf{R} - \mathbf{R}'|} \left[\nabla_{t'}' \Phi(\mathbf{R}', t') + \frac{\nabla'}{v} |\mathbf{R} - \mathbf{R}'| \frac{\partial \Phi(\mathbf{R}', t')}{\partial t'} \right] \cdot d\mathbf{s}(\mathbf{R}')$$

$$- \oiint\limits_{A} \Phi(\mathbf{R}', t') \nabla' \frac{1}{|\mathbf{R} - \mathbf{R}'|} \cdot d\mathbf{s}(\mathbf{R}')$$

$$= \begin{cases} 4\pi \Phi(\mathbf{R}, t) & \text{observation point within } A \\ 0 & \text{observation point outside of } A \end{cases}$$

$$= + \iiint\limits_{V} \left[\frac{\rho_v(\mathbf{R}', t')}{|\mathbf{R} - \mathbf{R}'|} \right] dV(\mathbf{R}')$$

$$- \oiint\limits_{A} \frac{1}{|\mathbf{R} - \mathbf{R}'|} \left\{ \left[\frac{\Phi(\mathbf{R}', t')}{|\mathbf{R} - \mathbf{R}'|} + \frac{1}{v} \frac{\partial \Phi(\mathbf{R}', t')}{\partial t'} \right] \mathbf{u}_{\mathbf{R}-\mathbf{R}'} - \nabla_{t'}' \Phi(\mathbf{R}', t') \right\} \cdot d\mathbf{s}(\mathbf{R}')$$

$$\tag{12.58}$$

Thus we have calculated the potential at a field point at a time t in terms of the retarded potential at the source point at a time earlier by the amount $|\mathbf{R} - \mathbf{R}'|/v$, that is, by the time it takes the "effect" at the source to propagate to the point of observation. Equation (12.58) is called the Kirchhoff solution to the wave equation.

If as A goes to infinity the integrand decreases faster than $[\mathbf{R} - \mathbf{R}']^{-1}$, then the surface integral vanishes and Eq. (12.58) reduces to

$$\frac{1}{4\pi} \iiint_{\substack{\text{all} \\ \text{space}}} \frac{\rho_v(\mathbf{R}', t')\, dV(\mathbf{R}')}{|\mathbf{R} - \mathbf{R}'|} = \Phi(\mathbf{R}', t') \tag{12.59}$$

the same result given in Eq. (12.49).

To determine the vector potential $\mathbf{T}$ in terms of the retarded vector source density, we start with Eq. (12.36) [see (Eq. (8.22k)]

$$\mathbf{T}(\mathbf{R}, t) = \nabla \times \iiint_{\substack{\text{all} \\ \text{space}}} \frac{\mathbf{F}(\mathbf{R}', t')\, dV(\mathbf{R}')}{4\pi\, |\mathbf{R} - \mathbf{R}'|} = \frac{1}{4\pi} \iiint_{\substack{\text{all} \\ \text{space}}} \frac{\nabla \times \mathbf{F}(\mathbf{R}', t')\, dV(\mathbf{R}')}{|\mathbf{R} - \mathbf{R}'|}$$

$$+ \frac{1}{4\pi} \iiint_{\substack{\text{all} \\ \text{space}}} \nabla \frac{1}{|\mathbf{R} - \mathbf{R}'|} \times \mathbf{F}(\mathbf{R}', t')\, dV(\mathbf{R}') \tag{12.36}$$

Since $\quad \nabla \times \mathbf{F}(\mathbf{R}', t') = \dfrac{\partial \mathbf{F}(\mathbf{R}', t')}{\partial t'} \times \nabla t'$

$$= \frac{1}{v} \frac{\partial \mathbf{F}(\mathbf{R}', t')}{\partial t'} \times \nabla' |\mathbf{R} - \mathbf{R}'|$$

$$= \frac{|\mathbf{R} - \mathbf{R}'|^2}{v} \frac{\partial \mathbf{F}(\mathbf{R}', t')}{\partial t'} \times \nabla' \frac{1}{|\mathbf{R} - \mathbf{R}'|}$$

Equation (12.36) may then be written

$$\mathbf{T}(\mathbf{R}, t) = \frac{1}{4\pi} \iiint_{\substack{\text{all} \\ \text{space}}} \left\{ \mathbf{F}(\mathbf{R}', t') + \frac{|\mathbf{R} - \mathbf{R}'|}{v} \frac{\partial \mathbf{F}(\mathbf{R}', t')}{\partial t'} \right\} \times \nabla' \frac{1}{|\mathbf{R} - \mathbf{R}'|}\, dV(\mathbf{R}')$$

$$\tag{12.60}$$

Since

$$\nabla' \times \left[\frac{\mathbf{F}(\mathbf{R}', t') + \dfrac{|\mathbf{R} - \mathbf{R}'|}{v} \dfrac{\partial \mathbf{F}(\mathbf{R}', t')}{\partial t'}}{|\mathbf{R} - \mathbf{R}'|} \right]$$

$$= \frac{1}{|\mathbf{R} - \mathbf{R}'|} \nabla' \times \left[\mathbf{F}(\mathbf{R}', t') + \frac{|\mathbf{R} - \mathbf{R}'|}{v} \frac{\partial \mathbf{F}(\mathbf{R}', t')}{\partial t'} \right]$$

$$+ \nabla' \frac{1}{|\mathbf{R} - \mathbf{R}'|} \times \left[\mathbf{F}(\mathbf{R}', t') + \frac{|\mathbf{R} - \mathbf{R}'|}{v} \frac{\partial \mathbf{F}(\mathbf{R}', t')}{\partial t'} \right]$$

we may write Eq. (12.60) as

$$\mathbf{T}(\mathbf{R}, t) = \frac{1}{4\pi} \iiint_{\substack{\text{all} \\ \text{space}}} \frac{1}{|\mathbf{R} - \mathbf{R}'|} \nabla' \times \left[\mathbf{F}(\mathbf{R}', t') + \frac{|\mathbf{R} - \mathbf{R}'|}{v} \frac{\partial \mathbf{F}(\mathbf{R}', t')}{\partial t'} \right] dV(\mathbf{R}')$$

$$- \frac{1}{4\pi} \iiint_{\substack{\text{all} \\ \text{space}}} \nabla' \times \left[\frac{\mathbf{F}(\mathbf{R}', t') + \dfrac{|\mathbf{R} - \mathbf{R}'|}{v} \dfrac{\partial \mathbf{F}(\mathbf{R}', t')}{\partial t'}}{|\mathbf{R} - \mathbf{R}'|} \right] dV(\mathbf{R}')$$

$$= \frac{1}{4\pi} \iiint_{\substack{\text{all} \\ \text{space}}} \frac{\nabla' \times \mathbf{F}(\mathbf{R}', t')}{|\mathbf{R} - \mathbf{R}'|} dV(\mathbf{R}')$$

$$+ \frac{1}{4\pi v} \iiint_{\substack{\text{all} \\ \text{space}}} \nabla' \times \frac{\partial \mathbf{F}(\mathbf{R}', t')}{\partial t'} dV(\mathbf{R}')$$

$$+ \frac{1}{4\pi v} \iiint_{\substack{\text{all} \\ \text{space}}} \frac{1}{|\mathbf{R} - \mathbf{R}'|} \nabla' |\mathbf{R} - \mathbf{R}'| \times \frac{\partial \mathbf{F}(\mathbf{R}', t')}{\partial t'} dV(\mathbf{R}')$$

$$- \frac{1}{4\pi} \iiint_{\substack{\text{all} \\ \text{space}}} \nabla' \times \left[\frac{\mathbf{F}(\mathbf{R}', t')}{|\mathbf{R} - \mathbf{R}'|} \right] dV(\mathbf{R}')$$

$$- \frac{1}{4\pi v} \iiint_{\substack{\text{all} \\ \text{space}}} \nabla' \times \frac{\partial \mathbf{F}(\mathbf{R}', t')}{\partial t'} dV(\mathbf{R}') \tag{12.61}$$

We now observe that

$$\nabla' \times \mathbf{F}(\mathbf{R}', t') = \nabla'_{t'} \times \mathbf{F}(\mathbf{R}', t') - \frac{\nabla' |\mathbf{R} - \mathbf{R}'|}{v} \times \frac{\partial \mathbf{F}(\mathbf{R}', t')}{\partial t'}$$

so that Eq. (12.61) becomes

$$\mathbf{T}(\mathbf{R}, t) = \frac{1}{4\pi} \iiint_{\substack{\text{all} \\ \text{space}}} \frac{\nabla'_{t'} \times \mathbf{F}(\mathbf{R}', t')}{|\mathbf{R} - \mathbf{R}'|} dV(\mathbf{R}')$$

$$- \frac{1}{4\pi v} \iiint_{\substack{\text{all} \\ \text{space}}} \frac{\nabla' |\mathbf{R} - \mathbf{R}'|}{|\mathbf{R} - \mathbf{R}'|} \times \frac{\partial \mathbf{F}(\mathbf{R}', t')}{\partial t'} dV(\mathbf{R}')$$

$$+ \frac{1}{4\pi} \iiint_{\substack{\text{all} \\ \text{space}}} \frac{\nabla' |\mathbf{R} - \mathbf{R}'|}{|\mathbf{R} - \mathbf{R}'|} \times \frac{\partial \mathbf{F}(\mathbf{R}', t')}{\partial t'} dV(\mathbf{R}')$$

$$- \frac{1}{4\pi} \iiint_{\substack{\text{all} \\ \text{space}}} \nabla' \times \left[\frac{\mathbf{F}(\mathbf{R}', t')}{|\mathbf{R} - \mathbf{R}'|} \right] dV(\mathbf{R}') \tag{12.62}$$

If we consider Eq. (9.40) as V expands to include all space under the condition that $F(R', t')$ decreases faster than $|R - R'|^{-1}$ on A, we see that the last integral in Eq. (12.62) vanishes. Thus Eq. (12.62) becomes

$$T(R, t) = \frac{1}{4\pi} \iiint_{\substack{\text{all} \\ \text{space}}} \frac{\nabla'_{t'} \times F(R', t')}{|R - R'|} \, dV(R') \qquad (12.63a)$$

By analogy with previous discussions concerning the relationship between the curl of a field and the vector source density, it is reasonable to write

$$T(R, t) = \frac{1}{4\pi} \iiint_{\substack{\text{all} \\ \text{space}}} \frac{K_s(R', t')}{|R - R'|} \, dV(R') \qquad (12.63b)$$

where $K_s(R', t') \equiv \nabla'_{t'} \times F(R', t')$ is the vector source density at t'. Equation (12.63b) gives the vector potential at R and at t' in terms of the vector source density at the retarded time t'.

By treating each component of T in a manner analogous to that employed in deriving Eq. (12.58), we can obtain an integral expression for the vector potential when the vector source density is known within a finite volume V if the T and its normal derivative are known on A, that is,

$$\frac{1}{4\pi} \iiint_V \frac{K_s(R', t')}{|R - R'|} \, dV(R')$$

$$- \frac{1}{4\pi} \iiint_A \frac{1}{|R - R'|} \left\{ \left[\frac{T(R', t')}{|R - R'|} - \frac{1}{v} \frac{\partial T(R', t')}{\partial t'} \right] u_{R-R'} \cdot u_n \right.$$

$$\left. - \frac{1}{|R - R'|} [(u_n \cdot \nabla'_{t'}) T(R', t')] \right\} |ds(R')|$$

$$= \begin{array}{ll} T(R, t) & \text{if the observation point is within } V \\ 0 & \text{if the observation point is not in } V \end{array} \qquad (12.64)$$

12.4 Electromagnetic Potentials

The electromagnetic field, as its name implies, consists of two members: the electric field and the magnetic field. In Section 12.3 we discussed fields which, although quite general in nature, consist of only one member. When extending the ideas of the previous section to electromagnetic fields, we must take cognizance of the experimental facts which relate the time-dependent electric field to the time-dependent magnetic field.

Furthermore, it would be valuable in the following discussion of electro-magnetic potentials to be able to so develop them that they satisfy the inhomogeneous wave equation. In this way the concepts discussed in the previous section can be carried over and utilized to treat electromagnetic fields.

We shall assume that we are dealing with homogeneous, isotropic media and that the electric field $\mathbf{F}_e$ and the magnetic field $\mathbf{F}_m$ both satisfy equations of the form of Eqs. (11.21b) and (11.37):

$$\nabla \cdot \mathbf{F}_e = \frac{\rho_{v_e}}{\epsilon} \tag{12.65}$$

$$\nabla \cdot \mathbf{F}_m = \frac{\rho_{vm}}{\epsilon} \tag{12.66}$$

$$\nabla \times \mathbf{F}_e = \mathbf{K}_{s_e}\mu \tag{12.67}$$

$$\nabla \times \mathbf{F}_m = \mathbf{K}_{s_m}\mu \tag{12.68}$$

where the ρ_v's are the scalar source densities and the $\mathbf{K}_s$'s are the vector source densities; ϵ and μ can at this time be thought of as constants which alter the units in which the source densities are measured.

Electric fields are related to magnetic fields by the fact that it is the flow of the scalar sources (electric charge) of the electric field that con-stitutes the vector source (current density) of the magnetic field. Since electrical charge is subject to a continuity equation, we may write (see Eq. 6.25)

$$\nabla \cdot \mathbf{J} + \frac{\partial \rho_{v_e}}{\partial t} = 0 \tag{12.69}$$

where $\mathbf{J}$ is the electrical current density and ρ_{v_e} is the electric charge density. From Eq. (12.65) we may write Eq. (12.69) as

$$\nabla \cdot \mathbf{J} + \epsilon \frac{\partial}{\partial t} \nabla \cdot \mathbf{F}_e = \nabla \cdot \left(\mathbf{J} + \epsilon \frac{\partial \mathbf{F}_e}{\partial t}\right) = 0 \tag{12.70}$$

If we take the divergence of Eq. (12.68), we see that

$$\nabla \cdot \nabla \times \mathbf{E}_m = \nabla \cdot \mathbf{K}_{s_m} = 0 \tag{12.71}$$

because the divergence of the curl is identically zero. Thus it is reasonable to take $\mathbf{K}_{s_m}$ as

$$\mathbf{K}_{s_m} = \mathbf{J} + \epsilon \frac{\partial \mathbf{F}_e}{\partial t} \tag{12.72}$$

so that Eq. (12.68) becomes

$$\nabla \times \mathbf{F}_m = \mu\mathbf{J} + \mu\epsilon \frac{\partial \mathbf{F}_e}{\partial t} \tag{12.73}$$

Electric fields are characterized by the absence of real vector sources, that is, there is no term like $\mathbf{J}$, the current density in Eq. (12.72). Magnetic fields are characterized by the absence of scalar sources, that is, $\rho_{v_m} = 0$. Since $\nabla \cdot \mathbf{F}_m$ is then zero, we would expect Eq. (12.67) to have the form

$$\nabla \times \mathbf{F}_e = \pm \frac{\partial \mathbf{F}_m}{\partial t}$$

Faraday's law states that we must choose the minus sign.

We may then write Eqs. (12.65) to (12.68) as

$$\nabla \cdot \mathbf{F}_e = \frac{\rho_{ve}}{\epsilon} \qquad \text{(Gauss's law)} \qquad (12.74)$$

$$\nabla \cdot \mathbf{F}_m = 0 \qquad \text{(no unit magnetic poles)} \qquad (12.75)$$

$$\nabla \times \mathbf{F}_e + \frac{\partial \mathbf{F}_m}{\partial t} = 0 \qquad \text{(Faraday's law)} \qquad (12.76)$$

$$\nabla \times \mathbf{F}_m = \mu \mathbf{J} + \mu\epsilon \frac{\partial \mathbf{F}_e}{\partial t} \qquad \text{(Ampere's law)} \qquad (12.77)$$

Collectively, these four equations are called Maxwell's equations. The discussion preceding them is not a derivation of them, for they are expressions of experimental facts, but rather it is to show that they are consistent with the development of Section 12.3.

Since $\nabla \cdot \mathbf{F}_m = 0$, $\mathbf{F}_m$ can be written as the curl of $\mathbf{A}$, a magnetic vector potential [see Eq. (11.66)]

$$\nabla \times \mathbf{A} = \mathbf{F}_m \qquad (12.78)$$

Thus Eq. (12.76) becomes

$$\nabla \times \mathbf{F}_e + \frac{\partial}{\partial t} \nabla \times \mathbf{A} = \nabla \times \left(\mathbf{F}_e + \frac{\partial \mathbf{A}}{\partial t} \right) = 0 \qquad (12.79)$$

Recalling that a vector whose curl is zero may be written as the (negative) gradient of a scalar field, Eq. (12.79) leads to

$$\mathbf{F}_e = -\nabla\psi - \frac{\partial \mathbf{A}}{\partial t} \qquad (12.80)$$

where ψ is a scalar field called the electrodynamic potential. The divergence of Eq. (12.80) is

$$\nabla \cdot \mathbf{F}_e = -\nabla^2\psi - \frac{\partial(\nabla \cdot \mathbf{A})}{\partial t}$$

$$= \frac{\rho_{ve}}{\epsilon} \qquad (12.81)$$

To preserve the form of the inhomogeneous wave equation for this scalar potential, we may now take advantage of the fact that only the curl of **A** has been defined (Eq. 12.78). To obtain the inhomogeneous wave equation from Eq. (12.81), we then choose $\nabla \cdot \mathbf{A}$ to be related to ψ by

$$\nabla \cdot \mathbf{A} + \mu\epsilon \frac{\partial \psi}{\partial t} = 0 \tag{12.82}$$

This relationship is referred to as the Lorentz condition. Then Eq. (12.81) becomes

$$\frac{\rho_{v_e}}{\epsilon} = -\nabla^2 \psi + \mu\epsilon \frac{\partial^2 \psi}{\partial t^2} \tag{12.83}$$

where, by analogy with Eq. (12.39), $\mu\epsilon = c^{-2}$, where c is the velocity of light.

Utilizing Eq. (12.78), we may write Eq. (12.77) as

$$\nabla \times \nabla \times \mathbf{A} = \mu\mathbf{J} + \mu\epsilon \frac{\partial \mathbf{F}_e}{\partial t}$$

or

$$\begin{aligned}
\mu\mathbf{J} &= [\nabla(\nabla \cdot \mathbf{A}) - \nabla^2 \mathbf{A}] - \mu\epsilon \frac{\partial \mathbf{F}_e}{\partial t} \\
&= -\frac{1}{c^2} \nabla\left(\frac{\partial \psi}{\partial t}\right) - \nabla^2 \mathbf{A} - \frac{1}{c^2} \frac{\partial \mathbf{F}_e}{\partial t} \\
&= -\frac{1}{c^2} \frac{\partial}{\partial t} \{\nabla \psi + \mathbf{F}_e\} - \nabla^2 \mathbf{A} \\
&= -\nabla^2 \mathbf{A} + \frac{1}{c^2} \frac{\partial^2 \mathbf{A}}{\partial t^2} \qquad \text{(see Eq. 12.80)}
\end{aligned} \tag{12.84}$$

We see, therefore, that by utilizing the Lorentz condition, **A** also satisfies the inhomogeneous wave equation.

The magnetic vector potential defined by Eq. (12.78) is not unique; we may replace **A** by a vector **A**′ given by

$$\mathbf{A}' = \mathbf{A} + \nabla\Theta \tag{12.85}$$

where Θ is a scalar field. Thus the form of Eq. (12.78) is unchanged by this gauge transformation,

$$\nabla \times \mathbf{A}' = \nabla \times [\mathbf{A} + \nabla\Theta] = \nabla \times \mathbf{A} = \mathbf{F}_m \tag{12.86}$$

However, if $\mathbf{F}_m$ in Eq. (12.76) is replaced by $\nabla \times \mathbf{A}'$, we see that

$$\nabla \times \left\{\mathbf{F}_e + \frac{\partial \mathbf{A}'}{\partial t}\right\} = 0 \tag{12.87}$$

Thus the quantity in the braces must be the (negative) gradient of a scalar field ψ',

$$\mathbf{F}_e = -\nabla\psi' - \frac{\partial \mathbf{A}'}{\partial t} \qquad (12.88)$$

Subtracting Eq. (12.80) from this equation yields

$$-\nabla(\psi' - \psi) - \frac{\partial(\mathbf{A}' - \mathbf{A})}{\partial t} = 0$$

$$= -\nabla(\psi' - \psi) + \frac{\partial \nabla\Theta}{\partial t} = \nabla\left\{(\psi - \psi') + \frac{\partial\Theta}{\partial t}\right\}$$

or

$$\psi' = \psi + \frac{\partial\Theta}{\partial t'} \qquad (12.89)$$

In terms of the new potentials ψ' and $\mathbf{A}'$, Eqs. (12.80) and (12.78) become

$$\mathbf{F}_e = -\nabla\psi' - \frac{\partial \mathbf{A}'}{\partial t} \qquad (12.90)$$

and

$$\mathbf{F}_m = \nabla \times \mathbf{A}' \qquad (12.91)$$

The divergence of Eq. (12.90) is

$$\nabla \cdot \mathbf{F}_e = \frac{\rho_{ve}}{\epsilon} = \nabla^2\psi' - \frac{\partial \nabla \cdot \mathbf{A}'}{\partial t} \qquad (12.92)$$

and the curl of Eq. (12.91) is

$$\nabla \times \mathbf{F}_m = \mu\mathbf{J} + \mu\epsilon\frac{\partial \mathbf{F}_e}{\partial t} \qquad \text{(see Eq. 12.73)}$$

$$= \nabla(\nabla \cdot \mathbf{A}') - \nabla^2\mathbf{A}' \qquad (12.93)$$

Now if we impose the Lorentz condition on $\mathbf{A}'$, and ψ',

$$\nabla \cdot \mathbf{A}' + \mu\epsilon\frac{\partial\psi'}{\partial t} = 0 \qquad (12.94)$$

so that Eqs. (12.92) and (12.93) become the inhomogeneous wave equations for ψ' and $\mathbf{A}'$, respectively, we find that Θ must satisfy the relation

$$\nabla^2\Theta - \mu\epsilon\frac{\partial^2\Theta}{\partial t^2} = \nabla \cdot \mathbf{A} + \mu\epsilon\frac{\partial\psi}{\partial t} = 0 \qquad (12.95)$$

The reason for the Lorentz condition and gauge transformation is obviously to preserve the similarity in form of the inhomogeneous wave equation for both potentials. They are of value in relativity because their use yields results which are independent of the coordinate system.

Finally, it is interesting to note that both the electric field and the magnetic field satisfy wave equations. To see this, we take the curl of Eq. (12.76),

$$\nabla \times \nabla \times \mathbf{F}_e + \frac{\partial \nabla \times \mathbf{F}_m}{\partial t} = 0$$

$$= \nabla(\nabla \cdot \mathbf{F}_e) - \nabla^2 \mathbf{F}_e + \frac{\partial}{\partial t}\left(\mu \mathbf{J} + \frac{1}{c^2}\frac{\partial \mathbf{F}_e}{\partial t}\right)$$

$$= \frac{\nabla \rho_{v_e}}{\epsilon} - \nabla^2 \mathbf{F}_e + \mu \frac{\partial \mathbf{J}}{\partial t} + \frac{1}{c^2}\frac{\partial^2 \mathbf{F}_e}{\partial t^2} \qquad (12.96)$$

Rearranging Eq. (12.96), we obtain

$$\nabla^2 \mathbf{F}_e - \frac{1}{c^2}\frac{\partial^2 \mathbf{F}_e}{\partial t^2} = \frac{\nabla \rho_{v_e}}{\epsilon} + \mu \frac{\partial \mathbf{J}}{\partial t} \qquad (12.97)$$

If the medium is ohmic, that is, if $\mathbf{J} = \sigma \mathbf{F}_e$, then Eq. (12.97) becomes

$$\nabla^2 \mathbf{F}_e - \frac{1}{c^2}\frac{\partial^2 \mathbf{F}_e}{\partial t^2} - \mu\sigma \frac{\partial \mathbf{F}_e}{\partial t} = \frac{\nabla \rho_{v_e}}{\epsilon} \qquad (12.98)$$

A similar treatment of Eq. (12.77) yields the fact that

$$\nabla^2 \mathbf{F}_m - \frac{1}{c^2}\frac{\partial^2 \mathbf{F}_m}{\partial t^2} + \mu\nabla \times \mathbf{J} = 0 \qquad (12.99)$$

Again, if the medium is ohmic, Eq. (12.99) becomes

$$\nabla^2 \mathbf{F}_m - \frac{1}{c^2}\frac{\partial^2 \mathbf{F}_m}{\partial t^2} - \mu\sigma \frac{\partial \mathbf{F}_m}{\partial t} = 0 \qquad (12.100)$$

Index